INTRODUCTION TO COMPLEX ANALYSIS

This book is in the

ADDISON-WESLEY SERIES IN MATHEMATICS

A. J. Lohwater, *Consulting Editor*

Introduction to
COMPLEX ANALYSIS

ROLF NEVANLINNA
Academy of Finland

V. PAATERO
University of Helsinki

Translated by

T. KÖVARI and G. S. GOODMAN
Imperial College of Science and Technology, London

ADDISON-WESLEY PUBLISHING COMPANY

Reading, Massachusetts · Menlo Park, California · London · Don Mills, Ontario

517.8
N 499

This volume is the only authorized English translation of *Einführung in die Funktionentheorie* by Rolf Nevanlinna and V. Paatero published by Birkhäuser Verlag, whose copyright notice on the original edition reads

© Birkhäuser Verlag Basel, 1964.

Copyright © 1969 by Rolf Nevanlinna.

FOREWORD

The present textbook is based upon lectures given by the authors at Helsinki University and at the University of Zürich, and is a translation of the German edition, *Einführung in die Funktionentheorie*, published by Birkhäuser Verlag, Basel, in 1964.

It is assumed that the reader is acquainted with analytic geometry and the calculus, so that this introduction to the theory of functions may be begun in the third or fourth year of undergraduate study in college.

As the Table of Contents indicates, the present volume is limited to the presentation of the elements of the theory of functions, and the authors have attempted to make the material both comprehensible and precise. Among the sections in which this volume deviates more or less from other presentations we must mention the following: the introduction of the complex numbers, the concept of homotopy and its application, the integral theorems, the theory and application of harmonic functions, in particular harmonic measure, and the correspondence of boundaries under conformal mapping.

Exercises have been placed at the end of each chapter, and all 320 of these exercises should be solved by the student for better insight into the subject matter, whether he learns the subject through lectures or by self-study.

In introducing the elementary functions (Chapters 2–7) we have followed in many places the presentation given by Ernst Lindelöf in his Finnish text-book, *Johdatus funktioteoriaan* (introduction to the theory of functions). This is particularly true for a considerable number of the exercises of these chapters.

We have received assistance in our work from various sources. First we owe thanks to Dr. G. S. Goodman and Dr. T. Kövari for the effort and interest which they have put into the translation of the book. We also express our appreciation to Addison-Wesley Publishing Company and, in particular, to Professor A. J. Lohwater for the valuable advice and generous assistance which he has given in the editing of this edition.

Helsinki, September, 1968

Rolf Nevanlinna
V. Paatero

CONTENTS

CHAPTER 1

THE CONCEPT OF
AN ANALYTIC FUNCTION

The theory of functions is concerned with complex-valued functions of a complex variable. Our study is confined to those functions which are *differentiable* in a sense which will be made precise later on; such functions are known as *analytic functions*. In order to create a basis for the theory, we begin by introducing the complex numbers in a manner which will lead us naturally to their interpretation as vectors in the plane.

§1. THE COMPLEX NUMBERS

1.1. Two-dimensional Vector Spaces

We begin by stating the axioms for a two-dimensional vector space over the real numbers.

Let there be given a set R, whose elements $a, b, \ldots, x, y, \ldots$ shall be called *points* or *vectors*, satisfying the following conditions.

I. To every two elements $a, b \in R$ there corresponds an element $c \in R$, known as their sum and written $c = a + b$, obeying the following rules:

    I.1. $a + b = b + a$ (the commutative law).

    I.2. $a + (b + c) = (a + b) + c$ (the associative law).

    I.3.   There is a zero in R, denoted $x = 0$, with the property that $a + 0 = a$ for every $a \in R$.

    I.4.   The equation $a + x = b$ has one and only one solution, $x = b - a \in R$.

II. To every vector a and every real number λ there corresponds a vector $b = \lambda a \in R$, known as their product, and obeying the following rules.

    II.1. $\lambda(\mu a) = (\lambda\mu)a$ (λ, μ real numbers).

    II.2. $(\lambda + \mu)a = \lambda a + \mu a, \lambda(a + b) = \lambda a + \lambda b$ (the distributive law).

    II.3. $1 \cdot a = a$.

    II.4.   The product λa vanishes if and only if $\lambda = 0$, or $a = 0$, or both $\lambda = 0$ and $a = 0$.†

    II.5.   *The axiom of dimension:* there exist two vectors a and b in R which are linearly independent, that is, for which the equation

---

† We shall use the symbol 0 for the number zero as well as for the vector zero without, we trust, provoking any confusion.

$\lambda a + \mu b = 0$ has only the solution $\lambda = \mu = 0$, but every three vectors a, b, c in R are linearly dependent, that is, the equation $\lambda a + \mu b + \nu c = 0$ always has a solution such that at least one of the three numbers λ, μ, ν does not vanish.

This axiom asserts that the dimension of the vector space R is equal to *two*. In the resulting "affine plane" every vector x admits a representation in terms of its coordinates in a two-dimensional reference system. Such a system is given by a *basis* for R, that is, by two linearly independent vectors e_1, $e_2 \in R$. From II.5 it follows that every vector $x \in R$ has two numbers ξ_1 and ξ_2 associated with it (its coordinates in this reference system) such that

$$x = \xi_1 e_1 + \xi_2 e_2.$$

1.2. Plane Euclidean Geometry

Axioms I and II define a two-dimensional vector space whose geometry is the geometry of the affine plane. It becomes a Euclidean geometry once we introduce a (Euclidean) measure of length and angle. We can arrive at such a measure by defining, for any two vectors x and y in R, a scalar product (x, y) with the following properties.

III.1. (x, y) is a real, symmetric function of its arguments x and y: $(x, y) = (y, x)$.

III.2. (x, y) is linear in each argument.†

III.3. (x, y) is positive definite, that is, $(x, x) \geq 0$, and equality holds only for $x = 0$.

The *length, norm,* or *modulus* $|x|$ of a vector x is defined by

$$|x| = +\sqrt{(x, x)}.$$

It is easily proved (Exercises 1 and 2)‡ that the following inequalities hold:

1) *Schwarz's inequality* $(x, y)^2 \leq |x|^2 |y|^2$;
2) *The triangle inequality* $|x + y| \leq |x| + |y|$.

The angle $[x, y]$ between two vectors x, y $(\neq 0)$ is defined by

$$\cos [x, y] = \frac{(x, y)}{|x| |y|}.$$

Two vectors are therefore orthogonal if $(x, y) = 0$.

---

† A function $f(x)$ is said to be linear, if $f(\lambda x) = \lambda f(x)$ and $f(x_1 + x_2) = f(x_1) + f(x_2)$. The linearity of the scalar product (x, y) asserts, therefore, that this product obeys the distributive law.

‡ Unless there are indications to the contrary, the numbers will always refer to the exercises at the end of the chapter.

If e_1, e_2 is a basis for R and if the vectors x, y have the representations

$$x = \xi_1 e_1 + \xi_2 e_2, \qquad y = \eta_1 e_1 + \eta_2 e_2,$$

in terms of this basis, then

$$(x, y) = (\xi_1 e_1 + \xi_2 e_2, \eta_1 e_1 + \eta_2 e_2) = \sum_{i,k=1}^{2} g_{ik} \xi_i \eta_k,$$

where the g_{ik} denote the real constants

$$g_{ik} = (e_i, e_k) \qquad (g_{12} = g_{21}).$$

The square of the norm of x is the quadratic form

$$|x|^2 = (x, x) = \sum_{i,k} g_{ik} \xi_i \xi_k = g_{11} \xi_1^2 + 2 g_{12} \xi_1 \xi_2 + g_{22} \xi_2^2.$$

It reduces to the Pythagorean form

$$|x|^2 = \xi_1^2 + \xi_2^2$$

if and only if the coordinate system is orthonormal; that is,

$$(e_1, e_2) = 0, \qquad |e_1| = |e_2| = 1$$

(the Cartesian coordinate system).

1.3. Extension of the Set R to a Vector Algebra

In what follows, we shall not introduce a metric into the plane R for the time being, so that we shall be dealing with an affine geometry on R defined by the postulates in groups I and II. The problem before us is to see whether it is possible to extend I and II so as to give R the structure of a field (or algebra), and, if this is possible, to discover in how many different ways it can be done.

The vector space R becomes an algebra once we are able to define, for any two elements $x, y \in R$, a "product"

$$z = xy \in R$$

which satisfies the following axioms.

IV.1. The product is commutative: $xy = yx$.

IV.2. The product is bilinear, that is, linear in each factor.

IV.3. The product is associative: $x(yz) = (xy)z$.

IV.4. The product xy vanishes, $xy = 0$, if and only if at least one factor vanishes.

1.4.

Our task, then, is *to find all bilinear forms $xy \in R$ which satisfy these axioms IV.* In order to arrive at the general solution to this problem, we shall assume, at first, that we already have a product xy defined on R in accordance with axioms IV and see what this tells us.

If we fix the vector $y \neq 0$ in the product $z = xy$, we obtain a linear transformation in x which maps the plane R into itself. This mapping is one-to-one, for if $z_1 = x_1 y$, $z_2 = x_2 y$, then

$$z_1 - z_2 = (x_1 - x_2)y.$$

Since y was assumed to be different from 0, $z_1 - z_2$ will vanish if and only if $x_1 - x_2 = 0$. Different vectors x therefore have (for each fixed $y \neq 0$) different image vectors $z = xy$.

On the other hand, the range of the mapping $z = xy$ is the whole plane R. For, if x_1 and x_2 are two vectors in R, and λ_1 and λ_2 are two arbitrary real numbers, then

$$(\lambda_1 x_1 + \lambda_2 x_2)y = \lambda_1 x_1 y + \lambda_2 x_2 y = \lambda_1 z_1 + \lambda_2 z_2,$$

where $z_1 = x_1 y$, $z_2 = x_2 y$. From this we see that the image vectors z_1, z_2 are linearly independent if and only if the vectors x_1, x_2 are linearly independent. Hence, if x_1, x_2 is a basis for R, then z_1, z_2 will also be a basis. If the vector x has the coordinates λ_1, λ_2 in the system (x_1, x_2), then its image vector has the same coordinates in the system (z_1, z_2), for $z = xy = \lambda_1 z_1 + \lambda_2 z_2$. Hence, the set of image vectors $z = xy$ covers the plane R exactly once if x runs through all values in R (for y fixed).

Thus, for any given vector $y \neq 0$, there is precisely one vector x which makes the product xy take a prescribed value z; that element is the "quotient" $x = z/y$.

1.5. Definition of the Unit Vector e

If, in particular, we take $z = y (\neq 0)$, then there is a definite vector $e = e_y \in R$ having the property that $e_y y = y$. We shall show that e_y is *independent* of the choice of y. Let y_1 and y_2 be two non-zero vectors. If $e_1 y_1 = y_1$, $e_2 y_2 = y_2$, then

$$e_2 y_2 = y_2 = y_1 \frac{y_2}{y_1} = (e_1 y_1)\frac{y_2}{y_1},$$

and this last expression is, by axiom IV.3 (the associative law), equal to $e_1(y_1 y_2/y_1) = e_1 y_2$. Hence, $e_2 y_2 = e_1 y_2$, or $(e_1 - e_2)y_2 = 0$, from which it follows that $e_1 = e_2$, since $y_2 \neq 0$.

The element $e (\neq 0)$ defined uniquely by the equation

$$ey = ye = y \tag{1.1}$$

is called the *unit vector*, or *unit*, in R.

1.6. Definition of the Vector i

Let a be an arbitrary vector in R and consider the equation

$$x^2 = a.$$

If this equation has a solution $x = x_1$, $x_1^2 = a$, then, for every vector $x \in R$, we have

$$x^2 - a = x^2 - x_1^2 = (x - x_1)(x + x_1),$$

so that the equation $x^2 - a = 0$ has, in addition to $x = x_1$, one further solution $x = -x_1$.

Let us choose $a = -e$ and solve the equation

$$x^2 + e = 0. \tag{1.2}$$

The existence of a solution will be shown in an exercise (Exercise 3). We denote the solutions by $x = \pm i$ ($\neq 0$). The vector i is linearly independent of the vector e, for, if $i = \lambda e$ (λ real), then we would have $-e = i^2 = (\lambda e)^2 = \lambda^2 e^2 = \lambda^2 e$, or $(1 + \lambda^2)e = 0$, which is impossible, since both $1 + \lambda^2 \neq 0$ and $e \neq 0$.

The vectors $x = e$ and $x = i$ span the entire plane R. An arbitrary vector $x \in R$ has the coordinate representation

$$x = \xi e + \eta i.$$

This representation has been found under the assumption that there is a product, defined for pairs of vectors x_1, $x_2 \in R$, which satisfies the axioms IV. If x_1 and x_2 are written in terms of coordinates,

$$x_1 = \xi_1 e + \eta_1 i, \qquad x_2 = \xi_2 e + \eta_2 i,$$

it follows from IV and the definition of the basis vectors e and i via (1.1) and (1.2) that the product $x_1 x_2$ must have the form

$$\begin{aligned} x_1 x_2 &= (\xi_1 e + \eta_1 i)(\xi_2 e + \eta_2 i) \\ &= (\xi_1 \xi_2 - \eta_1 \eta_2)e + (\xi_1 \eta_2 + \eta_1 \xi_2)i. \end{aligned} \tag{1.3}$$

The quotient x_1/x_2 ($x_2 \neq 0$) is defined to be that vector $x = \xi e + \eta i$ which, when multiplied by the vector $x_2 = \xi_2 e + \eta_2 i$, yields the vector $x_1 = \xi_1 e + \eta_1 i$. With the aid of (1.3), we can obtain the coordinates ξ, η of x from the equations

$$\xi_2 \xi - \eta_2 \eta = \xi_1, \qquad \eta_2 \xi + \xi_2 \eta = \eta_1.$$

Therefore the quotient x_1/x_2 is given by the expression

$$\frac{x_1}{x_2} = \frac{\xi_1 e + \eta_1 i}{\xi_2 e + \eta_2 i} = \frac{\xi_1 \xi_2 + \eta_1 \eta_2}{\xi_2^2 + \eta_2^2} e + \frac{\eta_1 \xi_2 - \xi_1 \eta_2}{\xi_2^2 + \eta_2^2} i. \tag{1.4}$$

1.7. The Solution of the Extension Problem

We now turn all this around and choose any two linearly independent vectors in R, label them e and i, and *define* the product $x_1 x_2$ of two vectors $x_j = \xi_j e + \eta_j i$ ($j = 1$, 2) by means of Eq. (1.3). We shall then have $ex = xe = x$ and $i^2 + e = 0$, and all the axioms IV will be satisfied. The verification of axioms IV.1–3 we leave to the reader. To prove IV.4, we observe that the equation $x_1x_2 = 0$ is equivalent, by (1.3), to the coordinate equations

$$\xi_1\xi_2 - \eta_1\eta_2 = 0, \qquad \xi_1\eta_2 + \eta_1\xi_2 = 0.$$

Squaring and then adding, we obtain

$$(\xi_1^2 + \eta_1^2)(\xi_2^2 + \eta_2^2) = 0.$$

Consequently, $\xi_1 = \eta_1 = 0$ or $\xi_2 = \eta_2 = 0$, that is, $x_1 = 0$ or $x_2 = 0$ (or $x_1 = x_2 = 0$), as required by axiom IV.4.

We have, therefore, completely solved the problem before us:

If the vectors e and i are any two arbitrarily chosen linearly independent vectors, then (1.3) *furnishes a definition for the product of two vectors in R which makes R into a field* (or algebra, that is, a vector space which satisfies the axioms IV), *and this definition of the product is the only one that is compatible with all the axioms.*

1.8. Notation for Complex Numbers. Absolute Value and Argument

Having made R into a field in which every vector, or *complex number*, can be written as $\xi_1e + \xi_2i$, we want to say something about notation. Vectors ξe (ξ real) along the e-axis we shall denote, for brevity, by ξ alone, by dropping the e. In view of the property $xe = ex = x$ which defines the unit, this can hardly lead to confusion. Furthermore, in keeping with a long-standing custom we shall denote the coordinates of a complex number $z = \xi_1e + \xi_2i = \xi_1 + \xi_2i$ by $\xi_1 = x, \xi_2 = y$, and write

$$z = x + iy.$$

The real number x is called the *real part* of z, and the real number y is called the *imaginary part* of z. These terms can be abbreviated to

$$x = \operatorname{Re} z, \qquad y = \operatorname{Im} z.$$

We now introduce a Euclidean metric into the "complex plane" R by defining the scalar product (z_1, z_2) of two complex numbers $z_1 = x_1 + iy_1$, $z_2 = x_2 + iy_2$ as

$$(z_1, z_2) = x_1x_2 + y_1y_2.$$

This means that the basis vectors e and i are orthogonal to one another, and that their lengths are one: $|e| = |i| = 1$.

The *modulus* or *absolute value* of a complex number $z = x + iy$ is then given by

$$|z| = +\sqrt{(z, z)} = +\sqrt{x^2 + y^2}.$$

If we go over to polar coordinates, we get

$$z = r(\cos \phi + i \sin \phi),$$

where $r = |z|$, $\phi = $ arc tan y/x. The quantity ϕ is called the *argument* of z:

$$\arg z = \phi = \text{arc tan } y/x.$$

As long as $z \neq 0$, ϕ is defined up to a multiple of 2π (we say "modulo 2π," and write "mod 2π").

In this notation, the product of two complex numbers

$$z_k = r_k(\cos \phi_k + i \sin \phi_k) \ (k = 1, 2)$$

is

$$z_1 z_2 = r_1 r_2\{\cos (\phi_1 + \phi_2) + i \sin (\phi_1 + \phi_2)\}.$$

From this it follows that

The absolute value of the product of two complex numbers is equal to the product of their absolute values, while the argument of the product is equal to the sum (mod 2π) of the arguments of the factors:

$$|z_1 z_2| = |z_1| \, |z_2|, \qquad \arg (z_1 z_2) = \arg z_1 + \arg z_2 \text{ (mod } 2\pi).$$

The latter rule presupposes that the factors are different from zero, since the argument of the number $z = 0$ is indeterminate.

From the product rule it follows that

$$\left|\frac{z_1}{z_2}\right| = \frac{|z_1|}{|z_2|}, \qquad \arg \frac{z_1}{z_2} = \arg z_1 - \arg z_2 \text{ (mod } 2\pi).$$

If all n factors, $z = r(\cos \phi + i \sin \phi)$, of a product are equal we obtain

$$[r(\cos \phi + i \sin \phi)]^n = r^n(\cos n\phi + i \sin n\phi).$$

This yields as a special case, for $r = 1$, *de Moivre's formula*

$$(\cos \phi + i \sin \phi)^n = \cos n\phi + i \sin n\phi. \tag{1.5}$$

The numbers $x + iy$ and $x - iy$ are said to be *complex conjugates*. The complex conjugate of the complex number z is denoted by $\bar{z}$; obviously,

$$z\bar{z} = |z|^2; \qquad \text{Re } z = \frac{1}{2}(z + \bar{z}), \qquad \text{Im } z = \frac{1}{2i}(z - \bar{z}).$$

Geometrically speaking, the addition of complex numbers corresponds to vector addition (according to the parallelogram rule). The difference $z_1 - z_2$ corresponds to a vector whose initial point is at z_2 and whose end-point is at z_1. The modulus of the difference $|z_1 - z_2|$ gives the distance between the points z_1 and z_2.

Since the complex numbers form an algebra (axioms I–IV), the rational operations of arithmetic (addition, subtraction, multiplication, and division) obey the same rules as in the real case. Over and beyond this, the defining equation $i^2 = -1$ must be taken into account.

§2. POINT SETS IN THE COMPLEX PLANE

1.9. Convergent Sequences

A sequence of complex numbers

$$z_1, z_2, \ldots, z_n, \ldots \tag{1.6}$$

tends to a limit,

$$\lim_{n \to \infty} z_n = z, \tag{1.7}$$

if, to any arbitrarily prescribed number $\epsilon > 0$, a number $n_\epsilon > 0$ can be found such that

$$|z_n - z| < \epsilon \quad for \quad n \geq n_\epsilon. \tag{1.8}$$

The condition (1.8) says, geometrically, that all the points z_n ($n \geq n_\epsilon$) lie in a circle about z with radius ϵ.

Let $z = x + iy$, $z_n = x_n + iy_n$.

Then the conditions

$$\lim_{n \to \infty} x_n = x \quad and \quad \lim_{n \to \infty} y_n = y \tag{1.9}$$

are necessary and sufficient for (1.7) to hold.

The necessity of the condition (1.9) follows immediately from the inequalities

$$|x_n - x| \leq |z_n - z|, \quad |y_n - y| \leq |z_n - z|.$$

Conversely, if (1.9) is fulfilled, then there exists a number N with the property that

$$|x_n - x| < \frac{\epsilon}{2} \quad and \quad |y_n - y| < \frac{\epsilon}{2} \quad for \quad n \geq N.$$

Consequently, for all $n \geq N$ we have

$$|z_n - z| = \sqrt{(x_n - x)^2 + (y_n - y)^2} < \frac{\epsilon}{\sqrt{2}} < \epsilon,$$

which shows that the condition (1.9) is also sufficient. The following theorem is also easy to prove (Exercise 16):

If $z \neq 0$, the conditions

$$\lim_{n \to \infty} |z_n| = |z| \quad and \quad \lim_{n \to \infty} \arg z_n = \arg z \pmod{2\pi}$$

are necessary and sufficient for the validity of (1.7).

When the sequence z_n ($n = 1, 2, \ldots$) is such that

$$\lim_{n \to \infty} |z_n| = \infty,$$

we say that the sequence tends to ∞ and write simply

$$\lim_{n \to \infty} z_n = \infty.$$

This limit, ∞, is taken as a point, the *point at infinity*, of the complex plane. The plane, completed by the single point at infinity, is called the *extended*, or *closed*, plane.† In many questions, the point $z = \infty$ has an equal status with the finite points of the plane (cf. Section 3.13).

1.10. The Topology of the Complex Plane

The set of points z belonging to the interior of a disk of radius r with center at the point $z_0 = x_0 + iy_0 \neq \infty$:

$$K_r: \qquad |z - z_0| < r$$

is called a *circular neighborhood* of z_0. A circular neighborhood of the point $z = \infty$ will be taken to mean the set of points which lie outside some circle of radius r about the origin: $|z| > r$.

A set of points $\{z\}$ in the extended plane $|z| \leqq \infty$ is said to be *open* if each of its points is the center of some circular neighborhood which belongs entirely to the set.

An open set of points $\{z\}$ in the extended plane $|z| \leqq \infty$ forms a *domain* if it is possible to join any two points in $\{z\}$ by a polygonal path which lies entirely in $\{z\}$. (This condition makes the open set *connected*.)

Any domain containing the point z_0 is called a *neighborhood* of z_0.

A point a is called a *cluster point* (or sometimes, a *limit point* or *accumulation point*) of a set of complex numbers $\{z\}$ if every circular neighborhood of a contains at least one point $z \neq a$ of $\{z\}$. From this it follows that every neighborhood of a cluster point a must contain infinitely many points of the set.

If a set contains all of its cluster points, the set is said to be *closed*.

The set of points $|z| < \infty$ is open. The extended plane $|z| \leqq \infty$ is both open and closed (Exercise 18). Open sets and closed sets are important particular classes of sets, but an arbitrary set of points is, in general, neither open nor closed.

A closed set which cannot be split into two disjoint closed subsets is called a *continuum*.

A set of points $\{z\}$ is said to be *compact* if any infinite subset of it has a cluster point belonging to $\{z\}$. (A compact set is therefore closed.) The closed plane $|z| \leqq \infty$ is compact.

The set of points in the plane which do not belong to a given set $\{z\}$ forms what is called the *complement* of $\{z\}$. The complement of an open set is closed, and the complement of a closed set is open (Exercise 20).

---

† The finite plane can also be extended in other ways. For example, in projective geometry, there is the so-called line at infinity with its infinitely many, infinitely distant points.

Let G be a domain. If G does not contain every point of $|z| \leqq \infty$, then the points of the complement of G fall into two classes:

a) *Boundary points of G.* These do not belong to G, but are cluster points of G. The set of boundary points forms the *boundary* of G.

b) *Exterior points of G.* These are points which belong neither to G nor to the boundary of G. This set can be empty.

If Γ is the boundary of the domain G, then the union $G \cup \Gamma$ (that is, the set of all points which belong either to G or Γ) is a closed set (Exercise 21). It is called the *closure* of the domain G.

The union of a domain and its boundary is also called a *closed domain.*

§3. FUNCTIONS OF A COMPLEX VARIABLE

1.11. Definition of a Function. Continuity

Functions of a complex variable are defined in the same manner as functions of a real variable:

If to every value z in a domain G there corresponds a definite complex value w, then the mapping f: z → w is said to be a function defined in the domain G.

The number $w = f(z)$ is called the value of the function at the point z.

In what follows we shall consider first only those functions which assume *finite* values in a *finite* domain, that is, a domain belonging to the finite plane $|z| < \infty$.

The real and imaginary parts, u and v, of the function $f(z)$ are real functions of the real variables x and y $(z = x + iy)$:

$$u = u(x, y), \qquad v = v(x, y).$$

Conversely, any two such functions always define one complex function $f(z) = u + iv$ of $z = x + iy$.

Continuity is defined in the same way as in the real case:

A function w = f(z) is continuous at the point z if, to every positive number ϵ, there corresponds a positive number ρ_ϵ, such that

$$|f(z + \varDelta z) - f(z)| < \epsilon \qquad whenever \qquad |\varDelta z| < \rho_\epsilon.$$

Geometrically speaking, the continuity of a function $w = f(z)$ at $z = z_0$ means this: to an arbitrarily small disk K_w centered at $w_0 = f(z_0)$ there corresponds a disk K_z about z_0 with the property that $w = f(z)$ lies in K_w whenever z lies in K_z.

The limit of a function is defined in the same way as the limit of a sequence in Section 1.9. Everything that was said there about the limit of a sequence of complex numbers applies here as well. Combining the definitions of continuity and of a limit we can say that a function $f(z)$ is continuous at a point z if

$$\lim_{\Delta z \to 0} f(z + \Delta z) = f(z).$$

The real and imaginary parts of a continuous function are obviously continuous functions themselves, and conversely. The same holds for the absolute value and the argument of a continuous function, provided that the function does not vanish ($f(z) \neq 0$).

1.12. Differentiable Functions

The derivative of a function of a complex variable is defined in the same way as in the real case.

Let $f(z)$ be a function defined in a neighborhood of the point z. If the difference quotient

$$\frac{\Delta f}{\Delta z} = \frac{f(z + \Delta z) - f(z)}{\Delta z}$$

tends to a finite limit A whenever Δz tends to zero, then the number A is called the derivative of f at the point z and is denoted by

$$f'(z) = A = \lim_{\Delta z \to 0} \frac{\Delta f}{\Delta z}. \tag{1.10}$$

The difference $\epsilon = \Delta f / \Delta z - A$ therefore tends to zero with Δz. Hence, Δf has the expansion

$$\Delta f = A\Delta z + \Delta z \, \epsilon = A\Delta z + \Delta z(\Delta z), \tag{1.10'}$$

where (Δz) denotes a number which tends to zero as $\Delta z \to 0$.

If, on the other hand, there exists a constant A such that (1.10)' is satisfied, then $\Delta f / \Delta z = A + (\Delta z)$. Accordingly, the difference quotient $\Delta f / \Delta z$ tends to the limit A as $\Delta z \to 0$. Hence, A is the derivative $f'(z)$ of the function $f(z)$.

Equations (1.10) and (1.10)' are therefore equivalent.

The expansion (1.10)' expresses the fact that the function f is *differentiable* at the point z. The first term is the *differential*

$$df = f'(z)\Delta z$$

corresponding to the increment Δz. The total increment Δf of the function f is obtained by adding to the differential df the remainder term $\Delta z(\Delta z)$.

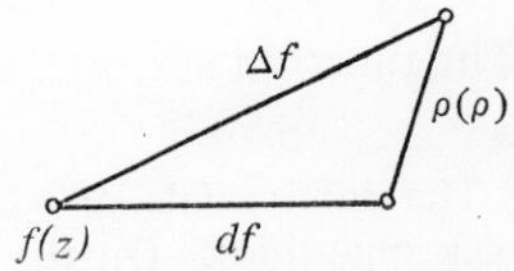

If $f'(z) \neq 0$, this remainder term is negligible in comparison with df as $\Delta z \to 0$. Therefore, for small values of $|\Delta z|$, the differential df is a good approximation to the increment Δf: the ratio of

Figure 1

the length of the vector $\rho(\rho)$ (where $\rho = |\varDelta z|$) to $|df|$ tends to zero with $\varDelta z$.

If, in particular, we choose $f(z) \equiv z$, then $dz = \varDelta z$. Accordingly, we can write $df = f'(z)\,dz$. The derivative f' is therefore the quotient† of two differentials df and dz:

$$\frac{df}{dz} = f'(z).$$

(This notation is due to Leibniz.)

1.13. The Cauchy-Riemann Differential Equations

We shall now investigate what form the equations that define the derivative (1.10, 1.10′) assume when we separate the variables into their real and imaginary parts:

$$z = x + iy, \qquad f(z) = u(x, y) + i\,v(x, y).$$

Accordingly, $\varDelta z = \varDelta x + i\varDelta y$ and

$$u(x + \varDelta x, y + \varDelta y) - u(x, y) = \varDelta u,$$
$$v(x + \varDelta x, y + \varDelta y) - v(x, y) = \varDelta v.$$

We also write

$$A = \alpha + i\beta, \qquad \varDelta z(\varDelta z) = \rho((\rho)_1 + i(\rho)_2),$$

where $(\rho)_1$ and $(\rho)_2$ denote real numbers which tend to zero with

$$\rho = |\varDelta z| = \sqrt{(\varDelta x)^2 + (\varDelta y)^2}.$$

If the function f is differentiable, then, by (1.10)′,

$$\varDelta u + i\varDelta v = (\alpha + i\beta)(\varDelta x + i\varDelta y) + \rho((\rho)_1 + i(\rho)_2).$$

Comparison of the real and imaginary parts yields

$$\varDelta u = \alpha\varDelta x - \beta\varDelta y + \rho(\rho)_1, \qquad \varDelta v = \beta\varDelta x + \alpha\varDelta y + \rho(\rho)_2.$$

These formulas say that $u(x, y)$ and $v(x, y)$, considered as functions of the real variables x and y, are differentiable at the point (x, y). If we set $\varDelta y = 0$ (so that now $\rho = |\varDelta x|$) and then divide by $\varDelta x$, the first equation yields

$$\frac{\varDelta u}{\varDelta x} = \alpha + \frac{|\varDelta x|}{\varDelta x}(\varDelta x) \to \alpha \qquad \text{as} \qquad \varDelta x \to 0.$$

The function $u(x, y)$ therefore possesses the partial derivative $u_x = \alpha$.

---

† The differentials $dz = \varDelta z$ and $df = f'\,dz$ are *finite* (and not "infinitesimal") complex quantities. On the other hand, as we have already seen, the differential df approximates $\varDelta f$ better and better, the smaller the modulus of $\varDelta z = dz$ is.

In a similar way, we can prove that $u_y = -\beta$, $v_x = \beta$ and $v_y = \alpha$. We thus have the following result.

If the function $f(z) = u + iv$ is differentiable, then the functions $u(x, y)$ and $v(x, y)$ are also differentiable. The partial derivatives are related by the equations

$$u_x = v_y, \qquad u_y = -v_x. \tag{1.11}$$

These partial differential equations, which relate the real and imaginary parts of a differentiable function, are known as the *Cauchy-Riemann differential equations*.

The converse of this result is also true.

If $u(x, y)$ and $v(x, y)$ are differentiable functions of x and y, and if their partial derivatives u_x, u_y, v_x, v_y satisfy the Cauchy-Riemann differential equations, then the complex function

$$f(z) = u(x, y) + iv(x, y)$$

is differentiable with respect to the variable $z = x + iy$. Its derivative, $f'(z)$, is

$$f'(z) = u_x + iv_x = v_y - iu_y.$$

Proof. The assumption that u and v are differentiable at the point (x, y) means that they have the expansions

$$\Delta u = u_x \Delta x + u_y \Delta y + \rho(\rho)_1, \qquad \Delta v = v_x \Delta x + v_y \Delta y + \rho(\rho)_2. \tag{1.12}$$

Here, the quantities $(\rho)_1$ and $(\rho)_2$ vanish when $\rho = \sqrt{(\Delta x)^2 + (\Delta y)^2}$ tends to 0. If we multiply the second equation in (1.12) by i and add it to the first equation, we get

$$\Delta f = \Delta u + i\Delta v = (u_x + iv_x)\Delta x + (u_y + iv_y)\Delta y + \rho(\rho),$$

where $(\rho) \equiv (\rho)_1 + i(\rho)_2 \to 0$ as $\rho \to 0$. Since, by hypothesis, the Cauchy-Riemann equations (1.11) are satisfied, we can write

$$\Delta f = (u_x + iv_x)\Delta x + (-v_x + iu_x)\Delta y + \rho(\rho)$$
$$= (u_x + iv_x)(\Delta x + i\Delta y) + \rho(\rho).$$

But, according to (1.10)′, this means that $f(z)$ is differentiable and has the derivative $f'(z) = u_x + iv_x = v_y - iu_y$.

Remark. If a function $u(x, y)$ of two real variables is differentiable at a point (x, y):

$$\Delta u = \alpha \Delta x + \beta \Delta y + \rho(\rho) \quad ((\rho) \to 0 \quad \text{as} \quad \rho = \sqrt{(\Delta x)^2 + (\Delta y)^2} \to 0),$$

then, as we pointed out above, it possesses partial derivatives $u_x = \alpha$ and $u_y = \beta$ at this point. We know from the theory of real functions of several variables that, conversely, the mere existence of the derivatives u_x and u_y at the point (x, y) in no way implies the differentiability of the function $u(x, y)$ at this point. If, however, we make the additional hypothesis that the partial derivatives u_x and u_y also exist in a neighborhood of the point (x, y) and are *continuous* at this point, then one can conclude that u is differentiable at the point. (We use the mean-value theorem; cf. Exercises 27 and 28.)

1.14. The Definition of an Analytic Function

If $f(z)$ is defined in a finite domain G, and is differentiable in z at each point of G, then $f(z)$ is said to be an analytic function in G.

A function is said to be *analytic at a point* if it is analytic in a neighborhood of the point.

The definition of an analytic function in the domain G says that at every point of G this function possesses a finite derivative

$$f'(z) = \lim_{\Delta z \to 0} \frac{\Delta f}{\Delta z}.$$

This definition of an analytic function was given by the founder of the theory of complex functions, Augustin Cauchy (1789–1857). From what we have just discussed, it is equivalent to the following definition, given by Bernhard Riemann (1826–1866).

A function $f(z) = u(x, y) + i\,v(x, y)$ is analytic in a domain G if the functions $u(x, y)$ and $v(x, y)$ are differentiable throughout G and the Cauchy-Riemann differential equations

$$u_x = v_y, \qquad u_y = -v_x$$

are satisfied.

Later on, we shall show that still more follows from these assumptions, namely, that an analytic function is *continuously* differentiable (that is, it possesses a continuous derivative), and the same holds for its real and imaginary parts. In their original definition of an analytic function, the founders of complex function theory, Cauchy and Riemann, required the continuity of the derivatives. That this property already follows from the differentiability assumption was proved only at a later date (Édouard Goursat, 1900).

We shall see, in fact, that the existence of *all* the higher derivatives follows from the analyticity of a function. Despite its apparent simplicity, then, the definition of an analytic function constitutes an enormous restriction compared with the general definition of a complex function.

The real and imaginary parts u and v of an analytic function have continuous partial derivatives of all orders, as we shall prove later on. From the Cauchy-Riemann differential equations (1.11) it follows that u and v satisfy Laplace's equation

$$\Delta U \equiv \frac{\partial^2 U}{\partial x^2} + \frac{\partial^2 U}{\partial y^2} = 0$$

(cf. Exercise 32). Functions of this sort are called *harmonic* functions.

Two harmonic functions which are related by the Cauchy-Riemann equations are said to be *harmonic conjugates*. The real part and the imaginary part of an analytic function are therefore conjugate harmonic functions.

1.15. The Rules of Differentiation

The derivative of a complex function has been defined in precisely the same way as the corresponding notion in the case of a function of a single real variable. The definition is based upon the rational operations of arithmetic and the notion of limit, both of which remain unchanged when we go over from the real domain to the complex domain. Accordingly, all the rules of differential calculus (for example, for the derivative of a sum, or a product, or a quotient) remain intact and can be applied, without further ado, to complex functions.

The same also holds for the *composition* of functions. Suppose that the function $w = w(z)$ is analytic in the domain G_z of the z-plane and that its values lie in a domain G_w of the w-plane. If, further, $\zeta = \zeta(w)$ is an analytic function of w in the domain G_w, then the composite function $z \to w \to \zeta$

$$\zeta = \zeta(w(z)) \equiv f(z)$$

is analytic in G_z.

To prove this, it is only necessary to show that f is a differentiable function of z. We leave this to the reader as an exercise (Exercise 29). At the same time, we note that the chain rule for the derivative of a composite function holds in the complex domain:

$$\frac{d\zeta}{dz} = f'(z) = \frac{d\zeta}{dw}\frac{dw}{dz}.$$

1.16. Conformal Mapping by Analytic Functions

Suppose that the function $w = w(z)$ is continuous in a neighborhood of the point z_0 and is differentiable at z_0. Suppose, further, that $w'(z_0) \neq 0$.

If the point z moves along the ray $\arg (z - z_0) = \phi$ ($=$ const.), then its image $w(z) = w(z_0) + \Delta w$ moves along a well-defined curve γ_ϕ which starts at $w_0 = w(z_0)$ and is such that

$$\frac{\Delta w}{\Delta z} = w'(z_0) + (\Delta z) = w'(z_0)[1 + \epsilon(\Delta z)],$$

where $\epsilon(\Delta z) = (\Delta z)/w'(z_0) \to 0$ as $\Delta z \to 0$. Therefore, as $\Delta z \to 0$, we have

$$\frac{|\Delta w|}{|\Delta z|} \to |w'(z_0)|, \qquad \arg \frac{\Delta w}{\Delta z} = \arg \Delta w - \phi \to \arg w'(z_0). \qquad (1.13)$$

From the second formula in (1.13) it follows that γ_ϕ possesses a tangent at the point w_0 which makes an angle

$$\psi = \phi + \arg w'(z_0)$$

with the real axis.

If we take two rays, $\arg(z - z_0) = \phi_\nu$ ($\nu = 1, 2$), then the angle between the tangents to their image curves at the point w_0 turns out to be

$$\psi_2 - \psi_1 = \phi_2 - \phi_1.$$

Under the mapping from the z-plane into the w-plane this angle therefore remains fixed. If the angle of inclination of the ray in the z-plane increases, then the angle of inclination of the tangent to the image curve also increases: the orientation is preserved.

From the first formula in (1.13), we conclude that the ratio of corresponding distances $|\Delta w|$ and $|\Delta z|$ tends to the same limit $|w'(z_0)|$ independently of the direction chosen for the vector Δz.

Geometrically speaking, this means that the mapping of the z-plane into the w-plane resembles a similarity mapping in a neighborhood centered at z_0, and the resemblance becomes stronger as the size of the neighborhood shrinks.

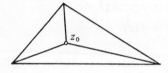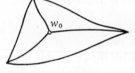

Figure 2

On the basis of these considerations we make the following definition:

If the function $w = w(z)$ has a non-vanishing derivative at the point z_0, then the mapping $z \to w$ is called *conformal* at the point z_0.

This definition is equivalent to the existence of the following (finite) limits:

$$\lim_{\Delta z \to 0} \arg \frac{\Delta w}{\Delta z}, \tag{a}$$

$$\lim_{\Delta z \to 0} \frac{|\Delta w|}{|\Delta z|} \neq 0, \tag{b}$$

where $\Delta w = w(z_0 + \Delta z) - w(z_0)$.

1.17.

In order to enlarge upon the foregoing considerations, we shall separate the complex function $w(z)$ into its real and imaginary parts. We shall assume that the real and imaginary parts of the function

$$w = w(z) = u(x, y) + i\, v(x, y)$$

are differentiable at the point z_0, and that the functional determinant is positive,

$$\frac{\partial(u, v)}{\partial(x, y)} = u_x v_y - u_y v_x > 0 \tag{1.14}$$

at the point z_0.

If, in addition, one of the two limits (a) and (b) mentioned in Section 1.16 exists, then $w(z)$ is differentiable at the point z_0 and $w'(z_0) \neq 0$.

To prove this, we shall first assume the existence of the limit (a). If we write $\Delta z = dz = dx + i\,dy \neq 0$ and $\Delta w = \Delta u + i\Delta v$, then

$$\lim_{\Delta z \to 0} \arg \frac{\Delta w}{\Delta z} = \arctan \frac{dv\,dx - du\,dy}{du\,dx + dv\,dy},$$

since, by (1.14), du and dv do not both vanish. This limit and therefore also the expression

$$\frac{dv\,dx - du\,dy}{du\,dx + dv\,dy} = \frac{v_x\,dx^2 + (v_y - u_x)\,dx\,dy - u_y\,dy^2}{u_x\,dx^2 + (u_y + v_x)\,dx\,dy + v_y\,dy^2}$$

is independent of dx and dy. From this it follows that the coefficients of the quadratic forms occurring in the numerator and denominator are proportional,

$$v_x = \lambda u_x, \qquad u_y = -\lambda v_y, \qquad v_y - u_x = \lambda(u_y + v_x),$$

where λ depends only upon z_0. Consequently,

$$(1 + \lambda^2)(v_y - u_x) = 0$$

and so

$$u_x = v_y, \qquad u_y = -v_x.$$

The Cauchy-Riemann equations therefore hold, and the existence of $w'(z_0) \neq 0$ follows from (1.14) and Section 1.13.

We shall now prove the same result from the existence of the limit (b) instead of (a). (The hypotheses made at the beginning of this section are still assumed to be in force.)

The expression

$$\lim_{\Delta z \to 0} \frac{|\Delta w|^2}{|\Delta z|^2} = \frac{du^2 + dv^2}{dx^2 + dy^2}$$

$$= \frac{(u_x^2 + v_x^2)\,dx^2 + 2(u_x u_y + v_x v_y)\,dx\,dy + (u_y^2 + v_y^2)\,dy^2}{dx^2 + dy^2} \quad (\neq 0)$$

is independent of dx and dy. From this it follows, as in the first case, that

$$u_x u_y + v_x v_y = 0, \qquad u_x^2 + v_x^2 = u_y^2 + v_y^2 > 0, \tag{1.15}$$

and, consequently,

$$\frac{u_x}{v_y} = \frac{-v_x}{u_y} = \mu \qquad \text{or} \qquad u_x = \mu v_y, \qquad -v_x = \mu u_y.$$

From the second equation in (1.15), we obtain $\mu = \pm 1$. Because of assumption (1.14), $\mu = 1$, and the Cauchy-Riemann equations hold. From this we conclude, as above, that the derivative $w'(z_0) \neq 0$ exists.

Remark. According to the foregoing proof, it follows from the existence of the limit (b) that $\mu = +1$ or $\mu = -1$, depending upon whether the functional determinant $u_x v_y - u_y v_x$ is positive or negative. In the latter case, the mapping $z \to w$ is indirectly conformal at the point z_0 (Exercise 39).

EXERCISES ON CHAPTER 1

1. Prove Schwarz's inequality $(x, y)^2 \leq |x|^2 |y|^2$ (Section 1.2). Under what conditions does equality hold?

Hint. $|\lambda x + \mu y|^2 = (\lambda x + \mu y, \lambda x + \mu y) = \lambda^2(x, x) + 2\lambda\mu(x, y) + \mu^2(y, y)$ is positive definite with respect to λ and μ (or it vanishes identically).

2. Prove the triangle inequality (Section 1.2):

$$||z_1| - |z_2|| \leq |z_1 + z_2| \leq |z_1| + |z_2|.$$

Under what conditions does equality hold? Generalize the inequality on the right to n complex numbers.

3. Prove, with the aid of axioms IV, Section 1.3, that the equation

$$x^2 + e = 0 \tag{1.2}$$

possesses a solution. Here e is that vector for which $ex = xe = x$ holds for all values of x.

Hint. Take as a basis for the x-plane the vector e and a vector f, linearly independent of e. Let

$$x = \alpha_1 e + \alpha_2 f, \qquad y = \beta_1 e + \beta_2 f, \qquad f^2 = \gamma_1 e + \gamma_2 f$$

be the coordinate representation of two arbitrary vectors x and y and of the vector f^2. Then

$$xy = \alpha_1\beta_1 e + (\alpha_1\beta_2 + \alpha_2\beta_1)f + \alpha_2\beta_2 f^2$$
$$= (\alpha_1\beta_1 + \gamma_1\alpha_2\beta_2)e + (\alpha_1\beta_2 + \alpha_2\beta_1 + \gamma_2\alpha_2\beta_2)f.$$

Since $xy = 0$ only if $x = 0$ or $y = 0$, the system of equations

$$\alpha_1\beta_1 + \gamma_1\alpha_2\beta_2 = 0, \qquad \alpha_2\beta_1 + (\alpha_1 + \gamma_2\alpha_2)\beta_2 = 0$$

has only the solutions $\alpha_1 = \alpha_2 = 0$ or $\beta_1 = \beta_2 = 0$. Such will be the case if and only if the determinant of the coefficients of β_1 and β_2,

$$\alpha_1(\alpha_1 + \gamma_2\alpha_2) - \gamma_1\alpha_2^2 = \alpha_1^2 + \gamma_2\alpha_1\alpha_2 - \gamma_1\alpha_2^2 \neq 0$$

for all $\alpha_1^2 + \alpha_2^2 > 0$. This quadratic form in α_1 and α_2 is therefore *definite*, and the discriminant of the form is positive:

$$-(4\gamma_1 + \gamma_2^2) > 0.$$

Now solve Eq. (1.2), setting $x = \alpha_1 e + \alpha_2 f$. The equation

$$x^2 + e = (\alpha_1^2 + \gamma_1\alpha_2^2 + 1)\,e + (2\alpha_1\alpha_2 + \gamma_2\alpha_2^2)f = 0$$

is equivalent to the system of equations

$$\alpha_1^2 + \gamma_1\alpha_2^2 + 1 = 0, \qquad \alpha_2(2\alpha_1 + \gamma_2\alpha_2) = 0,$$

which possesses two pairs of real roots:

$$\alpha_1 = \pm\frac{\gamma_2}{\sqrt{-(4\gamma_1 + \gamma_2^2)}}, \qquad \alpha_2 = \mp\frac{2}{\sqrt{-(4\gamma_1 + \gamma_2^2)}}.$$

4. Show that the product $x_1 x_2$ defined in Section 1.7 satisfies the axioms IV. 1–3.

5. What is the geometric interpretation of the multiplication of complex numbers?

6. Find the real and imaginary parts of the quotient of the complex numbers $z_1 = x_1 + iy_1$, $z_2 = x_2 + iy_2$ by multiplying top and bottom by the complex conjugate $\bar{z}_2$ of z_2.

7. Prove that the determinant of the real and imaginary parts of the complex numbers a and b is $(\bar{a}b - a\bar{b})/2i$.

8. The value of a rational expression goes over into its complex conjugate when every complex number occurring in the expression is replaced by its complex conjugate. (Show this.) Deduce from this the theorem:

If the coefficients of the algebraic equation $a_0 z^n + a_1 z^{n-1} + \cdots + a_n = 0$ are real, then the complex roots of the equation are conjugate in pairs.

9. Prove that $(z = x + iy)$

$$\frac{|x| + |y|}{\sqrt{2}} \leqq |z| \leqq |x| + |y|.$$

When does equality hold?

10. Prove that

$$\left|\frac{a - b}{1 - \bar{a}b}\right| = 1,$$

if a and b are complex numbers with $|a| = 1$ or $|b| = 1$.

11. Prove that

$$\left|\frac{a-b}{1-\bar{a}b}\right| < 1$$

if $|a| < 1$ and $|b| < 1$.

12. Prove that

$$\left|\frac{az+b}{\bar{b}z+\bar{a}}\right| = 1$$

for $|z| = 1$.

13. Derive the formulas

$$|z_1 + z_2|^2 = |z_1|^2 + |z_2|^2 + 2\,\mathrm{Re}\,(z_1\bar{z}_2),$$
$$|z_1 - z_2|^2 = |z_1|^2 + |z_2|^2 - 2\,\mathrm{Re}\,(z_1\bar{z}_2).$$

The second one includes the Law of Cosines.

14. Separate the following expressions into real and imaginary parts (z is complex):

$$iz^3, \quad \frac{1}{z-i}, \quad \frac{z-i}{z+i}, \quad \frac{1}{z^2}.$$

15. Explain the geometrical significance of the absolute value and the argument of the function $(z - i)/(z + i)$ and investigate how they vary as z varies.

16. Prove the following theorem:

$$\lim_{n\to\infty} z_n = z \neq 0$$

holds if and only if the conditions

$$\lim_{n\to\infty} |z_n| = |z| \quad \text{and} \quad \lim_{n\to\infty} \arg z_n = \arg z \,(\mathrm{mod}\, 2\pi)$$

are fulfilled.

17. Prove the *Bolzano-Weierstrass Theorem: Every bounded infinite set of points has a cluster point.*

18. Show that the set of points $|z| \leq \infty$ is both open and closed.

19. Give an example of a set of points in the plane which is neither open nor closed.

20. Show that in the complex plane (a) the complement of an open set is closed; (b) the complement of a closed set is open.

21. Prove that (a) the boundary of a domain is a closed set; (b) the union $G \cup \Gamma$ of a domain G with its boundary Γ is a closed set.

22. Prove that the union $A \cup B$ of two closed sets A and B is closed.

23. Prove that the intersection $A \cap B$ of two closed sets A and B (that is, the set of points common to A and B) is closed.

24. Prove that (a) the union $A \cup B$ and (b) the intersection $A \cap B$ of two open sets A and B are open.

25. Prove that the union of arbitrarily many open sets is open.

26. Prove the *Heine-Borel Theorem: If a bounded, closed set A is covered by a set C of open disks (that is, A is contained in the union of the disks in C), then there is a finite number of disks in C which cover A.*

27. Prove that if a real function $u(x, y)$ of two real variables possesses partial derivatives which are continuous at a point, then the function is differentiable at this point.

28. Show by means of the example $u = x^2y/(x^2 + y^2)$ that the continuity of a function and the existence of partial derivatives is not sufficient for the differentiability of the function.

29. Prove the chain rule for the differentiation of a composite function.

30. Verify that the real and imaginary parts of the functions of z given in Exercise 14 satisfy the Cauchy-Riemann equations.

31. By use of polar coordinates, investigate the real and imaginary parts of z^n and $1/z^n$, with particular rerefence to their sign.

32. Prove that the real and imaginary parts of an analytic function $w(z) = u(x, y) + i\,v(x, y)$ satisfy Laplace's equation

$$\Delta U = \frac{\partial^2 U}{\partial x^2} + \frac{\partial^2 U}{\partial y^2} = 0,$$

provided u and v possess continuous partial derivatives of the second order.

33. Prove that, in a disk on which the derivative of a complex function vanishes identically, the function is constant.

34. Show that every polynomial of the first degree $a + bx + cy$ with real coefficients is the real part of an analytic function of $z \,(= x + iy)$, and construct this function.

35. What are the most general polynomials, with real coefficients, of second degree

$$U(x, y) = a + bx + cy + dx^2 + exy + fy^2,$$
$$V(x, y) = a' + b'x + c'y + d'x^2 + e'xy + f'y^2,$$

for which $U(x, y) + i\,V(x, y)$ is an analytic function of $z = x + iy$? Show that the function in question is a polynomial of second degree in z.

36. What is the most general polynomial, with real coefficients, of the form

$$ax^3 + 3bx^2y + 3cxy^2 + dy^3$$

which is the real part of an analytic function? Construct this function.

37. Show that the form of the Cauchy-Riemann equations and of Laplace's equation is preserved when the coordinate system x, y is replaced by another rectangular coordinate system whose axes are in the same position relative to one another as were the original coordinate axes.

38. Show that in polar coordinates the Cauchy-Riemann equations have the form

$$\frac{\partial u}{\partial r} = \frac{1}{r}\frac{\partial v}{\partial \phi}, \qquad \frac{\partial v}{\partial r} = -\frac{1}{r}\frac{\partial u}{\partial \phi}$$

and Laplace's equation has the form

$$\frac{\partial^2 U}{\partial r^2} + \frac{1}{r}\frac{\partial U}{\partial r} + \frac{1}{r^2}\frac{\partial^2 U}{\partial \phi^2} = 0.$$

39. The real and imaginary parts of a function $w(z) = u(x, y) + i\, v(x, y)$ are differentiable at a certain point z_0 and $\partial(u, v)/\partial(x, y) = u_x v_y - u_y v_x < 0$. Prove that if the limit (b) in Section 1.16 exists, the mapping $z \to \bar{w} = u - iv$ is conformal at the point z_0 and the given mapping $z \to w$ is indirectly conformal (conformal with the sense of the angles reversed).

40. Suppose that the function $w(z)$ is analytic in a domain G which is symmetric with respect to the real axis. Show that $f(z) = \overline{w(\bar{z})}$ is then an analytic function of z in G.

CHAPTER 2

GENERAL PROPERTIES
OF RATIONAL FUNCTIONS

§1. THE n-TH POWER

2.1. Continuity and Differentiability

The function $w = z^n$ (n a positive integer) is a continuous function of z. For every value of z it possesses the derivative $dw/dz = nz^{n-1}$.

Proof. The increment Δw in the function w when z changes by Δz is, by the binomial formula,

$$\Delta w = (z + \Delta z)^n - z^n = nz^{n-1}\Delta z + \binom{n}{2} z^{n-2}(\Delta z)^2 + \cdots + (\Delta z)^n,$$

from which it follows that

$$|\Delta w| \leq n|z|^{n-1}|\Delta z| + \binom{n}{2} |z|^{n-2}|\Delta z|^2 + \cdots + |\Delta z|^n.$$

We see that $|\Delta w| < \epsilon$ whenever $|\Delta z|$ is sufficiently small. The n-th power is therefore a continuous function of z.

For the difference quotient of the function, we obtain

$$\frac{\Delta w}{\Delta z} = nz^{n-1} + \binom{n}{2} z^{n-2}\Delta z + \cdots + (\Delta z)^{n-1}$$

and, therefore,

$$\left|\frac{\Delta w}{\Delta z} - nz^{n-1}\right| \leq \binom{n}{2} |z|^{n-2}|\Delta z| + \cdots + |\Delta z|^{n-1}.$$

This yields, for the derivative, the formula

$$\frac{dw}{dz} = \frac{d(z^n)}{dz} = nz^{n-1}.$$

2.2. The Binomial Equation

We want to find out what values of z satisfy the equation

$$z^n = a \neq 0. \tag{2.1}$$

Introducing the notation

$$z = r(\cos \phi + i \sin \phi), \qquad a = \rho(\cos \psi + i \sin \psi),$$

23

we can write (2.1) in the form

$$r^n(\cos n\phi + i \sin n\phi) = \rho(\cos \psi + i \sin \psi).$$

This equation is fulfilled if and only if

$$r^n = \rho, \qquad n\phi = \psi + k \cdot 2\pi \qquad (k = 0, \pm 1, \pm 2, \ldots). \tag{2.2}$$

From Eq. (2.2) it follows that

$$r = \sqrt[n]{\rho}, \qquad \phi = \frac{\psi}{n} + k \frac{2\pi}{n}.$$

Those values of ϕ which differ by multiples of 2π, so that the difference of the corresponding values of k is divisible by n, give rise to the same value of z. The function z^n therefore assumes every value $a \neq 0$ at n different points, namely,

$$z = \sqrt[n]{\rho}\left[\cos\left(\frac{\psi}{n} + k \frac{2\pi}{n}\right) + i \sin\left(\frac{\psi}{n} + k \frac{2\pi}{n}\right)\right] \qquad (k = 0, 1, \ldots, n - 1). \tag{2.3}$$

As $a \to 0$, the values of z given by (2.3) all tend to zero, and for $z = 0$ they all coincide. At this point,

$$w^{(\nu)}(0) = 0 \qquad (\nu = 1, 2, \ldots, n - 1), \qquad w^{(n)}(0) \neq 0.$$

We say that the function $w = z^n$ possesses a *zero of n-th order* (or *n-tuple zero*) at the origin.

2.3. The Mapping by Means of the Power Function

The n-th power,

$$w = z^n \qquad (n \geq 2), \tag{2.4}$$

defines a function which is analytic in the entire z-plane. Its derivative, $w' = nz^{n-1}$, does not vanish for $z \neq 0$, so that by Chapter 1, (2.4) gives a mapping of the z-plane into the w-plane which is conformal whenever $z \neq 0$.

From (2.4) we have

$$|w| = |z|^n, \qquad \arg w = n \arg z. \tag{2.5}$$

Thus circles $|z| = $ const. in the z-plane correspond to circles $|w| = $ const. in the w-plane. *Every angle with vertex at the origin is multiplied by n.* The mapping is therefore not conformal at the origin $z = 0$, where $w' = 0$. If we let z make one circuit around the circle $|z| = r$, its image point w will go around the circle $|w| = r^n$ n times. Thus n different values of z, of the form (2.3), correspond to each value of $w = \rho(\cos \psi + i \sin \psi) \neq 0$. These values of z may also be written as

$$z_k = z_0 \epsilon_n^k \qquad (k = 0, 1, \ldots, n - 1), \tag{2.6}$$

where

$$z_0 = \sqrt[n]{\rho} \left(\cos \frac{\psi}{n} + i \sin \frac{\psi}{n} \right)$$

and

$$\epsilon_n = \cos \frac{2\pi}{n} + i \sin \frac{2\pi}{n}$$

is a root of the equation $z^n = 1$.

To every ray γ emanating from the origin in the z-plane there corresponds a ray from the origin in the w-plane which makes an angle with the positive real axis that is n times as large as the corresponding angle made by γ. When γ is rotated through the angle $2\pi/n$, its image ray turns through an angle of 2π. Thus, to the sector

$$F_0: \qquad 0 \leq \arg z \leq \frac{2\pi}{n}$$

there corresponds the entire w-plane. To every point on the positive real axis in the w-plane there corresponds one point on each of the two rays that bound the sector F_0; otherwise, the correspondence is one-to-one. We can obtain a correspondence which is everywhere one-to-one by slitting the w-plane along the positive real axis from the origin to infinity and associating the "upper edge" ($\arg w = 0$) of the slit with the positive real axis in the z-plane and the "lower edge" ($\arg w = 2\pi$) with the ray $\arg z = 2\pi/n$.

If the ray γ is rotated once more through the angle $2\pi/n$, its image ray turns through the whole angle 2π all over again. As in the previous case, the sector

$$F_1: \qquad \frac{2\pi}{n} \leq \arg z \leq 2\frac{2\pi}{n}$$

is therefore mapped one-to-one onto the entire slit plane. Two points z_0 and z_1 in the sectors F_0 and F_1, respectively, are mapped onto the same point in the w-plane whenever $z_1 = z_0 \epsilon_n$.

This procedure shows that the function (2.4) maps every sector

$$F_k: \qquad k\frac{2\pi}{n} \leq \arg z \leq (k+1)\frac{2\pi}{n} \qquad (k = 0, 1, \ldots, n-1)$$

in a one-to-one manner onto the whole plane slit along the positive real axis.

To every point in the z-plane there corresponds a definite point in the w-plane. Conversely, to every point $w \neq 0$ there correspond precisely n different points in the z-plane. The inverse of the function (2.4),

$$z = \sqrt[n]{w} = w^{1/n}, \tag{2.7}$$

has therefore n different values or *branches*: it is an n-valued function.

2.4. The Riemann Surface for the n-th Power

We can extend the mapping given by the n-th power $w = z^n$ by defining $w = \infty = \lim z^n$ $(z \to \infty)$ as the image of $z = \infty$. In order to make the mapping between the extended z-plane and the extended w-plane one-to-one, we now slit the w-plane along the positive real axis, make n replicas of it, and associate with each replica of the slit plane a different sector F_k ($k = 0$, $1, \ldots, n - 1$). We then bind these planes together along the edges of the slits and form a connected surface R_w in such a way that R_w will be completely

z-plane   w-plane

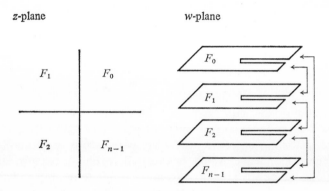

Figure 3

swept out by the image of a ray $\arg z = $ const. when this ray makes one complete turn about the origin. To achieve this, we join the "lower" edge of the first sheet to the "upper" edge of the second sheet, the lower edge of the second sheet to the upper edge of the third, etc., until, finally, we join the lower edge of the n-th sheet to the upper edge of the first sheet. Thus there arises a closed, n-sheeted surface R_w, which is known as a *Riemann surface* (cf. Fig. 3).†

The function (2.4) maps the extended z-plane in a one-to-one manner onto the n-sheeted Riemann surface R_w. Its inverse function (2.7) is therefore *single-valued* on this surface. Each point $w \neq 0$ appears on every sheet of the surface, and therefore n times in all, but the point $w = 0$ appears only once on the surface because all the sheets are joined together there.

If we go once around the point $w = 0$, we always proceed to a new sheet. Only after n revolutions do we return to our starting point. If we make k revolutions about the origin, where

$$\Delta \arg w = k \cdot 2\pi,$$

---

† The idea of making a multiple-valued function single-valued by defining it on a many-sheeted surface comes from Riemann.

then the image point in the z-plane moves, according to (2.5), in such a way that

$$\Delta \arg z = k \frac{2\pi}{n}.$$

The point z therefore returns to its starting point only when k is divisible by n; otherwise z ends up in some other sector $F_0, \ldots, F_{n-1}$ of the z-plane.

The n sheets of the surface are joined together at the points $w = 0$ and $w = \infty$. Such points are called *branch points of* $(n-1)$-*st order* of the Riemann surface R_w.

The Riemann surface R_w is also said to be a *covering surface* of the plane $|w| \leqq \infty$. This important topological notion is defined in the following way.

Let G_z and G_w be two domains in the complex planes $|z| \leqq \infty$ and $|w| \leqq \infty$, respectively. G_z is called an *unbranched covering surface* of G_w if the following conditions are fulfilled.

1) There is a mapping which associates to each point $z \in G_z$ a unique point $w \in G_w$.

2) Whenever this mapping takes a point $z = a$ into a point $w = b$, it maps a certain neighborhood U_a of $z = a$ topologically (one-to-one and continuously in both directions) onto a certain neighborhood U_b of $w = b$.

3) Every point $w \in G_w$ is the image of at least one point $z \in G_z$.

The mapping furnished by the power $w = z^n$ satisfies these properties for the domains G_z: $0 < |z| < \infty$, G_w: $0 < |w| < \infty$. Under the mapping the latter domain is covered precisely n times. The covering surface G_z is unbranched relative to the "underlying surface" G_w. If we add the branch points $z = w = 0$ and $z = w = \infty$, G_z is called a *branched* covering surface of the w-plane with branch points at 0 and ∞.

The many-sheeted surface R_w defined above is therefore a relatively branched covering surface of $|w| \leqq \infty$.

R_w can be made to a topological map of the plane G_z ($|z| \leqq \infty$) by taking the n-sheeted circular domains $|w| < r^n$ and $|w| > R^n$ that correspond under the mapping $w = z^n$ to the circular neighborhoods $|z| < r$ and $|z| > R$, respectively, as the "circular neighborhoods" of the branch points $w = 0, \infty$. R_w as well as G_z are therefore both coverings of G_w ($|w| \leqq \infty$). The surface R_w has been introduced "in space" to aid our geometrical intuition. But it is just as easy to grasp the structure of this surface by means of the domain G_z when, as above, it is divided up into "sheets" F_k ($k = 0, \ldots, n - 1$) each of which corresponds to a complete replica of the underlying surface G_w. This fact should be borne in mind when, later on, we construct Riemann surfaces which make the inverses of other single-valued mappings $z \rightarrow w$ single-valued.

2.5. The Cyclic Group of the n-th Roots

The points at which the function (2.4) assumes the same value w can be found, according to Eq. (2.6), by taking any one of them, say z, and making the substitution

$$S = z\epsilon_n^k \qquad (k = 0, \pm1, \pm2, \ldots). \tag{2.8}$$

These substitutions form what is called a *group*.

A group is defined in the following way.

A set R of elements $a, b, c, \ldots$ forms a group if the following postulates hold:

1) To every ordered pair of elements (a, b) in R there is associated an element c in R, written $c = ab$.

2) This operation is associative:

$$a(bc) = (ab)c.$$

3) There exists an element e in R, called the identity, such that, for every $a \in R$, the equation

$$ae = ea = a$$

holds.

4) Every element $a \in R$ possesses an inverse, a^{-1}, in R, satisfying

$$aa^{-1} = a^{-1}a = e.$$

In the set (2.8) we take as elements the substitutions S themselves, and we define as the group product S_1S_2 of

$$S_1 = z\epsilon_n^{k_1} \qquad \text{and} \qquad S_2 = z\epsilon_n^{k_2}$$

the result of composing them:

$$S_1S_2 = z\epsilon_n^{k_2}\epsilon_n^{k_1} = z\epsilon_n^{k_1+k_2},$$

which is again a substitution.

The conditions (1) and (2) are obviously fulfilled.

If we set

$$e = z\epsilon_n^0 = z,$$

then (3) is also satisfied.

Finally, the substitution inverse to $S = z\epsilon_n^k$ is

$$S^{-1} = z\epsilon_n^{-k} = z\epsilon_n^{n-k},$$

for

$$SS^{-1} = S^{-1}S = z\epsilon_n^{-k}\epsilon_n^k = z.$$

Since $\epsilon_n^{k+n} = \epsilon_n^k$ for every integer k, the number of different substitutions is finite, in fact equal to n. Such a group is said to be *finite* and *of order n*.

By repeated application of the substitution $S = z\epsilon_n$ we obtain all the substitutions of the group (2.8). If we set $S^2 = SS$, etc., the different substitutions of the group can be written as

$$S^0 = e, S, S^2, \ldots, S^{n-1}.$$

The elements of the group are thus powers of a single element S in the group. Such a group is said to be *cyclic*.

The group (2.8) (more generally, any cyclic group) is *commutative*, or *abelian*, that is, $S_1 S_2 = S_2 S_1$ is valid for all substitutions S_1, S_2 in the group.

§2. POLYNOMIALS

2.6. Zeros

A polynomial of degree n is an expression of the form

$$P_n(z) = a_0 z^n + a_1 z^{n-1} + \cdots + a_n. \tag{2.9}$$

The coefficients are given complex numbers $a_0, a_1, \ldots, a_n$, with $a_0 \neq 0$. It follows from Section 2.1 that $P_n(z)$ is continuous and, at every finite value of z, possesses a well-defined derivative which can be computed according to the rule familiar from the real case.

Replacing z by $x + iy$ in (2.9) and expanding $(x + iy)^{n-k}$ for each value of k $(k = 0, 1, \ldots, n - 1)$ according to the binomial formula, we obtain a decomposition of $P_n(z)$ into real and imaginary parts:

$$P_n(z) = U_n(x, y) + iV_n(x, y).$$

The functions $U_n(x, y)$ and $V_n(x, y)$ are polynomials in x and y of degree n. They are, according to Chapter 1 (Section 1.14), harmonic functions and satisfy the Cauchy-Riemann differential equations.

We want to find out what values a polynomial will assume when z varies. This question can be resolved with the help of the *Fundamental Theorem of Algebra*:

A polynomial $P_n(z)$ $(n \geq 1)$ vanishes for at least one value of z.

We shall defer the proof of this theorem until later (Section 9.13).

The following theorem also holds:

If the polynomial $P_n(z)$ vanishes for $z = z_1$, then

$$P_n(z) = (z - z_1)P_{n-1}(z), \tag{2.10}$$

where $P_{n-1}(z)$ is a polynomial of degree $n - 1$.

Indeed, if we divide $P_n(z)$ by $(z - z_1)$ until the remainder is independent of z, we obtain the identity

$$P_n(z) = (z - z_1)P_{n-1}(z) + R.$$

Setting $z = z_1$ yields $R = 0$, since $P_n(z_1) = 0$.

If we apply successively the Fundamental Theorem of Algebra and the theorem just proved, we find that

$$P_n(z) = a_0(z - z_1)(z - z_2) \ldots (z - z_n),$$

where the $z_1, z_2, \ldots, z_n$ are, apart from the ordering, uniquely determined complex numbers.

The polynomial $P_n(z)$ vanishes for the values $z = z_1, z_2, \ldots, z_n$, and only for these. The values z_i need not all be distinct. If ν_1 values of the z_i are equal to z_1, ν_2 equal to $z_2, \ldots, \nu_k$ equal to z_k ($z_1, \ldots, z_k$ all distinct), then

$$P_n(z) = a_0(z - z_1)^{\nu_1}(z - z_2)^{\nu_2} \ldots (z - z_k)^{\nu_k}, \qquad \sum_{i=1}^{k} \nu_i = n.$$

If $P(z)$ has the representation

$$P(z) = (z - z_0)^\mu Q(z) \qquad (\mu \geq 1),$$

where $Q(z)$ is a polynomial and $Q(z_0) \neq 0$, then $z = z_0$ is said to be a *zero of μ-th order* of the polynomial $P(z)$. The polynomial $P_n(z)$ above therefore has a zero of ν_i-th order at each point z_i ($i = 1, 2, \ldots, k$).

From the result just obtained, it follows that an algebraic equation of the n-th degree possesses exactly n roots (when each root is counted according to its multiplicity or order).

We speak of an *n-th order c-point* z_0 of a polynomial $P(z)$ when z_0 is an n-th order zero of the polynomial $P(z) - c$.

From this it follows that *the polynomial $P_n(z)$ assumes every finite value precisely n times*.

2.7. The Behavior at Infinity

We now want to investigate the behavior of a polynomial $P_n(z)$ when $|z| \to \infty$. If we write

$$P_n(z) = z^n \left(a_0 + \frac{a_1}{z} + \frac{a_2}{z^2} + \cdots + \frac{a_n}{z^n} \right),$$

then

$$|P_n(z)| = |z|^n \left| a_0 + \frac{a_1}{z} + \frac{a_2}{z^2} + \cdots + \frac{a_n}{z^n} \right|. \tag{2.11}$$

Since the second factor tends to the limit $|a_0| \neq 0$ when $|z| \to \infty$, we have

$$\lim_{|z| \to \infty} |P_n(z)| = \infty.$$

Moreover, it follows from (2.11) that

$$\lim_{|z| \to \infty} \left| \frac{P_n(z)}{z^n} \right| = |a_0| \neq 0.$$

We therefore say that the polynomial $P_n(z)$ possesses a *pole* of n-th order *at infinity*. Another way of expressing this is to say that the polynomial assumes the value ∞ exactly n times.

§3. RATIONAL FUNCTIONS

2.8. Zeros and Poles

A *rational function* is obtained whenever we apply the rational operations of arithmetic finitely many times to the variable z and to certain given complex numbers. We can write the result as

$$R(z) = \frac{P(z)}{Q(z)}, \tag{2.12}$$

where $P(z)$ and $Q(z)$ are polynomials

$$P(z) = a_0 z^m + a_1 z^{m-1} + \cdots + a_m,$$
$$Q(z) = b_0 z^n + b_1 z^{n-1} + \cdots + b_n$$

$(a_0, b_0 \neq 0)$ without common factors. The real and imaginary parts of the function $R(z)$ are rational functions of x and y.

From Section 1.15 it follows that a rational function $R(z)$ is differentiable whenever $Q(z) \neq 0$; the rule for differentiation is the same as in the real case.

2.9.

If we factor $P(z)$ and $Q(z)$ so that

$$P(z) = a_0(z - \alpha_1)^{\mu_1}(z - \alpha_2)^{\mu_2} \ldots (z - \alpha_k)^{\mu_k},$$
$$Q(z) = b_0(z - \beta_1)^{\nu_1}(z - \beta_2)^{\nu_2} \ldots (z - \beta_l)^{\nu_l},$$

where $a_0 \neq 0$, $b_0 \neq 0$ and $\alpha_i \neq \beta_j$ for all i, j, we obtain for $R(z)$ the representation

$$R(z) = K \frac{(z - \alpha_1)^{\mu_1}(z - \alpha_2)^{\mu_2} \ldots (z - \alpha_k)^{\mu_k}}{(z - \beta_1)^{\nu_1}(z - \beta_2)^{\nu_2} \ldots (z - \beta_l)^{\nu_l}} \tag{2.13}$$

with $K = a_0/b_0$.

The normal form (2.13) of the rational function $R(z)$ places in evidence all of its finite zeros and poles. From (2.13),

$$R(z) = (z - \alpha_1)^{\mu_1} R_1(z),$$

where $R_1(z)$ is a rational function which, at the point $z = \alpha$, assumes a finite, non-zero value. We thus designate the point α_1 as a *zero of order* μ_1 of the function $R(z)$. Similarly, $\alpha_2, \alpha_3, \ldots, \alpha_k$ are zeros of orders $\mu_2, \mu_3, \ldots, \mu_k$, respectively, of the function $R(z)$.

2*

Now let us write (2.13) in the form

$$R(z) = \frac{1}{(z - \beta_1)^{\nu_1}} R_2(z),$$

where $R_2(z)$ is again a rational function which, at the point $z = \beta_1$, has a finite, non-zero value. Therefore $|R(z)|$ increases beyond all bounds when $z \to \beta_1$, but in such a way that $(z - \beta_1)^{\nu_1}R(z)$ tends to a finite, non-zero limit. For this reason we say that $R(z)$ possesses a *pole of order* ν_1 at the point β_1. Similarly, β_2 is a pole of order ν_2, etc.

At every point z which is different from $\alpha_1, \alpha_2, \ldots, \alpha_k, \beta_1, \beta_2, \ldots, \beta_l$ the function $R(z)$ assumes a finite, non-zero value.

2.10. The Order of the Function $R(z)$

Let us consider the behavior of the function $R(z)$ when $|z|$ increases beyond all bounds. We write $R(z)$ in the form

$$R(z) = z^{m-n} \frac{a_0 + \dfrac{a_1}{z} + \cdots + \dfrac{a_m}{z^m}}{b_0 + \dfrac{b_1}{z} + \cdots + \dfrac{b_n}{z^n}}.$$

There are three different cases to treat, depending upon the relative magnitudes of m and n.

1) For $m > n$, $\lim\limits_{|z|\to\infty} R(z) = \infty$. Since

$$\lim_{z\to\infty} \frac{R(z)}{z^{m-n}} = \frac{a_0}{b_0} \neq 0, \infty,$$

∞ is a pole of order $m - n$ of $R(z)$.

2) For $m = n$,

$$\lim_{z\to\infty} R(z) = \frac{a_0}{b_0}.$$

The function therefore has a finite, non-zero value at $z = \infty$.

3) For $m < n$, $\lim\limits_{|z|\to\infty} R(z) = 0$ and, at the same time,

$$\lim_{z\to\infty} z^{n-m}R(z) = \frac{a_0}{b_0}.$$

The function has a zero of order $n - m$ at ∞.

We summarize these results in the following table.

	Number of Zeros			Number of Poles		
	In the finite plane	At infinity	All together	In the finite plane	At infinity	All together
$m > n$	m	—	m	n	$m - n$	m
$m = n$	m	—	$m = n$	n	—	$n = m$
$m < n$	m	$n - m$	n	n	—	n

The number of zeros of a rational function is equal to the number of its poles when both are counted according to multiplicity.

This number is called the *order* of the function. It is equal to the greater of the degrees m and n of the polynomials $P(z)$ and $Q(z)$ in (2.12), respectively.

2.11. c-Points of the Function

Now that we have treated the zeros and poles, we shall consider the c-points of the function $R(z)$, that is, those points z at which $R(z) = c \neq 0, \infty$. If z_0 is a c-point of the function

$$R(z) = \frac{P(z)}{Q(z)},$$

then z_0 is a zero of the function

$$R(z) - c = \frac{P(z) - cQ(z)}{Q(z)} . \qquad (2.14)$$

A zero of order μ of the function (2.14) is said to be a *c-point of order μ* of the function $R(z)$. The numerator and denominator of the function (2.14) can have no common factor, for if they did, it would be a factor of $P(z)$, and therefore $R(z)$ would not be in reduced form. From this it follows that the order of the function (2.14) is equal to the order p of $R(z)$. From what has just been proven, the function (2.14) takes the value zero p times. Therefore $R(z)$ takes the value c p times. Thus we have proved the following theorem:

A rational function assumes every value the same number of times as its order.

2.12. Decomposition into Partial Fractions

If the degree m of the polynomial $P(z)$ that forms the numerator of the rational function

$$R(z) = \frac{P(z)}{Q(z)}$$

is greater than, or equal to, the degree n of the polynomial $Q(z)$ in the denominator, we can divide the polynomial $P(z)$ by $Q(z)$ until the remainder $P_1(z)$ is of lower degree than the divisor $Q(z)$. Let $G_{m-n}(z)$ be the polynomial of degree $m - n$ obtained as the quotient. Then

$$P(z) = Q(z)G_{m-n}(z) + P_1(z)$$

and

$$R(z) = G_{m-n}(z) + \frac{P_1(z)}{Q(z)}.$$

Since $P_1(z)$ is of lower degree than $Q(z)$, the difference

$$R(z) - G_{m-n}(z)$$

has the value 0 at infinity.

We now split off all the parts of the function which become infinite at the remaining poles. According to (2.13), we have

$$R(z) = \frac{1}{(z - \beta_\lambda)^{\nu_\lambda}} \frac{P(z)}{Q_\lambda(z)} \qquad (\lambda = 1, 2, \ldots, l), \tag{2.15}$$

where $Q_\lambda(z)$ is a polynomial of degree $n - \nu_\lambda$ which does not contain $z - \beta_\lambda$ as a factor. $P(z)/Q_\lambda(z)$, therefore, has a finite, non-zero value at $z = \beta_\lambda$. Let us expand P and Q_λ into powers of $z - \beta_\lambda$:

$$P(z) = A_0 + A_1(z - \beta_\lambda) + \cdots + A_m(z - \beta_\lambda)^m,$$

$$Q_\lambda(z) = B_0 + B_1(z - \beta_\lambda) + \cdots + B_{n-\nu_\lambda}(z - \beta_\lambda)^{n-\nu_\lambda}.$$

Here, $A_0 = P(\beta_\lambda) \neq 0$ and $B_0 = Q_\lambda(\beta_\lambda) \neq 0$. If we divide the polynomial $P(z)$ by the polynomial $Q_\lambda(z)$ and terminate the division as soon as $(z - \beta_\lambda)^{\nu_\lambda}$ appears as a factor in the remainder, then

$$\frac{P(z)}{Q_\lambda(z)} = c_0 + c_1(z - \beta_\lambda) + \cdots + c_{\nu_\lambda - 1}(z - \beta_\lambda)^{\nu_\lambda - 1} + (z - \beta_\lambda)^{\nu_\lambda} \frac{P^*(z)}{Q_\lambda(z)},$$

where $c_0, c_1, \ldots, c_{\nu_\lambda - 1}$ are constants and $P^*(z)$ is a polynomial. By (2.15),

$$R(z) = G_{\nu_\lambda}\left(\frac{1}{z - \beta_\lambda}\right) + \frac{P^*(z)}{Q_\lambda(z)}, \tag{2.16}$$

where

$$G_{\nu_\lambda}\left(\frac{1}{z - \beta_\lambda}\right) = \frac{c_0}{(z - \beta_\lambda)^{\nu_\lambda}} + \frac{c_1}{(z - \beta_\lambda)^{\nu_\lambda - 1}} + \cdots + \frac{c_{\nu_\lambda - 1}}{z - \beta_\lambda}. \tag{2.17}$$

With the aid of (2.16) and (2.17), we see that

1) The difference

$$R(z) - G_{\nu_\lambda}\left(\frac{1}{z - \beta_\lambda}\right)$$

has a finite value at the point $z = \beta_\lambda$; and

2)

$$\lim_{z \to \infty} G_{\nu_\lambda}\left(\frac{1}{z - \beta_\lambda}\right) = 0.$$

2.13.

We claim that $R(z)$ is identically equal to the following sum $F(z)$:

$$F(z) = G_{m-n}(z) + \sum_{\lambda=1}^{l} G_{\nu_\lambda}\left(\frac{1}{z - \beta_\lambda}\right). \qquad (2.18)$$

The difference

$$R(z) - F(z) \qquad (2.19)$$

is a rational function. It is finite at every finite point $z \neq \beta_\lambda$ $(\lambda = 1, 2, \ldots, l)$. In order to study the difference at the point β_1, we write it as

$$\left\{R(z) - G_{\nu_1}\left(\frac{1}{z - \beta_1}\right)\right\} - G_{m-n}(z) - \sum_{\lambda=2}^{l} G_{\nu_\lambda}\left(\frac{1}{z - \beta_\lambda}\right).$$

By (1), the expression in brackets remains finite for $z = \beta_1$; the same holds for the remaining terms as well. The expression (2.19) therefore has a finite value even at β_1. In a similar way we can conclude that the difference is finite at every point β_λ. Therefore (2.19) is a polynomial in z.

Since the difference can also be written in the form

$$R(z) - F(z) = \{R(z) - G_{m-n}(z)\} - \sum_{\lambda=1}^{l} G_{\nu_\lambda}\left(\frac{1}{z - \beta_\lambda}\right),$$

it vanishes at infinity. The polynomial (2.19) therefore has no pole at infinity either. It is therefore a constant, whose value, from the above, must be zero. Thus our assertion is proved.

The rational function (2.12) can therefore be written in the form

$$R(z) = G_{m-n}(z) + \sum_{\lambda=1}^{l} G_{\nu_\lambda}\left(\frac{1}{z - \beta_\lambda}\right), \qquad (2.20)$$

and this representation in partial fractions is unique (see Exercise 6).

EXERCISES ON CHAPTER 2

1. Split the function $w = z^2$ into real and imaginary parts and investigate: (a) how straight lines in the z-plane are mapped into the w-plane; (b) how straight lines in the w-plane are mapped into the z-plane.

Hint. Consider first the lines parallel to the coordinate axes. If a configuration in the z-plane is rotated about the origin, what happens to its image in the w-plane?

2. Which curves in the z-plane correspond to the circles $|w - b| = \varrho$ under the mapping $w = z^2$? Check the dependence of these curves on the value of $|b|/\rho$.

Solution. The curves are lemniscates $|z - a||z + a| = \rho$ with $a = \sqrt{b}$.

3. What values does the function $\sqrt[4]{z}$ possess at the point $z = i$? Write these values in trigonometric and in algebraic form. In what sequence do these values come up, when, starting at $z = 1$ with the function value 1, z describes the unit circle once in the negative direction (that is, in the direction in which arg z decreases)?

4. Derive the rule for differentiation of a rational function.

5. Decompose the functions

$$\frac{1}{z^2 + 1}, \qquad \frac{z^4}{z^3 - 1}, \qquad \text{and} \qquad \frac{1}{z(z + 1)^2(z + 2)^3}$$

into partial fractions.

6. Show that the partial fraction decomposition (2.20) of a rational function is unique.

7. If the order of a rational function is p, then, by Section 2.11, the function assumes a given value c at p points, some of which may coincide for certain values of c. For which values of c does this happen?

CHAPTER 3

LINEAR TRANSFORMATIONS

§1. BASIC PROPERTIES OF LINEAR TRANSFORMATIONS

3.1. The Group of Linear Transformations

The term *linear* (or *bilinear*) *transformation* is used to designate a rational function $w = w(z)$ of first order. Its general form is

$$w = S(z) = \frac{az + b}{cz + d},\tag{3.1}$$

where the determinant of the coefficients is assumed to be different from zero:

$$ad - bc \neq 0.\tag{3.2}$$

Were this determinant zero, w would be either indeterminate ($a = b = c = d = 0$) or constant (and therefore a rational function of order zero).

The linear transformations satisfy the group axioms (1)–(4) given in Section 2.5. In particular, the identity transformation I ($w \equiv z$) plays the role of the identity in the group, and the inverse S^{-1} of the transformation (3.1) is the transformation

$$z = S^{-1}(w) = \frac{-dw + b}{cw - a}.$$

The collection (3.1) therefore forms a group under composition.

The linear transformation (3.1) furnishes a one-to-one mapping of the extended z-plane onto the extended w-plane (Section 1.9). In particular, it places in correspondence the points

$$z = \infty, \qquad w = \frac{a}{c} \qquad \text{and} \qquad z = -\frac{d}{c}, \qquad w = \infty.$$

The mapping is conformal at all other points in the plane, for when $z \neq -d/c$,

$$\frac{dw}{dz} = \frac{ad - bc}{(cz + d)^2} \neq 0.$$

3.2. The Invariance of the Cross-Ratio

Let z_1 ($\neq \infty, -d/c$) be an arbitrary point of the z-plane and let w_1 be its image:

$$w_1 = \frac{az_1 + b}{cz_1 + d}.$$

37

Then

$$w - w_1 = \frac{(ad - bc)(z - z_1)}{(cz_1 + d)(cz + d)}.$$

A similar formula holds for any other pair of associated points z_2, w_2 ($z_2 \neq \infty$, $-d/c$). Forming their quotient, we get

$$\frac{w - w_1}{w - w_2} = \lambda \frac{z - z_1}{z - z_2}, \tag{3.3}$$

where λ is the constant

$$\lambda = \frac{cz_2 + d}{cz_1 + d} \neq 0, \infty.$$

Equation (3.3) holds for all finite pairs z, $w = (az + b)/(cz + d)$. If z_3, w_3 is a third pair of corresponding points, then

$$\frac{w_3 - w_1}{w_3 - w_2} = \lambda \frac{z_3 - z_1}{z_3 - z_2}.$$

Elimination of λ between this equation and (3.3) converts the transformation (3.1) into the following form:

$$\frac{(w - w_1)/(w - w_2)}{(w_3 - w_1)/(w_3 - w_2)} = \frac{(z - z_1)/(z - z_2)}{(z_3 - z_1)/(z_3 - z_2)}. \tag{3.4}$$

Conversely, (3.4) defines a linear transformation which makes correspond to any three distinct given values $z = z_1, z_2, z_3$ any three arbitrarily prescribed values w_1, w_2, w_3.

On each side of formula (3.4) appears what is known as the *cross-ratio* of four points $\alpha, \beta, \gamma, \delta$:

$$(\alpha, \beta, \gamma, \delta) = \frac{(\alpha - \gamma)/(\alpha - \delta)}{(\beta - \gamma)/(\beta - \delta)}.$$

The equation

$$(w, w_3, w_1, w_2) = (z, z_3, z_1, z_2) \tag{3.4'}$$

asserts that *the cross-ratio of four points is invariant under a linear transformation.*

Up to now we have assumed that the points z_ν, w_ν ($\nu = 1, 2, 3$) are different from ∞. However, formula (3.4)' also holds when any one of these values is infinite. For example, if $w_3 = \infty$, then we have

$$(w, \infty, w_1, w_2) = \frac{w - w_1}{w - w_2}.$$

It is easy to see that even in this case (3.4)' determines a linear transformation which carries the points $z = z_\nu$ into the points $w = w_\nu$ ($\nu = 1, 2, 3$).

3.3. The Steiner Circles

Let us choose two arbitrary points $z = z_1$, z_2 ($\neq \infty$, $-d/c$) and denote their images under (3.1) by $w = w_1$, w_2, respectively. The transformation (3.1) can then be put into the form (3.3), where the constant λ is non-zero. Consequently,

$$\frac{|w - w_1|}{|w - w_2|} = |\lambda|\, \frac{|z - z_1|}{|z - z_2|}, \tag{3.3$'$}$$

$$\arg \frac{w - w_1}{w - w_2} = \arg \lambda + \arg \frac{z - z_1}{z - z_2} \pmod{2\pi}. \tag{3.3$''$}$$

Let ρ be a positive number. Then

$$\frac{|z - z_1|}{|z - z_2|} = \rho$$

is the equation of a circle known from elementary geometry as the *circle of Apollonius*: it is the locus of all points z for which the ratio of the distances from the "limiting points" z_1 and z_2 is constant. As z moves around this circle, the point w, according to (3.3)$'$, must move on a circle with the limiting points w_1 and w_2. The ratio of the distances from w to these limiting points is $|\lambda|\rho = $ const.

The expression

$$\phi = \arg \frac{z - z_1}{z - z_2} = \arg(z - z_1) - \arg(z - z_2)$$

gives the angle between the vectors $z - z_2$ and $z - z_1$ (Fig. 4). When z moves from z_1 to z_2 along a circular arc α, ϕ remains constant and equals the angle ϕ_0 between the tangent to this arc at z_1 and the vector $z_1 - z_2$. According to Eq. (3.3)$''$,

$$\psi = \arg \frac{w - w_1}{w - w_2} = \phi_0 + \arg \lambda$$

is also constant. Therefore the image point w also moves along a circular arc β which makes the angle $\phi_0 + \arg \lambda$ with the vector $w_1 - w_2$. If z now moves along the complementary arc of the arc α, $\phi = \phi_0 + \pi$ and, consequently, $\psi = \phi_0 + \arg \lambda + \pi$. Hence, w also moves along the complementary arc of β. The circle through the points z_1 and z_2 therefore corresponds to a circle through the points w_1 and w_2.

We shall now construct all the "Steiner circles" which belong to the limiting points z_1 and z_2. There are two kinds of circles to be distinguished. The first kind consists of the Apollonius circles (circles *about* the limiting points) which correspond to different values of ρ; the second kind consists of the circles through the limiting points which correspond to different values of ϕ (circles *through* the limiting points). From the foregoing, we see that a linear transformation (3.1) maps this system of Steiner circles onto a similar system in the w-plane having limiting points w_1 and w_2. Under this transformation circles of the first kind are mapped onto circles of the first kind, and circles of the second kind are mapped onto circles of the second kind.

From elementary geometry it is known (and, in any case, easy to prove) that through every point in the plane there passes exactly one circle of the first kind and one of the second kind in the Steiner system belonging to any two arbitrary limiting points. The two kinds of circles intersect orthogonally.

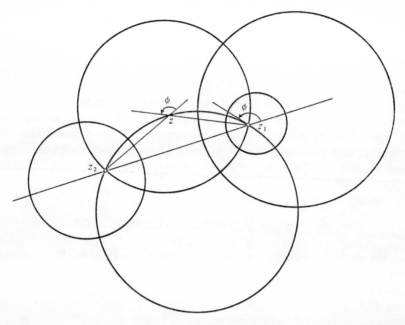

Figure 4

This result continues to hold when one or the other of the limiting points (z_1 or z_2, w_1 or w_2) moves off to infinity. If, for example, $z_1 \neq \infty$, $z_2 = \infty$, then the "circles" of the second kind become straight lines through the point z_1 and the circles of the first kind become concentric circles about this point.

For this reason, straight lines and circles are not distinguished in the theory of linear transformations: by a "circle" is understood either a (finite) circle or a straight line.

3.4. The Mapping of Circles

We now can prove easily:

A linear transformation is a circular collineation: it maps circles onto circles.

Proof. Let C_z be an arbitrary circle in the z-plane. We select two points z_1 and z_2 on it and denote their image points under the mapping (3.1) by w_1 and w_2. C_z can then be thought of as a circle of the second kind through the limiting points z_1 and z_2. Accordingly, it will be mapped by (3.1) onto a circle of the second kind through the limiting points w_1 and w_2, which proves our assertion.

A variety of other important consequences can be drawn from the above-mentioned properties of the Steiner circles.

Let C be a Steiner circle of the first kind with limiting points z_1 and z_2. The straight line through z_1 and z_2 cuts the circle C in two diametrically

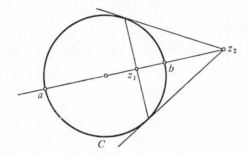

Figure 5

opposite points, $z = a$, $z = b$. By the definition of the circle C, the cross-ratio

$$(a, b, z_1, z_2) = \frac{(a - z_1)/(a - z_2)}{(b - z_1)/(b - z_2)} = -1. \tag{3.5}$$

Such a sequence of points a, b, z_1, z_2 is said to be *harmonic*. The points z_1 and z_2 are called *symmetric points* with respect to the circle C. It is easy to show that z_1 and z_2 are *polar* with respect to the circle C; this means that z_1 (or z_2) is the mid-point of the chord which joins the points of contact with the circle of the tangents drawn from the point z_2 (z_1, respectively).

From (3.5) it follows that $r_1 r_2 = \rho^2$, where r_1 and r_2 are the distances of the points z_1 and z_2 from the center of the circle C and ρ is the radius of C.

In particular, if C is a straight line, then C is the perpendicular bisector of the segment $z_1 z_2$, and the reflected points z_1 and z_2 are symmetric with respect to C.

Now we shall prove:

If a linear transformation maps a circle C_z onto a circle C_w, and if z and z^* are symmetric points with respect to C_z, then their image points w and w^* are symmetric with respect to C_w.

Indeed, C_z is a Steiner circle of the first kind with limiting points z and z^*. By Section 3.3, C_w is then also a Steiner circle of the first kind with limiting points w and w^*. Therefore, w and w^* are symmetric points with respect to C_w.

3.5. Fixed Points

We consider now the *fixed points* of a linear transformation (3.1); that is, the points z which coincide with their image points under the mapping. Such points must satisfy the condition

$$\zeta = \frac{a\zeta + b}{c\zeta + d},$$

or

$$c\zeta^2 + (d - a)\zeta - b = 0. \tag{3.6}$$

If the discriminant

$$\Delta = (a - d)^2 + 4bc = (a + d)^2 - 4(ad - bc) \tag{3.7}$$

of the quadratic equation (3.6) does not vanish, then (3.6) has two distinct roots $\zeta = \zeta_1, \zeta_2$, which are finite when $c \neq 0$. If, however, $c = 0$, then one of the roots is $\zeta = \infty$.

In the following, we shall suppose that $\Delta \neq 0$, and consider first the case $c \neq 0$, so that there are two distinct finite fixed points, ζ_1 and ζ_2. From Section 3.3 it follows that the system of Steiner circles with limiting points $z_1 = \zeta_1$ and $z_2 = \zeta_2$ remains fixed under the transformation (3.1), with circles of the first kind going over into circles of the first kind, and circles of the second kind going over into circles of the second kind.

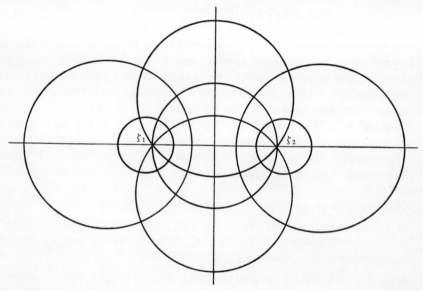

Figure 6

If $\Delta \neq 0$, but $c = 0$, then by (3.7), $\Delta = (a - d)^2$, so that $a \neq d$ and neither a nor d vanishes. The fixed points are

$$\zeta_1 = \frac{b}{d - a} \neq \infty \qquad \text{and} \qquad \zeta_2 = \infty,$$

and the mapping of the Steiner net is the same as in the case $c \neq 0$. The circles of the first kind are concentric circles about ζ_1, while the circles of the second kind are straight lines through ζ_1. The transformation (3.1) assumes the form

$$w - \zeta_1 = \lambda(z - \zeta_1), \tag{3.8}$$

with $\lambda = a/d$. This is a *similarity* (or *homothetic*) *transformation* with the fixed point ζ_1 as center.

3.6. Elliptic and Hyperbolic Transformations

If $\Delta \neq 0$ and $c \neq 0$, then, by Section 3.2, the transformation is of the form

$$\frac{w - \zeta_1}{w - \zeta_2} = \lambda \frac{z - \zeta_1}{z - \zeta_2}, \tag{3.9}$$

where $\lambda \neq 0$ is a finite constant.

If, in particular, $|\lambda| = 1$, then it follows from (3.9) (cf. Section 3.3) that every circle of the first kind in the Steiner system with limiting points ζ_1 and ζ_2 is left invariant. Under the mapping, then, the points z "flow" along these invariant circles in such a way that circles of the second kind pass over into one another. Such a mapping is said to be *elliptic*.

Similarly, one can speak of an elliptic transformation when $\Delta \neq 0$, $c = 0$. Now, the second fixed point is at infinity, and the transformation is of the form (3.8), with $|\lambda| = |a/d| = 1$, that is, $|a| = |d|$. The transformation (3.8) represents a *rotation* (through the angle $\arg \lambda$) about the fixed point ζ_1.

The value $\lambda = -1$ gives rise to an elliptic transformation of a particular kind. If we set $z_1 = w_1 = \zeta_1$, $z_2 = w_2 = \zeta_2$ in (3.3)″, then the circles of the second kind are also invariant: the arcs bounded by the limiting points are merely interchanged. This elliptic transformation is *involutory*; that is, if the point z is mapped into the point w, then w is mapped into z, as we can easily see from (3.9) ($\lambda = -1$).

Now suppose that λ is *real and positive*. Comparing the arguments of the left and right sides of (3.9) shows that, in the Steiner system belonging to the limiting points ζ_1 and ζ_2, the circles of first kind go over into one another, while the circles of second kind remain fixed. The transformation therefore represents a "flow" along the circle of second kind. A transformation of this kind is said to be *hyperbolic*.

In case $\Delta \neq 0$, $c = 0$, ζ_2 equals infinity; the transformation is of the form (3.8). It is hyperbolic when $\arg \lambda = \arg a - \arg d = 0 \pmod{2\pi}$. The mapping is *homothetic*; ζ_1 is the center and λ is the quotient or scale factor.

The general mapping (3.9) can always be thought of as the result of composing an elliptic transformation with a hyperbolic transformation. Let arg $\lambda = \phi$. We first effect the elliptic transformation in which λ is replaced by $\lambda_1 = \cos \phi + i \sin \phi$ ($|\lambda_1| = 1$), and then the hyperbolic transformation with the λ-value $\lambda_2 = |\lambda|$. The resulting general linear transformation has two different fixed points and is called *loxodromic*.

3.7. Parabolic Transformations

We now turn to the case $\varDelta = 0$. The transformation (3.1) is then called *parabolic*.

First let us assume that $c = 0$. Then, by (3.7), $a = d \neq 0$, and the linear transformation (3.1) is thus of the form

$$w = z + \omega \qquad (\omega = b/d \neq \infty). \tag{3.10}$$

If $\omega = 0$ (that is, $b = 0$), this is the identity transformation. Every point is a fixed point. If $\omega \neq 0$, (3.10) is a simple *translation* (parallel displacement) with the "displacement vector" ω. The only fixed point is $\zeta = \infty$. The straight lines L_1 in the direction ω are the streamlines; their perpendiculars, the lines L_2, pass over into one another under the flow.

It remains for us to investigate the case $\varDelta = 0$, $c \neq 0$. Equation (3.6) then yields one finite fixed point

$$\zeta = \frac{a - d}{2c}.$$

This is the only fixed point of the parabolic mapping, since the point $z = \infty$ goes over into the point $w = a/c$, so that ∞ is not a fixed point.

We now obtain

$$w - \zeta = \frac{az + b}{cz + d} - \frac{a\zeta + b}{c\zeta + d} = \frac{ad - bc}{c\zeta + d} \frac{z - \zeta}{cz + d},$$

and if we set $cz + d = c(z - \zeta) + c\zeta + d$ in the last expression, we obtain

$$\frac{1}{w - \zeta} = c \frac{c\zeta + d}{ad - bc} + \frac{(c\zeta + d)^2}{ad - bc} \frac{1}{z - \zeta}.$$

Here

$$c\zeta + d = \frac{a + d}{2}, \qquad ad - bc = \frac{(a + d)^2}{4} - \frac{\varDelta}{4} = \frac{(a + d)^2}{4},$$

and so

$$\frac{(c\zeta + d)^2}{ad - bc} = 1.$$

Thus, the transformation assumes the form

$$\frac{1}{w - \zeta} = \frac{1}{z - \zeta} + \omega',$$

where

$$\omega' = c \frac{c\zeta + d}{ad - bc} = \frac{2c}{a + d} \qquad (\neq 0, \infty).$$

If we set

$$w' = \frac{1}{w - \zeta}, \qquad z' = \frac{1}{z - \zeta}, \qquad (3.11)$$

then (3.1) reduces to the form

$$w' = z' + \omega'. \qquad (3.12)$$

This is a parallel displacement of the z'-plane. Under this mapping all straight lines L_1' in the direction ω' are left invariant. The lines L_2' which cut them orthogonally go over into one another, being displaced by an amount equal to the magnitude of ω'.

We can return to the original variables (z and w) by use of the inverse transformation of (3.11), $z = \zeta + 1/z'$. The lines L_1' thereupon go into circles L_1 which are mutually tangent at the point $z = w = \zeta$, but have no other points in common. Their common tangent is the line $z = \zeta + 1/(\tau\omega')$, which is the image of the straight line $z' = \tau\omega'$ (τ a real parameter). The perpendiculars L_2' go over into circles L_2, which are also tangent to one another at $z = \zeta$ and cut the circles L_1 orthogonally. Under a parabolic transformation the circles L_1 appear as invariant "streamlines"; the orthogonal family of circles L_2 remains unchanged as a whole, but individual circles are transformed into other circles of the family.

The parabolic transformations arise as the limiting case of the elliptic and hyperbolic transformations when the fixed points coincide; the systems of circles L_1 and L_2 can thereupon be regarded as the limiting case of the Steiner system when the limiting points ζ_1 and ζ_2 coincide.

From (3.11), it follows that for $\zeta = 0$

$$z' = \frac{1}{z}. \qquad (3.13)$$

This transformation is called an *inversion*. Since

$$|z'| = \frac{1}{|z|}, \qquad \arg z' = -\arg z,$$

we can obtain (3.13) by a reflection in the real axis followed by a further reflection in the unit circle (cf. Section 3.4.). Each of these two transformations is itself indirectly conformal.

§2. MAPPING PROBLEMS

3.8. The Conformal Mapping of Two Circular Domains onto one Another

By a circular domain K we mean a domain whose boundary consists of a circle C, so that K is either the interior or the exterior of C. If, in particular, C is a straight line, then K is one of the two half-planes bounded by C.

We pose the following problem:

Map a given circular domain K_z of the z-plane conformally onto a given circular domain K_w of the w-plane.

Solution 1. We choose three arbitrary points z_1, z_2, z_3 on the periphery of K_z and three arbitrary points w_1, w_2, w_3 on the periphery of K_w and ordered in the same sense as z_1, z_2, z_3.† The equation $(w, w_3, w_1, w_2) = (z, z_3, z_1, z_2)$, or

$$\frac{(w - w_1)/(w - w_2)}{(w_3 - w_1)/(w_3 - w_2)} = \frac{(z - z_1)/(z - z_2)}{(z_3 - z_1)/(z_3 - z_2)},$$

defines a linear transformation of z into w which carries the points z_ν into the points w_ν $(\nu = 1, 2, 3)$. Since a linear transformation maps circles onto circles, the circle C_z which passes through the points z_1, z_2, z_3 corresponds to the circle C_w through w_1, w_2, w_3. Each circular domain bounded by C_z corresponds to a circular domain bounded by C_w; it is the ordering of the points z_ν and w_ν which forces K_z to be mapped onto K_w.

From this we see that the mapping problem can be solved when three pairs of boundary points (z_ν, w_ν) $(\nu = 1, 2, 3)$ are *arbitrarily* chosen, so long as they have the same sense. The mapping is then uniquely determined by the choice of these boundary points.

Solution 2. We can also construct the mapping of K_z onto K_w so that two arbitrary points z_0 and w_0 in the *interiors* of K_z and K_w, respectively, correspond. According to §1, if such a linear mapping exists at all, it carries the symmetric point z_0^* of z_0 relative to the circle C_z onto the symmetric point w_0^* of w relative to C_w. It is therefore of the form

$$\frac{w - w_0}{w - w_0^*} = \lambda \frac{z - z_0}{z - z_0^*} \qquad (\lambda \text{ constant}). \tag{3.14}$$

As we know, such a mapping transforms the Steiner circles about the limiting points z_0, z_0^* into the Steiner circles about the limiting points w_0, w_0^*. The circles

---

† If K is the interior of C, and therefore a finite circular domain, the point z traverses the circle C in the *positive sense with respect to* K if the function arg $(z - a)$, for a an arbitrary interior point of K, *increases*. It is easy to show that this property is independent of the choice of the point a. On the other hand, if K is the exterior of C, the definition of the positive sense is reversed, so that the boundary point z moves in the negative sense with respect to the interior of C. If, in particular, C is a straight line, so that K is a half-plane, the positive direction on C with respect to K is defined as above: it is the direction in which arg $(z - a)$ increases when a is any interior point of K. *Intuitively*, this means the following: if we set up the coordinate axes in the $z(= x + iy)$-plane in the usual way (that is, so that the positive y-axis when turned in a clockwise sense through 90° will coincide with the positive x-axis), then the domain K remains to the left of the boundary when a point traverses the boundary in the positive sense (cf. Exercise 15).

C_z and C_w themselves belong to these pencils, however, and there exists one value of λ which forces (3.14) to map C_z onto C_w. We determine this value of λ in the following way.

Let z_1 and w_1 be arbitrary points on the circles C_z and C_w, respectively. If λ is calculated from the equation

$$\frac{w_1 - w_0}{w_1 - w_0^*} = \lambda \frac{z_1 - z_0}{z_1 - z_0^*} \tag{3.14$'$}$$

and substituted into (3.14), we can see that the transformation (3.14) maps the circle C_z onto the circle C_w. w_1 is thereby the image of z_1, and the mapping problem is solved.

This course of reasoning shows that we can find a conformal mapping of the domain K_z onto the domain K_w in which we can choose two pairs of corresponding points: a pair of interior points (z_0, w_0) and a pair of boundary points (z_1, w_1). Once they are picked, the linear mapping (3.14) is uniquely determined.

One may ask whether there exist analytic functions $w = w(z)$ other than linear transformations which perform this conformal mapping, under the side conditions mentioned above. Later (Section 9.16) we shall show that there are no others. The linear transformation determined above is therefore the only solution of the mapping problem.

3.9. The Conformal Mapping of the Unit Disk onto Itself

We shall now consider in more detail the mapping problem posed in Section 3.8, for the special case in which K_z and K_w are the *unit disks* $|z| \leq 1$, $|w| \leq 1$. Using the second method of solution, we choose two interior points z_0 ($0 < |z_0| < 1$) and w_0 ($0 < |w_0| < 1$) which are to correspond to one another. The transformation we are seeking is then of the form (3.14), where the constant λ is still to be determined. In the calculation of the symmetric points of z_0 and w_0 we observe that $|z_0|\,|z_0^*| = 1$, $\arg z_0^* = \arg z_0$, so that

$$z_0^* = \frac{1}{\bar{z}_0}, \qquad w_0^* = \frac{1}{\bar{w}_0}.$$

Equation (3.14) therefore becomes

$$\frac{w - w_0}{1 - \bar{w}_0 w} = \eta \frac{z - z_0}{1 - \bar{z}_0 z}, \tag{3.15}$$

in which the constant $\eta = \lambda \bar{z}_0/\bar{w}_0$. If $|z| = 1$, then

$$\left|\frac{z - z_0}{1 - \bar{z}_0 z}\right| = \left|\frac{z\bar{z} - z_0\bar{z}}{1 - \bar{z}_0 z}\right| = \left|\frac{1 - z_0\bar{z}}{1 - \bar{z}_0 z}\right| = 1.$$

Hence, the circles $|z| = 1$ and $|w| = 1$ correspond if and only if the constant η is unimodular (that is, has modulus 1).

Formula (3.15) therefore embraces all the linear transformations which map the unit disk onto itself and make the interior points z_0 and w_0 correspond.

3.10.

If, in particular, we choose $w_0 = 0$, then

$$w = \eta \, \frac{z - z_0}{1 - \bar{z}_0 z}$$

defines a mapping of the disk $|z| \leq 1$ onto the disk $|w| \leq 1$, which carries the point z_0 to the origin. We can also write this transformation in the form

$$w = \frac{az + b}{\bar{b}z + \bar{a}}; \tag{3.16}$$

here a, b are arbitrary complex numbers with $|b| < |a|$. Formula (3.16) arises when we set $\eta = a/\bar{a}$ and $z_0 = -b/a$. It therefore embraces (under the condition $|b| < |a|$) all (directly) conformal mappings of the unit disk onto itself.

Let us compute the fixed points of this transformation. We obtain these when $z = w = \zeta$:

$$\bar{b}\zeta^2 - (a - \bar{a})\zeta - b = 0.$$

If we put $a = \alpha + i\beta$, then $a - \bar{a} = 2i\beta$ (β real), and the fixed points are therefore

$$\zeta_{1,2} = \frac{i\beta \pm \sqrt{|b|^2 - \beta^2}}{\bar{b}}.$$

For $|b| = |\beta|$ $(\neq 0)$ there is only one fixed point, $\zeta_1 = \zeta_2 = \zeta = i\beta/\bar{b}$, which lies on the circumference of the unit disk: $|\zeta| = 1$. The mapping is *parabolic*.

For $|b| > |\beta|$ there are two distinct fixed points, $\zeta = \zeta_1, \zeta_2$, which both lie on the unit circle:

$$|\zeta|^2 = \zeta\bar{\zeta} = \frac{\beta^2 + (|b|^2 - \beta^2)}{|b|^2} = 1.$$

The mapping is *hyperbolic*.

For $|b| < |\beta|$, finally, the fixed points are

$$\zeta_{1,2} = \frac{i}{\bar{b}} (\beta \pm \sqrt{\beta^2 - |b|^2}).$$

Both points lie upon the same straight line through the origin and are symmetric with respect to the unit circle. The mapping is *elliptic*.

In the parabolic mapping, the circles which go through the fixed point and which are tangent to the unit circle (the so-called *oricycles*) are invariant, while, in the hyperbolic case, the Steiner circles of second kind through the fixed points (the *hypercycles*) and, in the elliptic case, the circles of first kind about the fixed points (the *cycles*), are invariant. From our previous discussion, it then follows that there is, for each case, a flow along the designated circles (see Fig. 7).

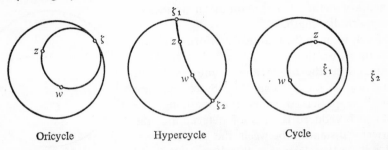

| Oricycle | Hypercycle | Cycle |

Figure 7

3.11. Conformal Self-Mappings of the Unit Disk and Non-Euclidean Geometry

If we write (3.15) in the form

$$\frac{w - w_0}{z - z_0} = \eta\,\frac{1 - \overline{w}_0 w}{1 - \overline{z}_0 z},$$

we then get, for $z \to z_0$, $w = w(z) \to w(z_0) = w_0$,

$$\frac{dw}{dz} = \eta\,\frac{1 - |w_0|^2}{1 - |z_0|^2}.$$

If we take the absolute value on both sides of this equation, we have

$$\frac{|dw|}{1 - |w_0|^2} = \frac{|dz|}{1 - |z_0|^2}.$$

Under a conformal mapping of the unit disk onto itself the differential expression

$$d\sigma = \frac{|dz|}{1 - |z|^2}$$

therefore remains invariant.

In the terminology of Henri Poincaré (1854–1912) $d\sigma$ defines the "hyperbolic length" of an element of arc dz at the point z ($|z| < 1$). In this metric, a regular curve which joins the points z_1 and z_2 and lies within the unit disk has the length

$$\int_{z=z_1}^{z_2} d\sigma = \int_{z=z_1}^{z_2} \frac{|dz|}{1 - |z|^2}. \tag{3.17}$$

If we subject the curve to an arbitrary transformation $w = S(z)$ which maps the unit disk conformally onto itself, the hyperbolic length of the curve remains fixed. This fact allows us to determine the *geodesic*, that is, the shortest path—in the given metric—which joins two points. The path must be chosen in such a way that the integral (3.17) extended over it is minimized. We can solve this problem in the calculus of variations directly by use of an elementary method based upon the invariance of the hyperbolic length.

First, we map the unit disk conformally onto itself by a function $w = S(z)$ which carries the point z_1 into the origin and z_2 into the point ρ $(0 < \rho < 1)$ on the real axis. Since the "arc length" is preserved under this mapping, the problem is reduced to that of determining the shortest "distance" between the points $z = 0$ and $z = \rho$. We claim that the shortest distance is associated with the straight line path along the segment $(0, \rho)$ of the real axis. If we set $|z| = t$, then $|dz| \geq |dt|$, and accordingly (Fig. 8),

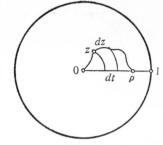

Figure 8

$$\int_{z=0}^{\rho} d\sigma = \int_{z=0}^{\rho} \frac{|dz|}{1-t^2} \geq \int_{z=0}^{\rho} \frac{|dt|}{1-t^2} \geq \int_{t=0}^{\rho} \frac{dt}{1-t^2} = \tfrac{1}{2} \log \frac{1+\rho}{1-\rho}.$$

The shortest distance is obtained precisely when the arc $(0, \rho)$ coincides with the segment $(0, \rho)$.

The segment $(0, \rho)$ is therefore the path of shortest length between the points $z = 0$ and $z = \rho$; its length is $(1/2) \log [(1 + \rho)/(1 - \rho)]$. The path of shortest length between two arbitrary points z_1 and z_2 $(|z_\nu| < 1, \nu = 1, 2)$ is therefore the circular arc $z_1 z_2$ which maps onto the segment $(0, \rho)$ under the transformation $S(z)$. This arc intersects the circumference of the unit disk orthogonally. It is uniquely determined by this property, once the points z_1 and z_2 are given.

3.12.

If we conceive of the points z in the unit disk $(|z| < 1)$ as "points" in this metric and the circular arcs which are orthogonal to the unit circle as "lines", then the rules of the non-Euclidean (hyperbolic) geometry of Bolyai and Lobachevsky apply in the resulting "plane", provided that we look upon two "segments" and two "angles" as equal when they can be transformed into one another by a conformal self-mapping $S(z)$ of the unit disk.†

We can easily show that the congruence axioms of plane Euclidean geometry hold here, as well as the remaining Euclidean axioms (for example, "through any two distinct points there is one and only one line"), with one

---

† The angle of intersection between two curves is therefore the same in the Euclidean and in the non-Euclidean metrics. But the arc lengths are different from one another, as (3.17) shows.

single exception: the *parallel axiom*. One sees immediately that, if a line L is given, then, through every point P not on L, there pass infinitely many "lines" which do not intersect L. They lie in a zone formed by two extreme "lines" through P which "point in the same direction" as L. The latter are represented in Fig. 9 by the "parallels" to L; that is, the circular arcs which are tangent at the unit circle to the arc which represents the given "line" L.

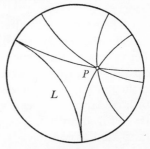

The boundary of the unit disk represents the "infinitely distant", or the "horizon", since the distance of a point z from the origin,

$$\tfrac{1}{2} \log \frac{1 + |z|}{1 - |z|},$$

Figure 9

exceeds all bounds when z approaches the boundary $|z| = 1$.

With the aid of this so-called "Poincaré model" we are able to obtain an intuitive insight into the rules of non-Euclidean geometry.

Now let us turn our attention to the figures which represent *circular arcs* in the unit disk.

As already mentioned, circular arcs which meet the unit circle $|z| = 1$ orthogonally represent non-Euclidean lines. Let us now consider a "pencil of lines" (L) through a given point $z = a$ ($|a| < 1$). The corresponding circles intersect one another at the point $z = 1/\bar{a}$ which is symmetric to a with respect to the unit circle, and the curves which intersect these circles at right angles (the orthogonal trajectories) are Steiner circles of the first kind about the symmetric points. If these circles lie within the unit disk $|z| < 1$, they represent non-Euclidean circles or *cycles*. Like the circles of Euclidean geometry, each cycle is the locus of points which have the same (non-Euclidean) distance from the "center" $z = a$.

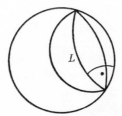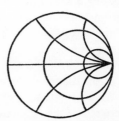

Figure 10

In Euclidean geometry, the locus of points at a fixed distance from a given line constitutes a parallel to the given line. This no longer holds in the non-Euclidean case. These loci, the so-called "contour-lines" or *hypercycles*, are represented by circular arcs which intersect the given "line" L at its two "infinitely distant" points on the unit circle. The "contour-lines" are not orthogonal to the circle $|z| = 1$; hence, they are not "lines" in the non-Euclidean geometry.

The orthogonal trajectories of a family of parallels in Euclidean geometry are likewise *parallel lines*. In non-Euclidean geometry this is no longer so. Let us consider a "pencil of lines" which is made up of "lines" L which are "parallels" to one another. They are therefore circular arcs L which are orthogonal to the boundary of the unit disk at the point ζ ($|\zeta| = 1$). Their orthogonal trajectories are the circles which are tangent at ζ to the unit circle $|z| = 1$ from within. These are neither cycles nor hypercycles, but represent a third kind of non-Euclidean "circle": *oricycles*.

The conformal mappings S of the unit disk onto itself represent motions of the non-Euclidean plane ($|z| < 1$). The *elliptic* mappings S correspond to "rotations" about the center (fixed point) $\zeta_1 = a$; the streamlines are, in this case, cycles. To the Euclidean parallel displacements there correspond two kinds of "displacements" in the non-Euclidean geometry. The first kind is made up of the *hyperbolic* transformations under which the streamlines are hypercycles joining the fixed points ζ_1 and ζ_2. The second kind consists of the *parabolic* transformations; the flow occurs here along the oricycles whose "infinitely distant" point is the fixed point ζ ($|\zeta| = 1$).

From the foregoing remarks, it is clear that the phenomena of non-Euclidean plane geometry are more varied than those of Euclidean geometry. We direct the reader to the exercises at the end of the chapter.

§3. STEREOGRAPHIC PROJECTION

3.13. Mapping of the z-Plane onto the Riemann Sphere

By the introduction of the point at infinity we succeeded in making the linear transformations one-to-one in the entire closed plane. The distinguished position afforded that point disappears when, following Riemann, we map the complex plane onto the surface of the sphere.

Let us consider a sphere which is tangent to the z-plane at the origin O. The diameter of the sphere shall have the length ρ; the point at the opposite end of the diameter through O we shall label P.

We associate to each point A of the complex plane that point A' of the sphere where the segment PA penetrates the surface of the sphere. If the point A goes off to infinity, A' goes to the "north pole", P, of the sphere, and conversely. If we associate the point at infinity with the north pole P, then the surface of the sphere is mapped in a one-to-one way onto the plane. This mapping of the surface of the sphere onto the plane is called *stereographic projection*.

The "meridians" of the sphere correspond to the lines of the z-plane which pass through O. Suppose that γ is a line of the z-plane which does not pass through O. The rays drawn from the pole P to the points of the line γ form a plane, and this plane cuts the sphere in a circle γ' through P. The tangent to γ' at the point P is parallel to γ, since it is the line of intersection of the plane through γ and the tangent plane to the sphere at P (which is parallel to the z-plane). Two lines γ_1 and γ_2 of the z-plane which intersect at the point A correspond to two circles γ_1' and γ_2' on the sphere, and these circles intersect at A', the image of A, and again at P. The angle between the circular arcs at A' has the same magnitude as the angle at P, and therefore the same magnitude as the angle between the lines γ_1 and γ_2. Since, under the mapping of a curve onto the sphere, its tangent maps onto a circle which is in contact with the image curve, we conclude that corresponding angles in the z-plane and on the Riemann sphere will have the same magnitude.

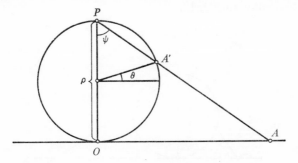

Figure 11

The mapping of the z-plane onto the Riemann sphere is therefore angle-preserving.

Let r and ϕ be the polar coordinates of a point A in the z-plane, and let λ and θ be the longitude and latitude of its image point A'. For the prime meridian (the meridian of zero longitude) we choose the meridian which maps onto the x-axis. Then

$$\phi = \lambda, \qquad r = \rho \tan \psi$$

(see Fig. 11). Since, however, $\theta + \pi/2 = 2\psi$, or $\psi = \theta/2 + \pi/4$, the equations of the mapping turn out to be

$$\phi = \lambda, \qquad r = \rho \tan\left(\frac{\theta}{2} + \frac{\pi}{4}\right).$$

Let a and a' be the distances of the points A and A', respectively, from the pole P. From Fig. 11, it is apparent that $aa' = \rho^2$, or

$$a' = \frac{\rho^2}{a}.$$

We thus obtain the mapping of the z-plane onto the Riemann sphere by reflection in a sphere whose center is P and whose radius is ρ.

From the above it follows that every linear transformation of the z-plane corresponds to a one-to-one, angle-preserving mapping of the Riemann sphere onto itself.

3.14. Rotations of the Riemann Sphere

As an application, we ask when a linear transformation represents a rotation of the Riemann sphere. In this instance, we set $\rho = 1$. In order that the mapping be a rotation of the sphere about a diameter, the end-points of every diameter must be mapped into end-points of a diameter. Let z be an arbitrary point in the z-plane, and let z^* be the point in the z-plane which is the pre-image of the point on the sphere that is diametrically opposite to the image point of z. Then, according to Fig. 12,

$$\arg z^* = \arg z + \pi, \qquad |zz^*| = 1.$$

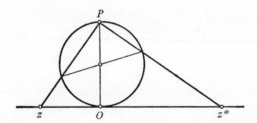

Figure 12

From this it follows that

$$z^* = -\frac{1}{\bar{z}}.$$

Together with the equation

$$w = \frac{az + b}{cz + d} \tag{3.18}$$

we must also have

$$-\frac{1}{\bar{w}} = \frac{-(a/\bar{z}) + b}{-(c/\bar{z}) + d} = \frac{-a + b\bar{z}}{-c + d\bar{z}}.$$

If we take conjugates and solve for w, we obtain

$$w = \frac{\bar{d}z - \bar{c}}{-\bar{b}z + \bar{a}}.$$

This, together with (3.18), gives

$$\frac{a}{\bar{d}} = -\frac{b}{\bar{c}} = -\frac{c}{\bar{b}} = \frac{d}{\bar{a}},$$

whence it follows that $|a| = |d|$, and therefore

$$d = \epsilon \bar{a}, \qquad c = - \epsilon \bar{b}, \qquad \text{where} \qquad |\epsilon| = 1.$$

Since we can write $1/\epsilon$ as the quotient of two conjugate complex numbers, $1/\epsilon = \mu/\bar{\mu}$, we obtain, finally,

$$w = \frac{az + b}{-\bar{b}z + \bar{a}}, \tag{3.19}$$

where we have written a and b in place of μa and μb, respectively.

If, conversely, a and b are two arbitrary complex numbers, then the linear transformation (3.19) represents a rotation of the sphere. We refer to Exercises 35 and 36 for the proof.

Formula (3.19) therefore expresses the general form of a rotation of the sphere.

It can be proved by elementary geometry that the most general congruence mapping (motion) of the surface of the sphere amounts to a rotation about a suitably chosen axis.

EXERCISES ON CHAPTER 3

1. Show that the linear transformations (3.1) satisfy the postulates (1) and (2) for a group (Section 2.5).

2. Show that the linear transformation which carries the points z_1 and z_2 ($\neq \infty$) into the points w_1 and $w_2 = \infty$, respectively, maps the Steiner circles belonging to z_1 and z_2 into circles about w_1 and straight lines through w_1.

3. Find the linear transformation which carries (a) the points $z = 0, 1, i$ into the points $w = -1, -i, 0$; (b) the points $z = -1, 1, i$ into the points $w = 0, 3, \infty$.

4. A linear transformation maps the points z_1, z_2, z_3, into the points w_1, w_2, w_3. Determine, *geometrically*, the point w which corresponds to a given point z.

5. Which transformations (3.1) map the plane congruently onto itself?

6. What linear transformation corresponds to a rotation of the z-plane through 90° about the point $z = 2$?

7. Map the z-plane congruently onto the w-plane in such a way that the points $z = 2, 3$ and $w = 2i, i$ correspond to one another. By what sort of rotation can this mapping be geometrically defined?

8. Determine the similarity transformation which carries the points $z = 1, 3$ into the points $w = -1, -2 + i$, and decompose it into a rotation and a perspectivity with the same point as center.

9. Show that under reflection in a circle about O (a) every line l which does not pass through O goes over into a circle through O whose tangent at O is

3

parallel to l, (b) every circle K drawn through O goes over into a line which is parallel to the tangent to K at O, (c) every circle which does not pass through O goes over into a circle homothetic with respect to O to the given circle.

10. Which circles correspond to the straight lines $y = x$, $y = x/2$ and to the unit circle when the z-plane ($z = x + iy$) is reflected in the circle $|z - 2| = 1$? Also construct the circles geometrically.

11. Show that there exists a linear transformation which maps four arbitrarily given points onto the points $1, -1, k, -k$, where k depends upon the given points. How many different solutions are there to this problem, and how are they related?

12. Determine the type of the following linear transformations:

$$w = \frac{z}{2z - 1}, \qquad w = \frac{2z}{3z - 1}, \qquad w = \frac{3z - 4}{z - 1}, \qquad w = \frac{z}{2 - z}.$$

13. Show that every involutory linear transformation is elliptic.

14. Separate the linear transformation (3.1) into a similarity transformation and an inversion.

Hint. First bring the transformation into the form $w - w_0 = \alpha/(z - z_0)$, where $z_0 = -d/c$, $w_0 = a/c$ and α is a constant.

15. Let a be a point in the interior of the circle $|z - z_0| = \rho$, so that $|a - z_0| < \rho$. Prove that if z moves along the circle in such a way that $\theta = \arg (z - z_0)$ increases, then $\phi = \arg (z - a)$ also increases.

Hint. If $|a - z_0| = r \ (< \rho)$, $\arg (a - z_0) = \alpha$, then

$$\phi = \arctan \frac{\rho \sin \theta - r \sin \alpha}{\rho \cos \theta - r \cos \alpha} \qquad \text{and} \qquad d\phi = \frac{\rho(\rho - r \cos (\theta - \alpha))}{|z - a|^2} \, d\theta.$$

From this it is apparent that $d\theta$ and $d\phi$ have the same sign.

16. Map the half-plane $\operatorname{Re} z \leq \frac{1}{2}$ conformally onto the unit disk $|w| \leq 1$ in such a way that the points $z = 0$, ∞ correspond to the points $w = 0, -1$. Divide up the w-plane by the coordinate axes and the bisectors of the angles between them, draw the corresponding curves in the z-plane, and investigate how the different sections of the two planes are associated.

17. Suppose that there are given two circles in the z-plane which have no common points. Show that the domain bounded by these two circles can be mapped onto an annulus whose boundary is made up of two concentric circles, and that the annulus is uniquely determined up to a similarity transformation. (The logarithm of the ratio of the radii of the image circles is termed the *modulus* of the domain.)

18. Map the domain bounded by the circles $|z| = 1$ and $|z - \frac{1}{4}| = \frac{1}{4}$ conformally onto an annulus whose outer boundary is the circle $|w| = 1$. How large is the radius of the inner circle?

Answer. $2 - \sqrt{3}$.

19. Reflect the point z in a given circle K_1, and reflect the image of z in another fixed circle K_2. Show that the resulting point w is related to the point z by a linear transformation and investigate how the type of this transformation depends upon the relative position of the circles K_1 and K_2.

20. Let K_1 and K_2 be two circles, one of which lies completely inside the other. Suppose that there exists a circle k_1 with the following properties: (a) it is tangent to K_1 and K_2; (b) if one draws a circle k_2 which is tangent to K_1, K_2, and k_1, and then a circle k_3 which is tangent to K_1, K_2, and k_2, etc., a circle k_n is eventually obtained which is tangent to K_1, K_2, k_{n-1} and to the first circle k_1, so that one has a closed chain of mutually tangent circles k_1, k_2, ..., k_n which are all tangent to the circles K_1 and K_2. Show that under this assumption the chain of circles always closes, no matter which of the circles tangent to K_1 and K_2 is taken as the initial circle k_1.

21. Prove that the sum of the angles $\alpha + \beta + \gamma$ of a non-Euclidean triangle in the Poincaré model is always less than two right angles.

Hint. An arbitrary triangle can always be brought by a non-Euclidean motion into such a position that one of its vertices lies at the origin.

22. Prove that the expression for arc length in the hyperbolic geometry of the half-plane $\eta = \operatorname{Im} \zeta > 0$ is

$$\int_{\zeta_0}^{\zeta} \frac{|d\zeta|}{2\eta}.$$

Hint. Map the disk $|z| < 1$ conformally onto the half-plane $\eta > 0$.

23. Prove that the so-called *angular defect* of a non-Euclidean triangle, $\pi - (\alpha + \beta + \gamma)$, is equal to quadruple the (non-Euclidean) area of the triangle.

Hint. In the Poincaré model the non-Euclidean element of area is computed from the expression

$$d\omega = \frac{df}{(1 - |z|^2)^2} = \frac{dF}{4\eta^2},$$

where df is the ordinary Euclidean element of area at the point $z = x + iy$ of the disk $|z| < 1$ ($df = dx\, dy$) and dF is the element of area at the point $\zeta = \xi + i\eta$ in the half-plane $\eta > 0$ ($dF = d\xi\, d\eta$).

It is simplest to treat first the case of a triangle in the half-plane $\eta > 0$ having one vertex at $\zeta = \infty$. An arbitrary triangle can be transformed by a non-Euclidean motion into a triangle which has two vertices A and B on a line $\xi = \text{const}$. If a parallel to the imaginary axis is drawn through the third vertex C, the problem reduces to the special case treated above.

24. Determine the (non-Euclidean) area of a triangle whose angles are all 0.

25. Prove that in the Poincaré model of non-Euclidean geometry the normal from a point a to the line L is the shortest distance from a to L.

26. Draw the normal N from a point z to a "line" L and two parallels through z. Calculate the angle between the two parallels with the aid of the (non-Euclidean) length of the normal N.

Hint. There is no restriction in taking for L the diameter $(-1, +1)$ and choosing z to lie on the imaginary axis.

27. Show that if the sum of the angles of a circular triangle ABC is smaller than π, then the sides of the triangle have a common orthocircle.

Hint. Make a linear transformation which carries the circles AB and AC into straight lines.

28. Show that if the sum of the angles in a circular triangle is equal to π, then the sides intersect at a common point.

Hint. Compare Exercise 27.

29. Let z_1 and z_2 be two points in the z-plane. Prove that the (chordal) distance between their image points on the Riemann sphere is

$$\frac{|z_1 - z_2|}{\sqrt{(1 + |z_1|^2)(1 + |z_2|^2)}},$$

when the diameter of the Riemann sphere has length one.

30. Show that the differential expression $|dz|/(1 + |z|^2)$, which represents the length of the element of arc on the Riemann sphere at the point which corresponds to the point z in the plane, is invariant under the transformation (3.19).

31. Determine by use of the differential expression given in the previous exercise and the procedure of Section 3.11 the shortest distance between two points on the Riemann sphere.

32. Prove that reflection in a sphere transforms (a) every plane which does not go through the center O into a sphere through O whose tangent plane at O is parallel to the given plane, (b) every sphere which does not go through O into a sphere which is homothetic to the given sphere with respect to O.

Hint. One can proceed in the same way as with the corresponding theorems concerning reflection in the plane (Exercise 9).

33. Prove that every circle in the z-plane corresponds to a circle on the Riemann sphere which does not pass through the pole P, and conversely.

34. Derive formula (3.16) in the way in which formula (3.19) was derived, bearing in mind that under a conformal mapping of the unit disk onto itself symmetric points z and $z^* = 1/\bar{z}$ go over into symmetric points w and $w^* = 1/\bar{w}$.

35. Let a and b be two arbitrary complex numbers. Prove that the transformation (3.19) is elliptic and that its fixed points correspond to the opposite ends of a diameter on the Riemann sphere.

36. Prove that if the fixed points of an elliptic transformation map onto the opposite ends of a diameter on the Riemann sphere, then this transformation corresponds to a rotation of the Riemann sphere about the said diameter.

37. Prove that reflection in a sphere is an angle-preserving transformation.

38. Show that the hyperbolic distance between the points z_1 and z_2 ($|z_1|, |z_2| < 1$) is given by the formula $\frac{1}{2} \log (z_1, z_2, \zeta_1, \zeta_2)$, where ζ_1 and ζ_2 ($|\zeta_1| = |\zeta_2| = 1$) are the "infinitely distant" points on the "line" L through z_1, z_2, situated on L in the order $\zeta_2, z_1, z_2, \zeta_1$.

Hint. The mapping S (Section 3.11) which carries z_1 to the origin and z_2 to the point ρ takes ζ_2 to -1 and ζ_1 to $+1$. By the invariance of the cross-ratio, $(z_1, z_2, \zeta_1, \zeta_2) = (0, \rho, +1, -1) = (1 + \rho)/(1 - \rho)$.

39. Prove that the constant λ in Eq. (3.9) satisfies the equation $\lambda + 1/\lambda + 2 = (a + d)^2/(ad - bc)$, where a, b, c, d are the constants appearing in (3.1).

Hint. By Section 3.2, $\lambda = (c\zeta_1 + d)/(c\zeta_2 + d)$; ζ_1 and ζ_2 can be calculated explicitly from (3.6).

40. What values does the function σ defined by the equation $\sigma + 4 = (a + d)^2/(ad - bc)$ assume when the transformation (3.1) is (a) elliptic, (b) hyperbolic, (c) loxodromic, (d) parabolic? What is the connection between σ and the discriminant Δ (cf. Eq. 3.7)?

CHAPTER 4

MAPPING BY RATIONAL FUNCTIONS OF SECOND ORDER

4.1. Reduction to the Function $w = z^2$

A rational function of second order has the general form

$$w = w(z) = \frac{P(z)}{Q(z)} = \frac{a_0 z^2 + a_1 z + a_2}{b_0 z^2 + b_1 z + b_2}, \tag{4.1}$$

where at least one of the coefficients a_0, b_0 does not vanish, and the numerator and denominator have no common zeros. In what follows, we shall show that by use of linear transformations one can always reduce (4.1) to the form $w = z^2$:

Equation (4.1) can be written as

$$\omega(w) = (\zeta(z))^2, \tag{4.2}$$

where ω and ζ are certain linear transformations of the variables w and z, respectively.

4.2.

We shall carry out the proof in three steps.

1) Suppose that $w(z)$ is a polynomial $(Q(z) \equiv b_2 \neq 0)$. Then

$$w(z) = c_0 z^2 + c_1 z + c_2 \qquad (c_0 \neq 0).$$

By completing the square, we obtain

$$w = c_0 (z - z_0)^2 + w_0,$$

where z_0 and w_0 are constants. Thus, if we set $\omega = (w - w_0)/c_0$, $\zeta = z - z_0$, we get an equation of the form (4.2).

2) Suppose the denominator is a perfect square: $Q(z) = b_0(z - z_1)^2$. By expanding P into powers of $z - z_1$ we obtain

$$w = \frac{P}{Q} = \frac{c_0}{(z - z_1)^2} + \frac{c_1}{z - z_1} + c_2 \qquad (c_0 \neq 0).$$

Thus, if we replace $1/(z - z_1)$ by a new variable, (2) reduces to the previous case (1), and the required transformations are

$$\omega = \frac{w - w_0}{c_0}, \qquad \zeta = \frac{1}{z - z_1} - z_0.$$

3) There still remains the case in which the polynomial Q has one or two *simple* zeros.

We form the derivative

$$w'(z) = \frac{Az^2 + 2Bz + C}{Q^2},$$ (4.3)

where

$$A = \begin{vmatrix} a_0 & b_0 \\ a_1 & b_1 \end{vmatrix}, \qquad B = \begin{vmatrix} a_0 & b_0 \\ a_2 & b_2 \end{vmatrix}, \qquad C = \begin{vmatrix} a_1 & b_1 \\ a_2 & b_2 \end{vmatrix}.$$ (4.3)'

At most one of these determinants can vanish. For the vanishing of two of them would imply the vanishing of the third; thus the coefficients a and b would be proportional, and w would reduce to a constant. But this is ruled out by our assumption in (4.1).

The equation

$$Az^2 + 2Bz + C = 0$$

is therefore of the first or second degree, and hence possesses at least one root $z = z_0$.

We claim that $Q(z_0) \neq 0$. For otherwise, the function $w(z)$ would have a simple pole at z_0, and therefore its derivative $w'(z)$ would have a double pole at z_0, as the partial fraction expansion of $w(z)$ shows. But, if $Q(z_0) = 0$, we could cancel out a common factor $z - z_0$ in (4.3), in which case w' would be left with a simple pole at z_0. Hence the case $Q(z_0) = 0$ cannot occur. From this it follows that $w'(z_0) = 0$.

Let us write $w(z_0) = w_0$ and form the difference

$$w(z) - w_0 = \frac{P(z)}{Q(z)} - \frac{P(z_0)}{Q(z_0)} = \frac{H(z)}{Q(z_0)Q(z)}.$$

The function $H(z)$ is a polynomial of at most second degree. Since the numerator H vanishes at $z = z_0$, it contains the linear factor $z - z_0$,

$$H(z) = (z - z_0)H_1(z),$$

from which it follows that

$$\frac{w(z) - w_0}{z - z_0} = \frac{H_1(z)}{Q(z_0)Q(z)}.$$ (4.4)

If we let z tend to z_0, the left-hand side of (4.4) will converge to $w'(z_0) = 0$. Hence $H_1(z_0) = 0$ and H_1 is divisible by $z - z_0$. Since, however, $H(z)$ can be of degree at most two, we must have $H = c_0(z - z_0)^2$ $(c_0 \neq 0)$, $H_1 = c_0(z - z_0)$. Therefore, by (4.4)

$$\frac{c_0}{w - w_0} = Q(z_0) \frac{Q(z)}{(z - z_0)^2}.$$ (4.4)'

We can now work with the right-hand side of this equation as we did in case (2). By so doing, we can easily determine linear transformations $\omega(w)$ and $\zeta(z)$ such that

$$\omega(w) = (\zeta(z))^2.$$

4.3. The Mapping $z \to w(z)$

The nature of the mapping effected by a rational function of the second order is revealed by (4.2). The function $\omega = \zeta^2$ maps the ζ-plane onto a two-sheeted Riemann surface R_ω having branch points of the first order at $\omega = 0$, ∞. At the corresponding points $\zeta = 0$, ∞ (and only at these) the mapping is not conformal.

Now, by means of the inverse $z = z(\zeta)$ of the linear transformation $\zeta = \zeta(z)$, we go back from ζ to the variable z. This mapping is everywhere conformal. Similarly, by inverting the equations $\omega = \omega(w)$, we obtain a second linear transformation, $w = w^*(\omega)$. Put $z(0) = z_1$, $z(\infty) = z_2$ and $w^*(0) = w_1$, $w^*(\infty) = w_2$. The mapping $w = w(z)$ is generated when we carry out the mappings: $z \to \zeta \to \omega \to w$ in succession. Hence, the composite mapping is conformal everywhere except at the points z_1, z_2. The image of the z-plane is a two-sheeted Riemann surface R_w with branch points of the first order at $w_1 = w(z_1)$, $w_2 = w(z_2)$. We can construct the surface R_w by slitting the w-plane along a curve l_w which joins the branch points w_1 and w_2, and then superposing this slit plane on a replica of itself in such a way that the opposing edges of the l_w-slit lying on different sheets are joined together in a cross-wise fashion.

The mapping $z \to w$ therefore has very much the same structure as the mapping $w = z^2$. The branch points $w = 0$, ∞ are merely shifted to $w = w_1$, w_2, and the pre-images $z = 0$, ∞ of these branch points are shifted to $z = z_1$, z_2. All this becomes particularly clear if one thinks in terms of the Riemann spheres associated with the z- and w-planes, instead of the planes themselves (cf. Section 3.13).

4.4.

The notation introduced above allows us to bring (4.2) into a simple analytic form. Since the linear mapping $z \to \zeta$ carries the points $z = z_1$, z_2 into the points $\zeta = 0$, ∞, it is of the form

$$\zeta = \alpha \frac{z - z_1}{z - z_2} \qquad (\alpha \text{ a constant} \neq 0),$$

provided z_1 and z_2 are both finite. In the same way

$$\omega = \beta \frac{w - w_1}{w - w_2} \qquad (\beta \text{ a constant} \neq 0).$$

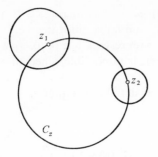
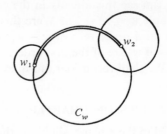

Figure 13

Thus (4.2) assumes the form

$$\frac{w - w_1}{w - w_2} = \lambda \left(\frac{z - z_1}{z - z_2}\right)^2 \qquad (\lambda \neq 0). \tag{4.5}$$

It is easy to see how these formulas are altered when one of the points z_1, z_2, w_1, w_2 is equal to ∞.

From (4.5) it follows that

$$\frac{|w - w_1|}{|w - w_2|} = |\lambda| \left(\frac{|z - z_1|}{|z - z_2|}\right)^2,$$

$$\arg \frac{w - w_1}{w - w_2} = \arg \lambda + 2 \arg \frac{z - z_1}{z - z_2}.$$

Thus the two families of Steiner circles with limiting points z_1 and z_2 (cf. Section 3.3) are transformed under the mapping (4.5) into the corresponding families of Steiner circles with limiting points w_1 and w_2. If z traverses once a circle of the first kind, then w will describe the corresponding circle twice. If z goes along a circle C_z of the second kind from z_1 to z_2, then w goes along the image circle C_w from w_1 to w_2. But if z continues further and goes along complementary arc $z_2 z_1$, then w will retrace the *same* arc of C_w in the opposite direction $w_2 w_1$.

Were we to choose the circular arc $w_1 w_2$ of C_w as the curve l_w in the construction of the Riemann surface described in Section 4.3, one sheet of the surface would correspond to the interior of the circle C_z while the other sheet would correspond to the exterior of this circle.

4.5. A Remark about Rational Functions of Higher Order

If $w(z)$ is a rational function of order ≥ 3, it cannot, in general, be brought into the special form

$$\frac{w - w_1}{w - w_2} = \lambda \left(\frac{z - z_1}{z - z_2}\right)^n \tag{4.6}$$

3*

by means of linear transformations $\zeta = \zeta(z)$, $\omega = \omega(w)$ analogous to (4.5). One can see this already in the case of a polynomial of third degree, by the example $w = z^3 - 3z$. Were this to have the representation (4.6), z_1 would be a third-order zero of $w - w_1$; this, however, is impossible, since all of the zeros of w' are of the first order.

We shall reconsider this question in greater detail in Chapter 9.

EXERCISES ON CHAPTER 4

1. Map the z-plane, slit along the positive real axis from 1 to ∞, conformally onto the unit disk in such a way that the points 0 and 1 remain fixed.

2. Investigate the mapping by the function

$$w = \left(1 + \frac{z}{n}\right)^n$$

for positive integer values of n.

3. Investigate the mapping by the function $w = \frac{1}{2}(z + 1/z)$.

4. Map the z-plane, slit along the positive real axis from 1 to ∞ and along the negative real axis from -1 to $-\infty$, conformally onto the unit disk in such a way that 0 and 1 are fixed points.

5. Map the z-plane, slit along the line segment joining the two points a and b, conformally onto the unit disk in such a way that the points $z = a$, ∞ correspond to the points $w = -1, 0$.

CHAPTER 5

THE EXPONENTIAL FUNCTION AND ITS INVERSE. THE GENERAL POWER

§1. DEFINITION AND BASIC PROPERTIES OF THE EXPONENTIAL FUNCTION

5.1. Extension of the Real Exponential into the Complex Domain

For real values of x

$$\lim_{n \to \infty} \left(1 + \frac{x}{n}\right)^n = e^x.$$

We shall take this property as the basis for our definition of the exponential function in the complex domain.

Let us replace x by the complex number $z = x + iy$; we shall show that the resulting sequence

$$c_n = \left(1 + \frac{z}{n}\right)^n \qquad (n = 1, 2, \ldots) \tag{5.1}$$

converges as $n \to \infty$.

A necessary and sufficient condition for the existence of a finite, non-zero limit of the sequence (5.1) is that both $|c_n|$ and $\arg c_n$ tend to definite finite values as $n \to \infty$, the first of which is positive. If we replace z by $x + iy$ in (5.1) we obtain

$$|c_n| = \left|1 + \frac{x}{n} + i\frac{y}{n}\right|^n = \left\{\left(1 + \frac{x}{n}\right)^2 + \left(\frac{y}{n}\right)^2\right\}^{n/2},$$

so that

$$\log|c_n| = \frac{n}{2} \log\left(1 + 2\frac{x}{n} + \frac{x^2 + y^2}{n^2}\right) = \frac{n}{2}\left\{\frac{2x}{n} + \left[\frac{1}{n^2}\right]\right\} = x + \left[\frac{1}{n}\right]. \tag{5.2}$$

The expression $[1/n^k]$ denotes a function of n which, when multiplied by n^k, remains bounded as $n \to \infty$. From (5.2) it is apparent that $\log|c_n| \to x$. Hence,

$$\lim_{n \to \infty} |c_n| = e^x.$$

The argument of c_n is

$$\arg c_n = n \arg\left(1 + \frac{z}{n}\right) = n \operatorname{Arc\,tan} \frac{y}{n + x}. \tag{5.3}$$

Here, for sufficiently large n, the principal branch of the function arc tan, assuming values in the interval $(-\pi/2, \pi/2)$, can be taken. From Eq. (5.3) it follows that

$$\lim_{n \to \infty} \arg c_n = y.$$

Hence, for every finite value of $z = x + iy$, the limit

$$\lim_{n \to \infty} \left(1 + \frac{z}{n}\right)^n = e^x(\cos y + i \sin y) \tag{5.4}$$

exists.

We now define the function e^z by means of the formula

$$e^z = \lim_{n \to \infty} \left(1 + \frac{z}{n}\right)^n. \tag{5.5}$$

From (5.4) and (5.5) it follows that

$$e^z = e^{x+iy} = e^x(\cos y + i \sin y), \tag{5.6}$$

and consequently

$$|e^z| = e^x, \qquad \arg e^z = y. \tag{5.7}$$

5.2. Properties of the Exponential Function

For real values of the variable z the exponential function is always different from zero. This property continues to hold for complex values of z, since, by (5.7), $|e^z| = e^x > 0$.

   If a function of z approaches a limit when z tends to infinity along some definite path, the limit is called an *asymptotic value* of the function along this path. According to the relations (5.7), the exponential function possesses an asymptotic value along every path $z = z(t) = x(t) + iy(t)$ $(0 \leq t < \infty)$ for which $|x(t)| \to \infty$ as $t \to \infty$. This asymptotic value is ∞ if $x(t) \to +\infty$, and it is 0 if $x(t) \to -\infty$.

   Next we may verify that the addition formula for the exponential function retains its validity. If $z_1 = x_1 + iy_1, z_2 = x_2 + iy_2$, then by (5.6)

$$e^{z_1+z_2} = e^{x_1+x_2}[\cos (y_1 + y_2) + i \sin (y_1 + y_2)].$$

On the other hand,

$$e^{z_1} e^{z_2} = e^{x_1} e^{x_2}(\cos y_1 + i \sin y_1)(\cos y_2 + i \sin y_2)$$
$$= e^{x_1+x_2}[\cos (y_1 + y_2) + i \sin (y_1 + y_2)].$$

The addition theorem

$$e^{z_1+z_2} = e^{z_1} e^{z_2} \tag{5.8}$$

therefore holds for complex values of z_1 and z_2.

From (5.8) and (5.6) it follows that

$$e^z e^{-z} = e^0 = 1,$$

hence,

$$e^{-z} = \frac{1}{e^z}.$$

When the addition formula is applied to a sum involving n terms, we obtain

$$(e^z)^n = e^{nz}, \tag{5.9}$$

where n is a positive integer. If we extend the definitions

$$a^0 = 1, \qquad a^{-n} = \frac{1}{a^n}$$

to complex values of a, then formula (5.9) holds for all integer values of n.

When z is chosen, in (5.6), to be purely imaginary, $z = iy$ or $z = -iy$, we obtain *Euler's formulas*:

$$e^{iy} = \cos y + i \sin y, \qquad e^{-iy} = \cos y - i \sin y \tag{5.10}$$

and

$$\cos y = \frac{e^{iy} + e^{-iy}}{2}, \qquad \sin y = \frac{e^{iy} - e^{-iy}}{2i}. \tag{5.11}$$

Equations (5.10) and (5.9) imply *de Moivre's formula*:

$$(\cos \phi + i \sin \phi)^n = (e^{i\phi})^n = e^{in\phi} = \cos n\phi + i \sin n\phi.$$

These formulas can be used to express powers and products of sines and cosines in terms of sines and cosines of multiple angles. For example,

$$\cos^3 \phi = \left(\frac{e^{i\phi} + e^{-i\phi}}{2}\right)^3 = \tfrac{1}{8}(e^{3i\phi} + e^{-3i\phi}) + \tfrac{3}{8}(e^{i\phi} + e^{-i\phi})$$

$$= \tfrac{1}{4} \cos 3\phi + \tfrac{3}{4} \cos \phi.$$

Euler's formulas offer a new and simple means of representing complex numbers z:

$$z = r(\cos \phi + i \sin \phi) = r\, e^{i\phi}.$$

If, for example, we set $r = 1$, $\phi = \pi$, we obtain

$$e^{i\pi} = -1.$$

For $\phi = n \cdot 2\pi$ it turns out that

$$e^{n \cdot 2\pi i} = 1 \qquad (n = 0, \pm 1, \pm 2, \ldots).$$

These formulas exhibit a remarkable connection between the numbers e, π, i, and -1.

5.3. The Derivative of the Exponential Function

Since the real and imaginary parts of the exponential function are continuous, the function itself is continuous. We are now going to show that e^z possesses a derivative for every value of $z = x + iy$.

Let us split the function $w = e^z$ into its real and imaginary parts:

$$w = u + iv = e^x \cos y + i\, e^x \sin y.$$

The increment in the functions u and v that corresponds to an increment $\Delta z = \Delta x + i\Delta y$ in the variable z can be written as

$$\Delta u = e^x \cos y\, \Delta x - e^x \sin y\, \Delta y + \rho(\rho),$$
$$\Delta v = e^x \sin y\, \Delta x + e^x \cos y\, \Delta y + \rho(\rho),$$

where $\rho = |\Delta z|$, and where (ρ) denotes a function of ρ which tends to zero when ρ tends to zero. Thus we obtain for the increment of the function w the expression

$$\Delta w = \Delta u + i\Delta v = e^x \cos y\, (\Delta x + i\Delta y) - e^x \sin y\, (\Delta y - i\Delta x) + \rho(\rho)$$
$$= e^x(\cos y + i \sin y)\Delta z + \Delta z(\Delta z).$$

From this it follows that

$$\frac{dw}{dz} = \frac{de^z}{dz} = e^z,$$

and the differentiation formula from the real case is the same in the complex domain. Consequently, *the exponential function is analytic in the whole z-plane* ($z \neq \infty$). Such functions are known as *entire* (or *integral*) *functions*.

From the differentiation formula it follows at once that the exponential function possesses derivatives of all orders, and that each of these derivatives is equal to e^z.

5.4. The Periodicity of the Exponential Function

Up to now we have discussed a number of properties of the exponential function which turn out to hold for both real and complex values of the independent variable. We now come to a new and remarkable property which appears only when we make the transition to complex values of z.

When z changes by an amount $n \cdot 2\pi i$ ($n = \pm 1, \pm 2, \ldots$), e^z remains unchanged since

$$e^{z+n \cdot 2\pi i} = e^z\, e^{n \cdot 2\pi i} = e^z. \tag{5.12}$$

The exponential function is therefore periodic, with $2\pi i$ as its period.

In general, a function $w = f(z)$ is called *periodic* if there exists a constant $\omega \neq 0$ (a *period*) with the property that for every value of z

$$f(z + \omega) = f(z).$$

If ω is a period, then $n\omega$ is also a period for n an arbitrary integer. For positive values of n this can be proved by induction. For negative values of n, it can be reduced to the case of positive values by setting $n = -k$, and writing

$$f(z - k\omega) = f(z - k\omega + k\omega) = f(z).$$

If the function $f(z)$ possesses no periods besides those of the form $n\omega$ ($n = \pm 1, \pm 2, \ldots$), the function is said to be *simply periodic*, and the number ω is said to be its *primitive period*.

5.5.

According to (5.12), $n \cdot 2\pi i$ is a period of the exponential function for every integer n. We shall now show that this function possesses no further periods. Let $z_1 = x_1 + iy_1$ and $z_2 = x_2 + iy_2$ be two values of z at which the exponential function assumes the same values:

$$e^{z_1} = e^{z_2}.$$

Then

$$\zeta = \frac{e^{z_1}}{e^{z_2}} = e^{z_1 - z_2} = 1, \tag{5.13}$$

so that

$$|\zeta| = e^{x_1 - x_2} = 1.$$

Since x_1 and x_2 are real, this is possible only for $x_1 - x_2 = 0$, or $x_1 = x_2$. According to (5.13), we also have that

$$\arg \zeta = y_1 - y_2 = n \cdot 2\pi.$$

Hence, $z_1 - z_2 = n \cdot 2\pi i$, or

$$z_1 = z_2 + n \cdot 2\pi i.$$

Accordingly, all the periods of the exponential function are multiples of the period $2\pi i$, which is thus the primitive period.

The points $z + n \cdot 2\pi i$ ($n = 0, \pm 1, \pm 2, \ldots$) are said to be *equivalent*. For each value of z, one of these points lies in the strip

$$0 \leq y < 2\pi \tag{5.14}$$

bounded by the parallel lines $y = 0$ and $y = 2\pi$. In this *period-strip* the function therefore assumes every value which it is capable of assuming.

The periodicity of the exponential function does not appear in the real domain, since the periods of the function are all imaginary.

§2. MAPPING BY MEANS OF THE EXPONENTIAL FUNCTION. THE LOGARITHM

5.6. The Riemann Surface of the Exponential Function

Now let us turn to the mapping effected by the exponential function and consider those curves along which the modulus or the argument of $w = e^z$ is constant.

Since $|e^z| = e^x$, $|w|$ is constant on every line parallel to the imaginary axis, but its values increase as we move out in the direction of the positive x-axis. To the lines parallel to the imaginary axis in the z-plane therefore there correspond circles about the origin in the w-plane. In particular, $|w| \to \infty$ as $x \to \infty$ and $|w| \to 0$ as $x \to -\infty$.

Since $\arg w = \arg e^z = y$ remains constant when z varies along lines parallel to the real axis

$$y = d, \tag{5.15}$$

every such line in the z-plane corresponds to a ray emanating from the origin in the w-plane. If the point z describes the line (5.15) from left to right, w describes the ray which is its image from the origin outwards to infinity. If d increases from 0 to 2π, so that the ray (5.15) sweeps out the strip (5.14), the image ray rotates about the origin, beginning with the positive real axis, through the angle 2π. The function $w = e^z$ therefore maps the parallel strip $0 \leqq y \leqq 2\pi$ onto the w-plane slit along the positive real axis in such a way that the line $y = 0$ corresponds to the upper edge of the slit and the line $y = 2\pi$ corresponds its lower edge.

Since the function possesses the period $2\pi i$, it maps every parallel strip

$$\nu \cdot 2\pi \leqq y \leqq (\nu + 1)2\pi \qquad (\nu = 0, \pm1, \pm2, \ldots) \tag{5.16}$$

onto a replica of the w-plane slit in the same manner. The points z which differ from one another by $\nu \cdot 2\pi i$ are thereby mapped onto the same point. One thus obtains infinitely many w-planes, all slit in an identical way, of which each represents the image of a parallel strip (5.16). These planes can be joined together into an infinite-sheeted Riemann surface by joining the lower edge of the slit on the ν-th sheet to the upper edge on the $(\nu + 1)$-st sheet. The branch points of the surface are 0 and ∞. All the sheets are joined together at these branch points; the order of each branch point is therefore *infinite*.

The function $w = e^z$ maps the entire z-plane in a one-to-one way onto the Riemann surface just described. Since $dw/dz = e^z \neq 0$ everywhere, the mapping is conformal at every finite point of the z-plane.

5.7. The Riemann Surface of the Exponential Function as the Limiting Case of the Riemann Surfaces for Powers

The exponential function $w = e^z$ is the limit of the rational functions

$$w_n = \left(1 + \frac{z}{n}\right)^n \tag{5.17}$$

when $n \to \infty$. In order to investigate the mapping effected by the function (5.17), we perform it in two steps:

$$\zeta = 1 + \frac{z}{n}, \qquad w_n = \zeta^n.$$

The first transformation amounts to a translation and a contraction. It carries the point $z = -n$ into the origin. The second transformation maps the ζ-plane onto an n-sheeted Riemann surface with branch point at the origin. The function (5.17) therefore maps the z-plane onto an n-sheeted Riemann surface in such a way that the point $z = -n$ replaces the origin as a branch point of the surface. To each sector $0 \leqq \arg (z + n) < 2\pi/n$ corresponds an entire

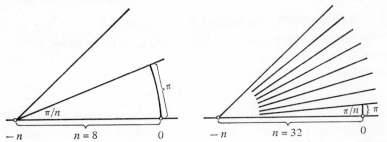

Figure 14

slit w-plane. As n increases, the vertex of the sector recedes more and more to the left and the sector differs less and less from the parallel strip (5.14). The mapping of an arbitrary finite region in the z-plane comes nearer and nearer to the mapping by the exponential function. On any finite domain one can therefore approximate the mapping furnished by the exponential function with arbitrary precision by the mapping given by a rational function (5.17) (cf. Exercise 7).

5.8. The Logarithm

Let us now determine the points $z = x + iy$ at which e^z assumes a given value $w = r\,e^{i\phi} \neq 0$. The condition $e^z = w$ yields the equation

$$e^{x+iy} = e^x\,e^{iy} = r\,e^{i\phi}.$$

This equation holds under the conditions

$$e^x = r \qquad \text{and} \qquad y = \phi + k \cdot 2\pi \qquad (k = 0, \pm1, \pm2, \ldots). \qquad (5.18)$$

The first equation yields

$$x = \log r,$$

where the logarithm of the positive number r has a well-defined real value. Consequently,

$$z = \log r + i(\phi + k \cdot 2\pi) = \log |w| + i \arg w + k \cdot 2\pi i. \qquad (5.19)$$

The function e^z assumes every value $w \neq 0$ at infinitely many places in the z-plane which differ only by integer multiples of $2\pi i$. Each parallel strip $v \cdot 2\pi \leqq y < (v + 1)2\pi$ is a *fundamental domain* of the exponential function: to every such fundamental domain there corresponds precisely one of the values (5.19).

5.9.

We are thus led to the inverse of the exponential function, for which we retain the notation $\log w$. The logarithm is an infinitely multiple-valued function:

$$z = \log w = \log |w| + i \arg w + k \cdot 2\pi i \qquad (k = 0, \pm 1, \pm 2, \ldots). \qquad (5.20)$$

The function $z = \log w$ maps the infinite-sheeted Riemann surface constructed in Section 5.6 onto the *schlicht* (that is, simply covered) z-plane. The single-valued branch of the function given by the formula

$$\log |w| + i \arg w,$$

where $0 \leqq \arg w < 2\pi$, is designated as the principal branch of the logarithm.

If w describes a closed curve γ in the w-plane which does not "wind" about the origin, i.e. one for which the increment of $\arg w$ is equal to zero when w describes the curve: $\Delta_\gamma \arg w = 0$ (Exercise 10), then z returns to its starting point. If, however, γ does wind about the origin, so that $\Delta_\gamma \arg w = k \cdot 2\pi$ ($k \neq 0$), then a new branch of the logarithm, $z + k \cdot 2\pi i$, is obtained.

5.10. Rules for Calculating with the Logarithm

The familiar properties of the real logarithm also hold for the complex logarithm. From (5.20) we see immediately that the real and imaginary parts of $\log w$ for $w \neq 0$ are continuous, and so the same is true for the function $\log w$ itself.

We shall show that each branch of the function $\log w$ has a derivative at every point $w \neq 0$. We give to w the increment Δw and designate the resulting increment of z by Δz. Then

$$\frac{\Delta z}{\Delta w} = \frac{1}{\Delta w / \Delta z}.$$

The increment $\Delta z \rightarrow 0$ when $\Delta w \rightarrow 0$. But $\Delta w / \Delta z \rightarrow dw/dz = e^z = w \neq 0$. Hence, the function $\log w$ possesses the derivative

$$\frac{dz}{dw} = \frac{d \log w}{dw} = \frac{1}{w}.$$

The rule for differentiation is thus the same as in the real case.

In the neighborhood $|w - w_0| < \rho_0$ of any point $w_0 = \rho_0 \, e^{i\theta_0}$ ($\rho_0 > 0$), every branch of log w is an analytic function.

From the addition theorem for the exponential function we obtain, as in the real case, the relations:

$$\log (w_1 w_2) = \log w_1 + \log w_2, \qquad \log \frac{w_1}{w_2} = \log w_1 - \log w_2,$$

provided one chooses the branches of the logarithm in a suitable way.

5.11. Problems of Conformal Mapping

Several interesting *conformal mappings* can be performed with the help of the exponential function. For example, a parallel strip can be mapped onto a disk. By means of a similarity transformation the strip can first be mapped onto the strip

$$0 < y < \pi.$$

The function $w = e^z$ carries this strip onto a half-plane. If we then map the half-plane onto a disk by means of a linear transformation, we get the conformal mapping of the original strip onto a disk.

One can likewise map the domain bounded by two tangent circles conformally onto a disk. Indeed, if one first carries out any sort of linear transformation which takes the point of tangency of the circles to ∞, the circles will be mapped onto parallel lines and the domain bounded by them will therefore be transformed into a parallel strip. One then proceeds as in the first example.

§3. THE GENERAL POWER

5.12.

The general power

$$w = z^\mu,$$

where μ is an arbitrary complex constant, is defined with the aid of the exponential function:

$$z^\mu = (e^{\log z})^\mu = e^{\mu \log z}. \tag{5.21}$$

Setting $\mu = \alpha + i\beta$ gives us

$$z^\mu = e^{\alpha \log |z| - \beta \arg z} \, e^{i(\beta \log |z| + \alpha \arg z)},$$

and therefore

$$|z^\mu| = e^{\alpha \log |z| - \beta \arg z}, \qquad \arg z^\mu = \beta \log |z| + \alpha \arg z. \tag{5.22}$$

In general, both the modulus and the argument of the power are multiple-valued functions. The modulus is single-valued only when $\beta = 0$, that is, when the exponent $\mu = \alpha$ is real. Then

$$|z^\mu| = |z|^\mu.$$

5.13.

We want to examine somewhat more closely the case in which the exponent is a rational real number: $\mu = m/n$ (m and n positive integers). Then, according to (5.22),

$$|w| = |z^{m/n}| = |z|^{m/n}, \qquad \arg w = \arg z^{m/n} = \frac{m}{n} \arg z.$$

We see from this that circles about the origin in the z-plane are mapped into circles about the origin in the w-plane. Rays emanating from the origin in the z-plane go over into rays of the same sort in the w-plane. Every angle whose vertex lies at the origin is multiplied by m/n.

In the particular case when $m = 1$, $\mu = 1/n$, the z-plane slit along the positive real axis corresponds to the sector

$$0 \leqq \arg w \leqq \frac{2\pi}{n}$$

of the w-plane. Hence, the function

$$w = z^{1/n} \tag{5.23}$$

effects a one-to-one mapping of the n-sheeted Riemann surface over the z-plane with branch points of the $(n - 1)$-st order at the origin and at infinity onto the schlicht w-plane. The function (5.23) is the inverse function $w = \sqrt[n]{z}$ of the function $z = w^n$, which we have already investigated explicitly in Section 2.3.

In the general case, $\mu = m/n$, we have, by (5.21),

$$w = z^{m/n} = e^{(m/n) \log z} = (e^{(1/n) \log z})^m = (z^{1/n})^m. \tag{5.24}$$

The mapping effected by the function (5.24) can thus be broken into two successive mappings: first, the mapping of an n-sheeted Riemann surface over the z-plane onto the schlicht plane, followed by the mapping of the schlicht plane onto an m-sheeted Riemann surface. The function (5.24) therefore maps an n-sheeted Riemann surface over the z-plane in a one-to-one way onto an m-sheeted Riemann surface over the w-plane. Both surfaces have 0 and ∞ as branch points. The mapping is, except at the branch points, everywhere conformal.

EXERCISES ON CHAPTER 5

1. Calculate the value of the function e^z at the points $z = -i\pi/2$, $3i\pi/4$, $1 - 2i$.

2. Change the following numbers into the form $re^{i\phi}$:

$$-3, \quad 2i, \quad -\frac{i}{2}, \quad -\frac{1}{2} + i\frac{\sqrt{3}}{2}, \quad 1 + 2i, \quad \frac{a + ib}{a - ib}.$$

3. At which points z does e^z assume the values $2, -1, i, -i/2, -1 - i, 1 + 2i$?

4. Show that the real and imaginary parts of the function e^z satisfy both the Cauchy-Riemann equations and Laplace's equation.

5. By use of Euler's formulas, write $\cos^5 \phi$, $\sin^6 \phi$, and $\cos^3 \phi \sin^2 \phi$ as linear expressions in the sine and cosine of integer multiples of ϕ.

6. Prove the formula

$$1 + 2 \cos \phi + 2 \cos 2\phi + \cdots + 2 \cos n\phi = \frac{\sin (n + \frac{1}{2})\phi}{\sin \frac{1}{2}\phi}.$$

7. Show that the limit

$$\lim_{n \to \infty} \left(1 + \frac{z}{n}\right)^n = e^z$$

holds uniformly in the disk $|z| \leq R$, where R is an arbitrary positive number.

8. How does e^z change when the point z goes off to infinity along a ray from the origin?

9. Determine which curves in the w-plane correspond to straight lines in the z-plane under the mapping $w = e^z$, and which curves in the z-plane correspond to straight lines in the w-plane under this mapping.

10. Let $z = z(\tau) \neq 0$ be a continuous function of τ ($\alpha \leq \tau \leq \beta$) and denote the curve $z = z(\tau)$ by γ. Show that arg z has a unique value at every point of γ, once a definite value for arg z at the point $z(\alpha)$ has been established and the curve is described in a continuous manner, starting at that point.

Hint. The interval (α, β) can be partitioned into subintervals $(\tau_{\nu-1}, \tau_\nu)$ ($\nu = 1, \ldots, n$, $\tau_0 = \alpha$, $\tau_n = \beta$) in such a way that $|z(\tau') - z(\tau'')| < d$ when τ' and τ'' belong to the same subinterval $(\tau_{\nu-1}, \tau_\nu)$ and $d = \min |z(\tau)|$ in the interval $\alpha \leq \tau \leq \beta$.

11. Determine the different values of the following logarithms:

$$\log 1, \quad \log (-\tfrac{1}{2}), \quad \log (-i), \quad \log (-1 + i), \quad \log (3 + 4i), \quad \log \frac{a - ib}{a + ib}.$$

12. Map that portion of the z-plane which lies outside the circles $|z - 1| = 1$ and $|z + 1| = 1$ conformally onto the exterior of the unit disk in the w-plane

so that the points at infinity correspond to one another and the mapping is symmetric in the coordinate axes.

Solution. $w = i(e^{\pi i/z} + 1)/(e^{\pi i/z} - 1)$.

13. Investigate the mapping defined by the function $w = \log [(z - a)/(z - b)]$, where a and b are two given complex numbers. Determine the locus of all points for which the real part of the function assumes a prescribed value and the locus of all points for which the imaginary part is constant.

14. Investigate how the branches of the function $\log [(z - a)/(z - b)]$ pass from one to another as z moves about the plane.

15. Construct an infinite-sheeted Riemann surface over the z-plane with branch points at 0 and ∞. Map that portion of the surface which lies inside the circle $|z| = \rho$ (> 1) conformally onto the unit disk in the w-plane in such a way that the points $z = 0$ and $w = 1$ correspond and so that the point $w = 0$ corresponds to the point $z = 1$ on the "principal sheet" (arg $z = 0$) of the surface.

Solution. $w = \log z/\log (z/\rho^2)$, where the principal value of the function is to be chosen at the point $z = \rho$ on the principal sheet.

16. Map the portion of the Riemann surface considered in the preceding problem that lies between the circles $|z| = \rho_1$ and $|z| = \rho_2$ $(> \rho_1)$ conformally onto the unit disk in the w-plane in such a way that the points $z = \sqrt{\rho_1\rho_2} = z_0$ and $z = \rho_2$ correspond to the points $w = 0$ and $w = 1$.

Solution.

$$w = -i(e^{(\pi i/2h) \log(z/z_0)} - 1)/(e^{(\pi i/2h) \log(z/z_0)} + 1),$$

where $z_0 = \sqrt{\rho_1\rho_2}$ and $h = \frac{1}{2} \log \rho_2/\rho_1$. The principal value of the function $\log (z/z_0)$ is to be chosen at the point $z = z_0$ on the principal sheet of the surface.

17. Map the surface of the sphere conformally onto a parallel strip in the plane so that the meridians correspond to lines parallel to the imaginary axis and the circles of latitude correspond to lines parallel to the real axis (the *Mercator projection*).

Hint. Use stereographic projection.

18. Let $w(z)$ be analytic and let $w = \rho e^{i\psi}$, $z = r e^{i\phi}$. Prove that at every point $z \neq 0$ where $w \neq 0$ the Cauchy-Riemann equations can be written in the form

$$\frac{\partial \rho}{\partial r} = \frac{\rho}{r} \frac{\partial \psi}{\partial \phi}, \qquad \frac{\partial \rho}{\partial \phi} = -\rho r \frac{\partial \psi}{\partial r}.$$

Hint. Consider the function $\log w(z)$.

19. Which branches of the function $z^{3/4}$ assume the value $-1 + i$, and at what points?

20. Determine the different values of the following expressions:

$$(-1)^{\sqrt{2}}, \qquad 2^{1-i}, \qquad (1 + i)^{\sqrt{3}}, \qquad i^i.$$

21. What value does the function z^i assume at the point $z = -1$, if one starts with the principal value of the function at the point $z = 1$ ($\arg z = 0$) and allows z to rotate one and a half turns continuously about the origin in the negative sense?

22. Show that under the mapping $w = z^\mu$ ($\mu = \alpha + i\beta$) the straight lines $\arg z = $ const. and the circles $|z| = $ const. correspond to logarithmic spirals in the w-plane which intersect orthogonally.

23. Map the domain $-\pi/6 < \phi < \pi/6$ in the z-plane ($z = r\,e^{i\phi}$) conformally onto the unit disk $|w| < 1$ in such a way that the points $z = 1, 0$ go over into the points $w = 0, -1$.

Solution. The mapping function is $w = (z^3 - 1)/(z^3 + 1)$.

24. Determine the function which maps the circular sector $-\pi/4 < \phi < \pi/4$, $r < 1$, conformally onto the unit disk in the w-plane in such a way that the points $z = 0, 1/\sqrt{2}$ go over into the points $w = -1, 0$. How does this function map the remaining portions of the plane?

Solution. $w = -(2z^4 + 3z^2 - 2)/(2z^4 - 3z^2 - 2)$ is the required function.

25. Map the domain $-h < y < h$, $x > 0$ of the z-plane ($z = x + iy$) conformally onto the unit disk in the w-plane in such a way that the points $z = 0$, a ($a > 0$) correspond to the points $w = -1, 0$.

Solution. The mapping function is

$$w = \frac{e^{\pi z/h} - 2k\,e^{\pi z/2h} - 1}{e^{\pi z/h} + 2k\,e^{\pi z/2h} - 1} \qquad \text{with} \qquad k = \tfrac{1}{2}(e^{\pi a/2h} - e^{-\pi a/2h}).$$

26. Map a domain bounded by two intersecting circular arcs conformally onto the unit disk.

CHAPTER 6

THE TRIGONOMETRIC FUNCTIONS

§1. THE SINE AND COSINE

6.1. Extension of the Definition to Complex Values. Basic Properties

The elementary definitions of the trigonometric functions do not hold for complex values of the argument. However, from the previous chapter, we know that for all real values of z

$$e^{iz} = \cos z + i \sin z, \qquad e^{-iz} = \cos z - i \sin z, \qquad (6.1)$$

from which it follows that

$$\cos z = \frac{e^{iz} + e^{-iz}}{2}, \qquad \sin z = \frac{e^{iz} - e^{-iz}}{2i}. \qquad (6.2)$$

We now define the cosine and sine for complex values of z by means of the formulas (6.2).

The formulas (6.1) then hold for all complex values of z.

The formulas (6.2) define the cosine and sine in terms of the complex exponential function. Thus these functions possess a derivative at every point z, and we see easily that

$$\frac{d \cos z}{dz} = - \sin z, \qquad \frac{d \sin z}{dz} = \cos z.$$

These two trigonometric functions are therefore analytic in the whole plane $z \neq \infty$, and thus they are entire functions.

The other familiar properties and formulas of the sine and cosine are also preserved. The defining equations (6.2) tell us that $\cos z$ is an even function and that $\sin z$ is odd:

$$\cos (-z) = \cos z, \qquad \sin (-z) = - \sin z.$$

The addition theorems for the sine and cosine come out of (6.2) when we make the substitution $z = z_1 + z_2$ and apply the addition theorem for the exponential function along with the formulas (6.1):

$$e^{i(z_1+z_2)} = e^{iz_1} e^{iz_2} = (\cos z_1 + i \sin z_1)(\cos z_2 + i \sin z_2)$$
$$= (\cos z_1 \cos z_2 - \sin z_1 \sin z_2) + i(\sin z_1 \cos z_2 + \cos z_1 \sin z_2),$$
$$e^{-i(z_1+z_2)} = (\cos z_1 \cos z_2 - \sin z_1 \sin z_2) - i(\sin z_1 \cos z_2 + \cos z_1 \sin z_2).$$

From this it follows, by addition and subtraction, that

$$\cos (z_1 + z_2) = \cos z_1 \cos z_2 - \sin z_1 \sin z_2,$$
$$\sin (z_1 + z_2) = \sin z_1 \cos z_2 + \cos z_1 \sin z_2. \tag{6.3}$$

We can obtain the other familiar trigonometric formulas from the addition formulas (6.3). By setting $z_1 = -z_2 = z$, the first one yields

$$\sin^2 z + \cos^2 z = 1.$$

For $z_2 = -\pi/2$, $z_1 = z$ we have

$$\cos (z - \tfrac{1}{2}\pi) = \sin z. \tag{6.4}$$

Finally, when $z_1 = z$, $z_2 = n \cdot 2\pi$, n an integer, we get

$$\cos (z + n \cdot 2\pi) = \cos z, \qquad \sin (z + n \cdot 2\pi) = \sin z.$$

The sine and cosine functions are thus periodic, with period 2π, even for complex values of z.

We shall show next that 2π is the *primitive period*. If ω is an arbitrary period of $\cos z$, then for all z

$$\cos (z + \omega) = \cos z.$$

When we set $z = 0$ in this formula, we get

$$\cos \omega = 1, \tag{6.5}$$

while for $z = -\pi/2$ we have, in view of (6.4),

$$\sin \omega = 0. \tag{6.6}$$

Hence, by (6.5) and (6.6), we have

$$e^{i\omega} = \cos \omega + i \sin \omega = 1.$$

But this can hold if and only if $i\omega = k \cdot 2\pi i$, or $\omega = k \cdot 2\pi$ ($k = 0, \pm1, \pm2, \ldots$). All of the periods are thus multiples of 2π, so that 2π is the primitive period of the cosine. In a similar way, we can show that the primitive period of the sine is 2π. This shows that the functions $\cos z$ and $\sin z$ are *simply periodic*. It is enough then to study them within a single period-strip, for example, $-\pi \leqq x < \pi$.

6.2.

On the imaginary axis $z = iy$ we have, by (6.2),

$$\cos iy = \frac{e^{-y} + e^y}{2} = \cosh y, \qquad \sin iy = \frac{e^{-y} - e^y}{2i} = i \sinh y. \qquad (6.7)$$

The addition theorem (6.3) now permits us to split $\cos z$ and $\sin z$ into real and imaginary parts:

$$\cos z = \cos (x + iy) = \cos x \cos iy - \sin x \sin iy$$
$$= \cos x \cosh y - i \sin x \sinh y, \qquad (6.8)$$
$$\sin z = \sin (x + iy) = \sin x \cosh y + i \cos x \sinh y.$$

It is clear from (6.8) that $\cos z$ is real when $\sin x = 0$ or when $\sinh y = 0$. The latter condition is fulfilled only on the real axis. The function $\cos z$ is therefore real on the lines parallel to the imaginary axis whose equations are $x = k\pi$ $(k = 0, \pm 1, \pm 2, \ldots)$ and on the real axis; otherwise, it is not real. On these parallel lines $|\cos z| = \cosh y \geq 1$ and $|\cos z| \to \infty$ for $|y| \to \infty$.

In a similar fashion, we can show that $\sin z$ is real on the real axis and on the straight lines $x = (k + \frac{1}{2})\pi$ $(k = 0, \pm 1, \pm 2, \ldots)$. On the latter we have $|\sin z| = \cosh y \geq 1$, and also $|\sin z| \to \infty$ for $|y| \to \infty$.

Let us now examine, more generally, the behavior of the modulus of each function for $|y| \to \infty$. From (6.2) we have

$$|\cos z| \leq \frac{|e^{iz}| + |e^{-iz}|}{2} = \frac{e^{-y} + e^y}{2} = \cosh y,$$

$$|\cos z| \geq \frac{||e^{iz}| - |e^{-iz}||}{2} = \frac{|e^y - e^{-y}|}{2} = |\sinh y|.$$

Hence we have, for all z,

$$|\sinh y| \leq |\cos z| \leq \cosh y.$$

The same inequalities can be obtained for the modulus of $\sin z$. It follows that

$$\lim_{|y| \to \infty} |\sin z| = \lim_{|y| \to \infty} |\cos z| = \infty.$$

6.3. The Distribution of Values in a Period-Strip

We are now going to examine more closely the distribution of the values of $\cos z$ in a period-strip and determine those points at which $\cos z$ assumes a prescribed value w. The condition $\cos z = w$ can be written, by means of the Euler equations, as

$$(e^{iz})^2 - 2w\, e^{iz} + 1 = 0. \qquad (6.9)$$

This quadratic equation in e^{iz} possesses two roots,

$$e^{iz} = w \pm \sqrt{w^2 - 1}, \tag{6.10}$$

whose product is 1. They are therefore different from zero for every finite value w. Let us set

$$w + \sqrt{w^2 - 1} = r\,e^{i\phi} \tag{6.11}$$

and choose the argument ϕ to lie in the interval $-\pi \leq \phi < \pi$. The second root is then

$$w - \sqrt{w^2 - 1} = \frac{1}{r}\,e^{-i\phi}. \tag{6.12}$$

The solution of the equation

$$e^{iz} = r\,e^{i\phi} \tag{6.13}$$

is

$$z = \frac{1}{i}\log\left(r\,e^{i\phi}\right) = \phi - i\log r + n\cdot 2\pi \qquad (n = 0, \pm 1, \pm 2, \dots).$$

The point z corresponding to the value $n = 0$ belongs to the fundamental period-strip

$$-\pi \leq x < \pi. \tag{6.14}$$

The second root (6.12) of Eq. (6.9) is

$$z = -\phi + i\log r + n\cdot 2\pi.$$

The point $z = -\phi + i\log r$ corresponding to the value $n = 0$ lies in the period-strip (6.14) (in the case $\phi = -\pi$ it would be the point corresponding to $n = -1$).

If we write

$$z_1 = \phi - i\log r,$$

then all the numbers

$$z_1 + n\cdot 2\pi \qquad \text{and} \qquad -z_1 + n\cdot 2\pi \qquad (n = 0, \pm 1, \dots)$$

are roots of the equation $\cos z = w$.

The two roots belonging to the fundamental period-strip coincide when $w = \pm 1$. When $w = +1$, Eq. (6.10) becomes $e^{iz} = 1$. Only the root $z = 0$ of this equation lies in the fundamental period-strip. Because the two roots z_1 and $-z_1$ now coincide, the equation $\cos z = 1$ has a double root at the origin.

If, on the other hand, $w = -1$, the equation

$$e^{iz} = -1 = e^{i\pi}$$

has the roots

$$z = \pi + n\cdot 2\pi \qquad (n = 0, \pm 1, \pm 2, \dots).$$

Among these, the value $z = z_1 = -\pi$ belongs to the fundamental period-strip.

This coincides with the root $-z_1 - 2\pi$. Hence, $z = -\pi$ is a double root of the equation $\cos z = -1$.

In the fundamental period-strip the function $\cos z$ assumes the value 0 at the points $\pi/2$ and $-\pi/2$, and these are the only zeros located there, for the function can assume no value more than twice in a single period-strip.

If we count a double root as two coincident, simple roots, we can formulate the result just obtained as follows:

In every period-strip the function $\cos z$ *assumes every finite value at two points.*

A period-strip is therefore *not* a fundamental domain for the cosine. We get such a domain by taking only half of a period-strip, for example, the part lying above the real axis. Only a part of the boundary is to be included, for example, $x = -\pi, y \geq 0$ and $x \leq 0, y = 0$ (the point $z = 0$ being "halved").

At no finite point of the plane does $\cos z$ attain the value ∞, but the function does tend to ∞ as a limit when z goes to infinity in such a way that its imaginary part tends either to $+\infty$ or $-\infty$. Thus, the value ∞ is an asymptotic value of $\cos z$.

The foregoing investigation shows that the value of $\cos z$ remains unchanged when we make the substitutions

$$z + n\cdot 2\pi, \qquad -z + n\cdot 2\pi \qquad (n = 0, \pm 1, \pm 2, \ldots). \tag{6.15}$$

These substitutions form a group. The *fundamental substitutions* of the group are $-z$ and $z + 2\pi$. We obtain all the elements of the group from these two by iterating them and their inverses a finite number of times.

The properties of the function $\sin z$ can be reduced to those of $\cos z$, by means of Eq. (6.4).

§2. THE TANGENT AND THE COTANGENT

6.4. Definition

The functions $\tan z$ and $\cot z$ are defined by the formulas

$$\tan z = \frac{\sin z}{\cos z}, \qquad \cot z = \frac{\cos z}{\sin z}. \tag{6.16}$$

By use of Euler's formulas, these trigonometric functions can be expressed in terms of the exponential function:

$$\tan z = \frac{1}{i} \frac{e^{iz} - e^{-iz}}{e^{iz} + e^{-iz}}, \qquad \cot z = i\frac{e^{iz} + e^{-iz}}{e^{iz} - e^{-iz}}. \tag{6.17}$$

Since $\tan z$ and $\cot z$ are reciprocals, it suffices to consider only one of them in detail. We shall start with the function

$$\cot z = \frac{\cos z}{\sin z} = i\frac{e^{iz} + e^{-iz}}{e^{iz} - e^{-iz}}. \tag{6.18}$$

Because of the relation $\sin^2 z + \cos^2 z = 1$, $\sin z$ and $\cos z$ cannot both vanish at the same time. Their quotient $\cot z$ therefore has a finite value at all points z ($\neq \infty$), except at the zeros $z = n\pi$ ($n = 0, \pm 1, \pm 2, \ldots$) of $\sin z$, where $\cot z$ becomes infinite.

The function $\cot z$ is continuous at the points $z \neq n\pi$. It follows immediately from the definition (6.16) that

$$\frac{d}{dz} \cot z = -\frac{1}{\sin^2 z},$$

so that the derivative of $\cot z$ has the same form as in the real case.

When we pass from the value z to the value $z + \pi$, the functions $\sin z$ and $\cos z$ merely change sign, so that π is a period of the function $\cot z$. Conversely, if $\omega \neq 0$ is an arbitrary period, $\cot (z + \omega) \equiv \cot z$, then, by setting $z = 0$ we obtain the condition $\cot \omega = \infty$. By (6.18), $e^{i\omega} = e^{-i\omega}$, or $e^{2i\omega} = 1$. This equation is satisfied only by the values $\omega = n\pi$ ($n = 0, \pm 1, \ldots$). The *primitive period* of the function $\cot z$ is therefore $\omega = \pi$. For the fundamental period-strip we can choose

$$-\frac{\pi}{2} \leq x < \frac{\pi}{2}.$$

The function $\cot z$ is analytic for all values z in this strip, except for $z = 0$, where $\cot z$ becomes infinite. In order to investigate the behavior of the function at this special point, we form the product

$$z \cot z = \frac{z}{\sin z} \cos z.$$

By the definition of the derivative of $\sin z$,

$$\frac{\sin z}{z} = \frac{\sin z - \sin 0}{z} \to \cos 0 = 1,$$

so that

$$z \cot z \to 1 \quad \text{as} \quad z \to 0.$$

Since $\cot z$ becomes infinite at the point $z = 0$ in such a way that $z \cot z$ tends to a finite non-zero limit, we call $z = 0$ a *simple pole* of the function $\cot z$ (cf. Section 2.9).

Because of the periodicity of the function, $\cot z$ possesses a simple pole at each of the points $z = n\pi$ ($n = 0, \pm 1, \pm 2, \ldots$). The function $\cot z$ is therefore analytic for all values $z \neq \infty$ except at those isolated points where the poles occur. Such a function is said to be a *meromorphic* function.

6.5. The Distribution of Values in the Period-Strips

We shall investigate the distribution of values of cot z in the fundamental period-strip by determining the roots of the equation

$$\cot z = i\frac{e^{2iz} + 1}{e^{2iz} - 1} = w \qquad (6.19)$$

for different values of w. Solving (6.19) for e^{2iz} gives

$$e^{2iz} = \frac{w + i}{w - i},$$

from which it follows that cot z nowhere assumes the values $\pm i$. On the other hand, if $w \neq \pm i$, we may write

$$\frac{w + i}{w - i} = r\,e^{i\phi} \qquad (r > 0,\ -\pi \leqq \phi < \pi)$$

and find that

$$2iz = \log r + i\phi + n\cdot 2\pi i$$

or

$$z = \frac{\phi}{2} - \frac{i}{2}\log r + n\pi \qquad (n = 0, \pm 1, \ldots).$$

Of these values, the one with $n = 0$, $z = (\phi - i\log r)/2$, belongs to the fundamental period-strip. Therefore, cot z assumes every value $w \neq \pm i$ at precisely one point in the period-strip; in particular, it assumes the value $w = \infty$ ($r = 1$, $\phi = 0$) at the pole $z = 0$.

The exceptional values $w = \pm i$, which cot z fails to assume for $z \neq \infty$, are asymptotic values to which cot z tends as $|y| \to \infty$. Indeed, $|e^{2iz}| = e^{-2y}$, so that it follows from (6.19) that cot $z \to \mp i$ when $y \to \pm\infty$.

6.6. The Function $w = \tan z$

All the properties of tan z result from (6.16) or, more simply, from the equation

$$\tan\left(z - \frac{\pi}{2}\right) = -\cot z. \qquad (6.20)$$

From this equation one sees that the function tan z also has the primitive period π and, in any period-strip, assumes every value $w \neq \pm i$ precisely once. It takes the value $w = \infty$ at the simple poles occurring at $z = \pi/2 + n\pi$. The exceptional values $w = \pm i$ are asymptotic values to which tan z tends when $y \to \pm\infty$.

The derivative of tan z has the familiar form

$$\frac{d}{dz}\tan z = \frac{1}{\cos^2 z}.$$

$\tan z$ is therefore a meromorphic function: it is analytic everywhere in the plane except at the points $z = \pi/2 + n\pi$ $(n = 0, \pm 1, \dots)$ where it has simple poles.

§3. THE MAPPINGS GIVEN BY THE FUNCTIONS tan z AND cot z. THEIR INVERSE FUNCTIONS

6.7. The Riemann Surface of the Function cot z

In order to investigate the mapping of the z-plane onto the w-plane given by the function

$$w = \cot z = i \frac{e^{2iz} + 1}{e^{2iz} - 1} \tag{6.21}$$

we carry it out in three stages:

$$z_1 = 2iz, \qquad z_2 = e^{z_1}, \qquad w = i \frac{z_2 + 1}{z_2 - 1}. \tag{6.22}$$

The fundamental period-strip $-\pi/2 \leqq x < \pi/2$ is mapped in a one-to-one way onto the strip $-\pi \leqq y_1 < \pi$ $(z_1 = x_1 + iy_1)$. The function $z_2 = e^{z_1}$ maps the latter strip onto the z_2-plane slit along the negative real axis. The boundary line $x = -\pi/2$ corresponds to the lower edge of the slit while the boundary line $x = \pi/2$ corresponds to the upper edge. The imaginary axis $x = 0$ goes over onto the positive real axis in the z_2-plane, and the segment $-\pi/2 \leqq x < \pi/2$, $y = 0$ goes over onto the unit circle $|z_2| = 1$. The origin $z = 0$ goes into the point $z_2 = 1$.

The last of the mappings (6.22) is a linear transformation of the z_2-plane into the w-plane which transforms the slit $(0, -\infty)$ into the slit $(-i, i)$ in the w-plane. The circumference $|z_2| = 1$ goes over into the real axis, the point $z = 0$ corresponds to $w = \infty$, and the boundary lines $x = +\pi/2$, $x = -\pi/2$ go over into the edges of the slit $(-i, i)$: the former into the right-hand edge, and the latter into the left-hand edge. Additional correspondences can be inferred from Figs. 15–18.

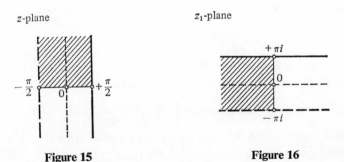

z-plane   z₁-plane

Figure 15   Figure 16

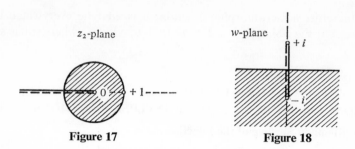

Figure 17   **Figure 18**

Since the function cot z is periodic, every period-strip $(2n - 1)\pi/2 \leqq x <$ $(2n + 1)\pi/2$ is mapped in the same way onto a slit w-plane. A one-to-one correspondence between the z- and w-planes can be achieved by joining the n-th plane F_n, slit along the segment $(-i, i)$, with the $(n + 1)$-st plane F_{n+1}, likewise slit, so that the right-hand edge of the slit in F_n is joined to the left-hand edge of the slit in F_{n+1}. In this way we obtain an infinite-sheeted Riemann surface R_w over the w-plane as the conformal image of the z-plane. Its branch points are the asymptotic values $w = \pm i$ of the function cot z; both are of infinite order.

The surface R_w is therefore constructed just like the Riemann surface of the exponential function, only the branch points are now at $\pm i$.

6.8. The Inverse Function arc cot z

By the preceding analysis we can now construct the inverse function, $z = $ arc cot w, of the function $w = $ cot z. It has infinitely many branches, and is single-valued on the Riemann surface R_w. Each of its branches is a single-valued analytic function in a w-plane slit along the segment $(-i, +i)$. The derivative is, as in the real case,

$$\frac{d}{dw} \text{ arc cot } w = \frac{1}{\dfrac{d}{dz} \cot z} = -\sin^2 z = -\frac{1}{1 + \cot^2 z} = -\frac{1}{1 + w^2},$$

and therefore exists for all values of $w \neq \pm i$.

By solving Eq. (6.21) for z, we can represent arc cot w in terms of the logarithm:

$$z = \frac{1}{2i} \log \frac{w + i}{w - i}.$$

6.9. The Mapping given by the Function tan z

From Eq. (6.20), which can be written in the form

$$\tan z = -\cot \left(z + \frac{\pi}{2}\right) = \frac{1}{\cot z},$$

we see that the function $w = \tan z$ maps the period-strip $0 \leqq x < \pi$ onto a plane slit in exactly the same way as the image of $-\pi/2 \leqq x < \pi/2$ under the mapping cot z. The image of the entire z-plane is the Riemann surface considered above with branch points at $\pm i$.

The inverse function $z = $ arc tan w maps this Riemann surface one-to-one conformally onto the schlicht z-plane. The derivative of the inverse function,

$$\frac{d}{dw} \text{ arc tan } w = \frac{1}{1 + w^2},$$

exists for $w \neq \pm i$, and arc tan w can also be expressed in terms of the logarithm:

$$z = \frac{\pi}{2} - \text{arc cot } w = \frac{1}{2i} \log \frac{i - w}{i + w}.$$

The branch $-\pi/2 \leq \text{Re } z < \pi/2$ is called the *principal branch* and is denoted by Arc tan w.

§4. THE MAPPINGS GIVEN BY THE FUNCTIONS sin z AND cos z. THE FUNCTIONS arc sin z AND arc cos z

6.10. The Image of a Period-Strip under the Function cos z

We consider now the mapping given by the function

$$w = \cos z = \frac{e^{iz} + e^{-iz}}{2} = \frac{(e^{iz})^2 + 1}{2 \, e^{iz}}. \tag{6.23}$$

We may break the mapping into the following succession of mappings:

$$z_1 = iz \qquad (z_1 = x_1 + iy_1), \tag{6.24}$$

$$z_2 = e^{z_1}, \tag{6.25}$$

$$w = \frac{z_2^2 + 1}{2z_2}. \tag{6.26}$$

The mapping (6.24) is just a rotation of the z-plane about the origin through an angle of $\pi/2$. To the period-strip F_0 $(-\pi \leq x < \pi)$ corresponds the parallel-strip $-\pi \leq y_1 < \pi$. The correspondence is shown in Figs. 19 and 20.

z-plane

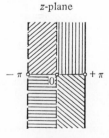

z_1-plane

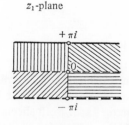

Figure 19

Figure 20

The transformation (6.25) maps the parallel-strip $-\pi \leqq y_1 < \pi$ onto the z_2-plane slit along the negative real axis from zero to infinity, as is shown in Figs. 20 and 21.

Finally the function (6.26) maps the entire z_2-plane onto a two-sheeted Riemann surface. To study the correspondence in more detail, we write (6.26) in the form given in Chapter 4. The zeros of the derivative of the function (6.26) lie at $z_2 = \pm 1$, where the function has the values $w = \pm 1$. If we now subtract these values from w and divide the expressions obtained, the transformation assumes the form

$$\frac{w - 1}{w + 1} = \left(\frac{z_2 - 1}{z_2 + 1}\right)^2.\tag{6.27}$$

This transformation is decomposed again:

$$\zeta = \frac{z_2 - 1}{z_2 + 1},\tag{6.28}$$

$$\omega = \zeta^2,\tag{6.29}$$

$$\omega = \frac{w - 1}{w + 1}.\tag{6.30}$$

The transformation (6.28) maps the z_2-plane linearly onto the ζ-plane in such a way that $z_2 = 1$ goes into the origin and $z_2 = -1$ goes into the point $\zeta = \infty$. The real axis remains fixed. The point $z_2 = 0$ goes into $\zeta = -1$ and $z_2 = \infty$ into $\zeta = 1$. Both the slit from -1 to ∞ along the negative real axis and the slit from 1 to ∞ along the positive real axis correspond to the slit along the negative real axis in the z_2-plane (Figs. 21 and 22).

z_2-plane

ζ-plane

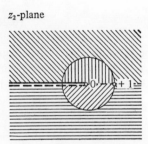
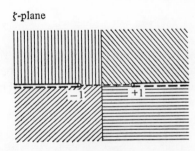

Figure 21   **Figure 22**

The transformation (6.29) maps the ζ-plane onto a two-sheeted Riemann surface over the ω-plane, whose branch points are at $\omega = 0, \infty$. The points 0 and ∞ remain fixed. Both sheets of the surface are slit along the positive real axis from 1 to ∞. The sheets of the surface are joined in a criss-cross fashion along the segment $(0, 1)$.

Finally we go from the ω-plane into the w-plane by means of the linear transformation (6.30), which carries the points $\omega = 0$, 1, ∞ into the points $w = 1$, ∞, -1, respectively. The real ω-axis goes over into the real w-axis; the upper and lower half-planes are each mapped into themselves. The slit between $\omega = 0$ and $\omega = 1$ is mapped onto a slit along the positive real axis from the point 1 to the point ∞. Along this slit the sheets of the resulting Riemann surface are joined together in a criss-cross manner. To the slit from 1 to ∞, which lies on both sheets, there corresponds in the w-plane another slit from -1 to ∞ along the negative real axis.

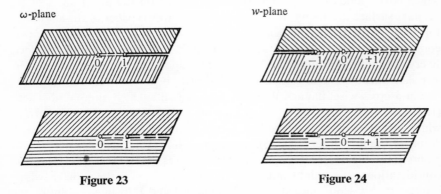

Figure 23   Figure 24

The final result of this analysis is to establish that the function $w = \cos z$ maps the fundamental period-strip

$$F_0: \qquad -\pi \leq x < \pi$$

onto a two-sheeted Riemann surface whose branch points are 1 and ∞; each sheet is slit along the negative real axis from -1 to ∞. The sheets are joined together in a cross-wise manner along a "seam" that runs from 1 to ∞ along the positive real axis. To the left half of the period-strip, $-\pi \leq x < 0$, corresponds the "bottom" sheet of the Riemann surface and to the right half, $0 \leq x < \pi$, corresponds the "top" sheet. To the line $x = -\pi$ is associated, in the bottom sheet, the edges of the slit from -1 to ∞. The other boundary line $x = \pi$ of the period-strip corresponds to the slit from -1 to ∞ in the top sheet. As z approaches the line $x = \pi$ in the upper half-plane, w approaches the slit in the top sheet from the lower half-plane. If, on the other hand, z approaches the line $x = \pi$ from the lower half-plane, w approaches the slit in the top sheet from the upper half-plane. The precise correspondence can be inferred from Figs. 19–24, in which corresponding regions are shaded in the same way.

6.11. The Riemann Surface of the Function cos z

Since the function $\cos z$ is periodic, it follows that every period-strip

$$F_\nu: \qquad (2\nu - 1)\pi \leq x < (2\nu + 1)\pi$$

is mapped in a similar way onto a slit, two-sheeted Riemann surface. Points which differ by an integer multiple of 2π occupy the same positions on these two-sheeted Riemann surfaces.

If z moves in the z-plane from the parallel-strip F_0 into the strip F_1, its image w must move from the Riemann surface corresponding to F_0 to the one that corresponds to F_1. The edges of the slit on the top sheet of the surface corresponding to F_0 must therefore be joined in a criss-cross manner to the edges of the slit on the bottom sheet of the surface that corresponds to F_1. On the other hand, if z goes from F_0 to F_{-1}, its image w goes to the surface which corresponds to F_{-1}. The edges of the slit on the lower sheet of the original surface are therefore joined cross-wise to the edges of the slit on the top sheet of the surface associated with F_{-1}. Going on in this way, we may combine all the two-sheeted surfaces into a connected Riemann surface. Every sheet of the resulting surface will correspond to half of a period-strip. The sheets are combined in such a way that each sheet is joined to the following one in a cross-wise manner along the edges of slits which alternate between $(1, \infty)$ and $(-1, -\infty)$. In this way a connected Riemann surface is formed which possesses at each of the two points 1 and -1 infinitely many branch points of the first order (Fig. 25). At infinity, however, there are two branch points of infinite order. We can convince ourselves of this fact by the following considerations. If a point winds once about the point ∞ in the w-plane, which is to say that it winds once about both points -1 and 1, its image point on the Riemann surface moves to another sheet. There is still another sheet between this sheet and the original sheet, so that in such a circuit around the point ∞, w always jumps over a sheet. If the image point in the z-plane starts off in the upper half-plane, it remains in the upper half-plane all the time. But, if one starts off on the Riemann surface with a point w which corresponds to a point z in the lower half-plane, then w moves on the Riemann surface only

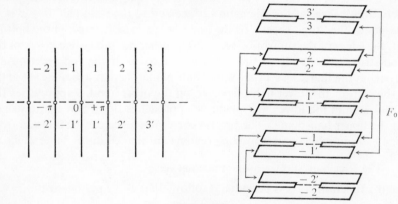

Figure 25

in such half-planes as correspond in the z-plane to portions of period-strips which lie in the lower half-plane.

6.12. The Inverse Function arc cos w

As we have already shown, the function $w = \cos z$ maps the entire z-plane conformally and one-to-one onto an infinite-sheeted Riemann surface. Its inverse function

$$z = \text{arc cos } w \tag{6.31}$$

is therefore an infinitely multiple-valued function whose different branches go over into one another when w makes a circuit about the points -1 and 1. The function is single-valued on the Riemann surface constructed above. As the principal branch of the function one generally takes the branch $0 \leq \text{Re } z < \pi$, and denotes it by Arc cos w.

The function (6.31) can be expressed in terms of the logarithm by means of Eqs. (6.24), (6.25) and (6.26). We obtain

$$z = \text{arc cos } w = \frac{1}{i} \log (w + \sqrt{w^2 - 1}).$$

6.13. The Mapping given by the Function sin z

The mapping given by the function $\sin z$ can be investigated in precisely the same way as we have dealt with $\cos z$. But one can also reduce $\sin z$ directly to $\cos z$ by means of (6.4). The mapping given by the sine is thus obtained from that given by the cosine by subjecting the z-plane to a parallel displacement of $\pi/2$.

All the trigonometrical functions have now been reduced to the exponential function, and their inverse functions to the logarithm.

§5. SURVEY OF THE RIEMANN SURFACES OF THE ELEMENTARY FUNCTIONS

6.14. The n-th Power

In Chapter 2 we saw that the n-th power $w = z^n$ (n a positive integer) maps the schlicht plane $0 \leq |z| \leq \infty$ in a one-to-one way onto an n-sheeted covering surface R_w lying over the plane $0 \leq |w| \leq \infty$. The mapping is conformal except at the points $z = 0, \infty$, which correspond to the branch points $w = 0$, ∞, of order $n - 1$.

The structure of the surface R_w can be described in the following way: We divide the plane into two half-planes: for instance, by the imaginary axis $u = 0$ ($w = u + iv$). The images in the z-plane of these two half-planes H_1: $u > 0$ and H_2: $u < 0$ consist of the sectors

$$F_v: \quad \left| \arg z - \frac{v\pi}{n} \right| < \frac{\pi}{2n} \quad (v = 0, \ldots, 2n - 1),$$

with ν even and with ν odd, respectively. If we connect these $2n$ sectors together, we obtain the entire z-plane. Its image in the w-plane is the n-sheeted covering surface R_w, with branch points $w = 0, \infty$ of order $n - 1$, which results from joining the $2n$ half-planes H_1 and H_2 together. We now take as representatives of the n half-planes H_1 the point $w = 1$ and of the n half-planes H_2 the point $w = -1$. Their image points $z_\nu = e^{\nu \cdot \pi i/n}$ $(\nu = 0, \ldots, 2n - 1)$ are associated with the sectors F_ν. If we denote the points z_ν with a cross for odd ν and a small circle for even ν, and join successive points by line segments, the structure of the surface R_w will be represented schematically by a graph (Fig. 26, right). Here the points denoted by circles or crosses represent half-planes H_1 and H_2, respectively. The graph divides the plane into two $2n$-gons (one inside the graph and one outside) which represent the two branch points of order $n - 1$ over $w = 0$ and $w = \infty$, respectively.

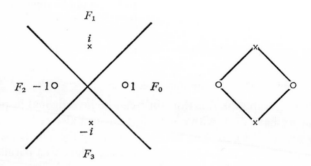

Figure 26

6.15. The Exponential Function

The Riemann surface of the exponential function $w = e^z$ can be represented in a similar way. If we define the two half-planes H_1 and H_2 as above, their image domains in the z-plane will be the parallel-strips

$$\left| y - 2\nu\pi \right| < \frac{\pi}{2} \quad \text{and} \quad \left| y - (2\nu + 1)\pi \right| < \frac{\pi}{2},$$

respectively, with $\nu = 0, \pm 1, \ldots$. The images of the points $w = 1$ and $w = -1$ are

$$z = 2\nu\pi i \quad \text{and} \quad z = (2\nu + 1)\pi i,$$

respectively, $\nu = 0, \pm 1, \ldots$. We take them as representatives of the half-planes H_1 and H_2, denoting them by a circle or a cross, respectively, and then join successive points by a line segment. This yields a graph (on the left in Fig. 27) which represents the infinite-sheeted Riemann surface R_w onto which $w = e^z$ maps the schlicht z-plane. The plane is divided by the graph into two polygons (the left- and right-hand half-planes) which represent the two branch points of R_w of infinite order lying over $w = 0$ and $w = \infty$, respectively.

6.16. The Trigonometrical Functions

We can obtain a similar representation for the functions $w = \sin z$ and $w = \cos z$. To each of the half-sheets $H_1 : v > 0$ and $H_2 : v < 0$ $(w = u + iv)$ of the corresponding Riemann surface R_w there is associated a "triangle" in the z-plane bounded by a segment of the x-axis and two rays parallel to the imaginary axis. If we again represent these "half-sheets" by circles and crosses, we obtain as the "schematic diagram" of R_w the graph on the right in Fig. 27; it gives a good over-all view of the structure of the surface. The plane is decomposed by the graph into infinitely many "polygons". The two upper and lower polygons (with infinitely many sides) correspond to the two branch points of the surface R_w over $w = \infty$. The two polygons are separated by a chain of infinitely many rectangles; these correspond alternately to the branch points of first order over the points $w = \pm 1$.

The surface of the function $w = \tan z$ (or $\cot z$) has the same structure as the surface for the exponential function. It can therefore be represented by the left-hand graph in Fig. 27.

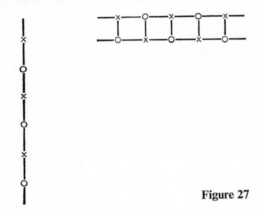

Figure 27

EXERCISES ON CHAPTER 6

1. Determine the following values:
$$\sin i, \qquad \cos i, \qquad \cos (\pi/4 - i), \qquad \tan (1 + i).$$

2. Determine all the roots of the following equations:
$$\sin z = i, \qquad \cos z = 2, \qquad \cot z = 1 + i.$$

Which of these roots belong to the fundamental domains of the functions, as given in the text?

3. Derive the differentiation formulas for $\cos z$ and $\sin z$ by use of the addition theorem.

Hint. The value of the limit

$$\lim_{z \to 0} \frac{\sin z}{z}$$

can be determined by using the definition of the sine once the derivative of the function e^z at the origin is known.

4. Show that the real and imaginary parts of the functions $\tan (x + iy)$ and $\cot (x + iy)$ satisfy the Cauchy-Riemann equations.

5. Draw about each pole of the function $\cot z$ a circle of fixed arbitrarily small radius ρ and show that when z lies outside these circles $|\cot z|$ is bounded by a finite number that depends only upon ρ.

6. Derive the most important properties of the function $\tan z$ from its mapping properties, which may be assumed known.

7. What values does the function Arc sin (ia) $(-\pi/2 \leqq \text{Re Arc sin } z < \pi/2)$ assume when a is a real number, and what values does Arc tan (ia) assume, when a is a real number whose modulus is smaller than 1 ?

8. Suppose the function arc cos z has, at the point $z = 2$, its principal value. Let z make one circuit about the point $z = 1$ and one circuit about the points $z = 1$ and $z = -1$ in a positive direction. What value does the function assume when z returns to the point $z = 2$?

9. Along what path in the plane must the point z move if (a) Arc cos z is to go into the branch $-$Arc cos $z - 2\pi$, (b) Arc sin z is to go into the branch Arc sin $z + 4\pi$, (c) Arc tan z is to go into the branch Arc tan $z - 3\pi$?

CHAPTER 7

INFINITE SERIES WITH COMPLEX TERMS

§1. GENERAL THEOREMS

7.1. Convergent Series

We shall consider an infinite series

$$\sum_{\nu=1}^{\infty} c_\nu = c_1 + c_2 + \cdots + c_n + \cdots \tag{7.1}$$

with complex terms

$$c_n = a_n + ib_n \qquad (n = 1, 2, \ldots).$$

The fact that the rational operations and the notion of limit remain formally unchanged in the transition from the real case to the complex case makes it possible to transfer the theory of infinite series to the complex domain.

Definition. *The series* (7.1) *is said to be convergent if the sequence of partial sums*

$$s_n = \sum_{\nu=1}^{n} c_\nu \qquad (n = 1, 2, \ldots)$$

tends to a finite limit s as n $\to$ ∞.

The limit s is called the *sum* of the convergent series, and we write

$$s = \sum_{\nu=1}^{\infty} c_\nu.$$

Whenever the series (7.1) converges, the series

$$\sum_{n+1}^{\infty} c$$

is also convergent, and its sum r_n, the *remainder after n terms*, is equal to $s - s_n$.

A series is said to be *divergent* if it does not converge.

Just as in the real case, we have the following result.

4*

Theorem 1. *The terms of a convergent series form a null sequence,*

$$\lim_{n \to \infty} c_n = 0.$$

Indeed, $\lim c_n = \lim (s_n - s_{n-1}) = s - s = 0$.

The generalization of the theory of infinite series from the real domain to the complex domain is based on the following theorem.

Theorem 2. *A necessary and sufficient condition for the convergence of the series* (7.1) *is that the series formed from the real and imaginary parts*

$$\sum_{\nu=1}^{\infty} a_\nu \quad and \quad \sum_{\nu=1}^{\infty} b_\nu \tag{7.2}$$

both converge.

Proof. Let

$$\sigma_n = \sum_{1}^{n} a_\nu, \qquad \tau_n = \sum_{1}^{n} b_\nu \qquad (s_n = \sigma_n + i\tau_n).$$

In order that $s = \lim s_n$ exist and be finite, it is necessary and sufficient that the limits $\sigma = \lim \sigma_n$ and $\tau = \lim \tau_n$ both exist and be finite, and this is the same as the convergence of the series (7.2).

We have

$$\sum_{1}^{\infty} c_\nu = \sum_{1}^{\infty} a_\nu + i \sum_{1}^{\infty} b_\nu.$$

7.2. The Cauchy Convergence Criterion

Of fundamental importance in the theory of convergence is *Cauchy's criterion*, which is as follows.

Theorem 3. *A necessary and sufficient condition for the existence of a finite limit s of a sequence of complex numbers*

$$s_1, s_2, \ldots, s_n, \ldots$$

is that for every $\epsilon > 0$, there is a number n_0 such that

$$|s_n - s_m| < \epsilon \quad for \quad n \geq n_0, \quad m \geq n_0. \tag{7.3}$$

By using Theorem 2, we could reduce this theorem to the corresponding criterion for real numbers. Nevertheless, we prefer to give a direct proof in the complex case.

Proof. The necessity follows directly from the triangle inequality. For if $\lim s_n = s$ exists, then

$$|s_n - s_m| = |(s - s_m) - (s - s_n)| \leq |s - s_m| + |s - s_n|,$$

which immediately implies (7.3).

Conversely, suppose that condition (7.3) is fulfilled. Then, for $n \geq n_0$, we have

$$|s_n| = |s_n - s_{n_0} + s_{n_0}| \leq |s_{n_0}| + |s_n - s_{n_0}| < |s_{n_0}| + \epsilon.$$

If M is the largest of the numbers $|s_\nu| + \epsilon$ ($\nu = 1, 2, \ldots, n_0$), then $|s_n| < M$ for every n. The sequence s_n is therefore bounded.

From this it follows (cf. Exercise 17, p. 20) that there is a number s ($|s| \leq M$) such that the inequality

$$|s - s_m| < \epsilon \tag{7.4}$$

holds for *infinitely* many indices m. Now let $n \geq n_0$ be chosen arbitrarily. Then, for every $m \geq n_0$, we have

$$|s - s_n| = |(s - s_m) + (s_m - s_n)| \leq |s - s_m| + \epsilon.$$

If we now fix the number $m \geq n_0$ so that (7.4) holds, then

$$|s - s_n| < 2\epsilon.$$

Since this is valid for every $n \geq n_0$, it follows that $s = \lim s_n$ as $n \to \infty$.

In the language of the theory of series, the Cauchy criterion takes the following form.

Theorem 4. *The series $\sum c_\nu$ converges if and only if to each $\epsilon > 0$, there is a number n_0 such that the inequality*

$$\left| \sum_n^{n+p} c_\nu \right| < \epsilon$$

holds for all $n \geq n_0$ and any $p \geq 0$.

7.3. Absolute Convergence

The series (7.1) is said to be *absolutely convergent* if the series of absolute values,

$$\sum_{\nu=1}^{\infty} |c_\nu|, \tag{7.5}$$

converges.

We shall prove:

Theorem 5. *If a series is absolutely convergent, then it converges.*

The converse is not true, as the example of the alternating harmonic series $\left(c_n = (-1)^n/n \right)$ shows.

A convergent series which does not converge absolutely is said to be *conditionally convergent*.

Proof of Theorem 5. Let the series (7.5) be convergent. Then, by the Cauchy criterion, for every $\epsilon > 0$ there is an integer n_0 such that the sequence of partial sums

$$\rho_n = \sum_1^n |c_\nu| \qquad (n = 0, 1, \ldots)$$

satisfies the condition

$$|\rho_m - \rho_n| = \sum_{\nu=n+1}^m |c_\nu| < \epsilon$$

when $m \geq n \geq n_0$. But then, for these same values m, n,

$$|s_m - s_n| = \left| \sum_{\nu=n+1}^m c_\nu \right| \leq \sum_{\nu=n+1}^m |c_\nu| < \epsilon$$

and the theorem follows from the Cauchy condition.

For absolutely convergent series we have:

Theorem 6. *One can interchange the order of the terms of an absolutely convergent series in any way without altering its sum.*

Proof. Let the series (7.1) converge absolutely, and let the series

$$\sum_{\nu=1}^\infty c_\nu' \tag{7.1}'$$

contain exactly the same terms, but in a different order. By hypothesis, for every $\epsilon > 0$, there exists an integer n_0 such that

$$\sum_{n_0+1}^\infty |c_\nu| < \epsilon.$$

Let n_1 ($\geq n_0$) be an arbitrary integer, so large that the numbers $c_1', \ldots, c_{n_1}'$ include all the numbers $c_1, \ldots, c_{n_0}$. Then, for $n \geq n_0$,

$$\left| \sum_1^n c_\nu - \sum_1^{n_1} c_\nu' \right| \leq \sum_{n_0+1}^\infty |c_\nu| < \epsilon.$$

If we let $n \to \infty$, it follows that

$$\left| \sum_1^\infty c_\nu - \sum_1^{n_1} c_\nu' \right| \leq \epsilon,$$

which implies the theorem.

One can also rearrange the series so that the terms are the sums of infinite subseries.

We mention, finally, *Cauchy's Product Rule*.

Theorem 7. *If the series*

$$U = \sum_{\nu=1}^\infty u_\nu \qquad and \qquad V = \sum_{\nu=1}^\infty v_\nu \tag{7.6}$$

converge, and if at least one of them converges absolutely, then

$$UV = \sum_{n=1}^{\infty} (u_1 v_n + u_2 v_{n-1} + \cdots + u_n v_1). \qquad (7.7)$$

The proof is carried out exactly as in the real case. The terms of the product series (7.7) and their order must be formed as written. If, however, *both* series in (7.6) converge absolutely, then we may group the terms in (7.7) and rearrange them arbitrarily. For in this case, the series remains convergent when the terms in the parentheses are replaced by their absolute values.

7.4. Uniform Convergence

We consider now the series

$$\sum_{\nu=1}^{\infty} w_\nu(z) = w_1(z) + w_2(z) + \cdots + w_n(z) + \cdots, \qquad (7.8)$$

whose terms $w_\nu(z)$ are functions of the complex variable z. All of the functions $w_\nu(z)$ are defined on a set A. We assume that the series (7.8) converges for each value $z \in A$. We denote the sum of the series by $s(z)$ and the n-th partial sum of the series by $s_n(z)$. If, for each $\epsilon > 0$, there exists an n_ϵ which is independent of z and which has the property that

$$|s_n(z) - s(z)| < \epsilon \qquad \text{for} \qquad n \geq n_\epsilon,$$

where z is an arbitrary point of A, the series (7.8) is said to be uniformly convergent on A.

The Cauchy criterion holds for the uniform convergence of the series (7.8):

Theorem 8. A necessary and sufficient condition for the uniform convergence of the series (7.8) on A is that for every $\epsilon > 0$ there exists an integer n_ϵ such that

$$\left| \sum_{\nu=n+1}^{n+p} w_\nu(z) \right| < \epsilon \qquad \text{for} \qquad z \in A,$$

for all $n \geq n_\epsilon$ and for all $p > 0$.

As a corollary, we have:

Theorem 9. If at every point $z \in A$

$$|w_n(z)| \leq r_n \qquad (n = 1, 2, \ldots)$$

and the "majorant series"

$$\sum_{1}^{\infty} r_n$$

converges, then the series $\sum w_n(z)$ converges absolutely and uniformly on A.

We shall prove the following theorem concerning a uniformly convergent series, which is already familiar in the real case.

Theorem 10. *If the series (7.8) converges uniformly in a domain G and if each of its terms $w_\nu(z)$ is continuous in G, then the sum of the series is a continuous function of z in G.*

Proof. Let z and $z + \Delta z$ be points of the domain G. Let us write

$$s(z) = s_n(z) + R_{n+1}(z),$$

so that

$$\Delta s = s(z + \Delta z) - s(z) = s_n(z + \Delta z) - s_n(z) + R_{n+1}(z + \Delta z) - R_{n+1}(z),$$

and thus

$$|\Delta s| \leqq |s_n(z + \Delta z) - s_n(z)| + |R_{n+1}(z + \Delta z)| + |R_{n+1}(z)|.$$

Since the series converges uniformly, to any arbitrary $\epsilon > 0$ there corresponds an n_ϵ such that for $n \geqq n_\epsilon$, $|R_{n+1}(z)| < \epsilon/3$, independently of the choice of $z \in G$. We shall choose a fixed n which fulfils this condition. Since the function $s_n(z)$ is a finite sum of continuous functions, it is itself continuous. Consequently, there exists a $\delta_\epsilon > 0$ such that

$$|s_n(z + \Delta z) - s_n(z)| < \frac{\epsilon}{3}$$

whenever $|\Delta z| < \delta_\epsilon$ and $z + \Delta z \in G$. From this it follows that

$$|\Delta s| < 3\,\frac{\epsilon}{3} = \epsilon \qquad \text{for} \qquad |\Delta z| < \delta_\epsilon.$$

This proves the continuity of the function $s(z)$.

§2. POWER SERIES

7.5. The Circle of Convergence

In this section we shall investigate *power series*

$$\sum_{n=0}^{\infty} c_n(z - z_0)^n = c_0 + c_1(z - z_0) + c_2(z - z_0)^2 + \cdots, \qquad (7.9)$$

in which the $c_0, c_1, c_2, \ldots$ and z_0 are complex numbers.

The first question before us is to determine those (complex) values of z for which the series converges. We shall begin by proving the following theorem of N. H. Abel (1802–1829).

Theorem 1. *If the series (7.9) converges for any value z', $z' \neq z_0$, then for every value of z which satisfies the condition*

$$|z - z_0| < |z' - z_0| \qquad (7.10)$$

the series not only converges, but converges absolutely.

Thus, if one draws a circle about z_0 with radius $|z' - z_0|$, the series converges at every point inside the circle.

Proof. Since the series

$$\sum_{n=0}^{\infty} c_n(z' - z_0)^n$$

converges, there exists a positive number M such that, for every n,

$$|c_n(z' - z_0)^n| < M.$$

From this it follows that

$$|c_n| < \frac{M}{|z' - z_0|^n} \qquad (n = 0, 1, 2, \ldots).$$

Thus, for the general term of the series (7.9), we have the estimate

$$|c_n(z - z_0)^n| \leqq M \left| \frac{z - z_0}{z' - z_0} \right|^n.$$

But the series

$$\sum_{n=0}^{\infty} \left| \frac{z - z_0}{z' - z_0} \right|^n \tag{7.11}$$

is a convergent geometric series, since, by hypothesis, the ratio

$$q = \left| \frac{z - z_0}{z' - z_0} \right| < 1.$$

Accordingly, the series (7.9) converges absolutely at every point z which satisfies condition (7.10).

7.6.

The series (7.9) obviously converges at the point z_0. It can happen that it converges only at this point. In the sequel we leave this case aside and assume that there is at least one other point $z' \neq z_0$ at which the series converges. We denote by $\{z'\}$ the set of all points for which the series converges and by R the least upper bound of the numbers $|z' - z_0|$:

$$R = \sup |z' - z_0| \leqq \infty. \tag{7.12}$$

Theorem 2. *The series (7.9) converges at every interior point of the circle*

$$|z - z_0| < R, \tag{7.13}$$

and it diverges at every point exterior to the circle.

Proof. First let z be an interior point of (7.13). By (7.12), the set $\{z'\}$ contains a number z' such that

$$|z - z_0| < |z' - z_0| \leqq R.$$

Since the series converges at the point z', it also converges at the point z by Abel's theorem. The divergence of the series in the exterior of the circle (7.13) is an immediate consequence of the definition (7.12) of R.

The circle $|z - z_0| = R$ will be called the *circle of convergence* of the series (7.9) and its radius R will be called the *radius of convergence*.

Theorem 3. *If the radius of convergence R is finite, then the least upper bound of the terms $|c_n| \, |z - z_0|^n$ is infinite for every $|z - z_0| > R$.*

Indeed, if for some point z_1 of $|z - z_0| > R$ the inequality

$$|c_n(z_1 - z_0)^n| < M < \infty$$

held for every n, then the same argument as was used to prove Abel's theorem would show that the series converges for every point z which satisfies the condition

$$|z - z_0| < |z_1 - z_0|.$$

If we choose z here to lie in the annulus $R < |z - z_0| < |z_1 - z_0|$, we would have a contradiction, as the radius of convergence would then be greater than R.

7.7. Determination of the Radius of Convergence

The radius of convergence R can be determined from the coefficients c_0, $c_1, \ldots$ of the series.

Since the series converges for $|z - z_0| = r < R$, $|c_n|r^n \to 0$ as $n \to \infty$. Hence, there exists a number n_0 such that $|c_n|r^n < 1$, or

$$r < \frac{1}{\sqrt[n]{|c_n|}} \qquad \text{for} \qquad n > n_0.$$

This number r is thus at most equal to the smallest cluster point of the sequence on the right. Since, however, r is an arbitrary number less than R, it follows that R itself has this property:

$$R \leqq \liminf_{n \to \infty} \frac{1}{\sqrt[n]{|c_n|}}.$$

If, in particular, $R = \infty$, then the number on the right is also infinite.

If $R < \infty$, then for $|z - z_0| = r > R$, the least upper bound of the numbers $|c_n|r^n$, $n = 0, 1, \ldots$, is *infinite* (Theorem 3). Therefore the inequalities $|c_n|r^n > 1$, $r > 1/\sqrt[n]{|c_n|}$, hold for infinitely many indices n. Accordingly,

$$r \geqq \liminf_{n \to \infty} \frac{1}{\sqrt[n]{|c_n|}},$$

and, since r can be chosen arbitrarily close to R, this inequality also holds for $r = R$.

Therefore we have the result:

Theorem 4. *The radius of convergence of the power series (7.9) is*

$$R = \liminf_{n \to \infty} \frac{1}{\sqrt[n]{|c_n|}}. \tag{7.14}$$

7.8. The Power Series as an Analytic Function

We wish to investigate further the sum of a power series inside the circle of convergence. For the sake of simplicity, we shall choose the "center" $z_0 = 0$; there is no real loss of generality in doing this. The power series we consider is therefore of the form

$$\sum_{n=0}^{\infty} c_n z^n. \tag{7.15}$$

Its radius of convergence R is assumed to be positive. The series is then absolutely convergent for $|z| < R$. We also have that the power series (7.15) is *uniformly* convergent on every disk $|z| \leq r < R$. In fact, for these values of z the series is majorized by the convergent series $\sum |c_n| r^n$, and the uniformity follows from Theorem 9 (p. 99).

It turns out therefore (if we apply Theorem 10, p. 100) that *the sum $S(z)$ of a power series is continuous throughout the circle of convergence $|z| < R$.*

7.9.

If we differentiate the series (7.15) term by term, we obtain a new power series

$$\sum_{n=1}^{\infty} n c_n z^{n-1}. \tag{7.15'}$$

By (7.14) its radius of convergence is

$$R_1 = \liminf_{n \to \infty} \frac{1}{\sqrt[n]{n} \sqrt[n]{|c_n|}}.$$

However, $\sqrt[n]{n} \to 1$ as $n \to \infty$, whence

$$R_1 = \liminf_{n \to \infty} \frac{1}{\sqrt[n]{|c_n|}} = R.$$

Hence, the derived series (7.15)' has the same radius of convergence as the original series (7.15).

If we differentiate the series (7.15)' term by term once again, we obtain the series

$$\sum_{n=2}^{\infty} n(n-1) c_n z^{n-2}, \tag{7.16}$$

whose radius of convergence is again equal to R.

We now prove that the sum $S(z)$ of the series (7.15) has a derivative, equal to the sum $S_1(z)$ of the series (7.15)':

$$S'(z) = S_1(z).$$

In view of the definition of the derivative, we must show that

$$\lim_{\Delta z \to 0} \frac{S(z + \Delta z) - S(z)}{\Delta z} = S_1(z)$$

holds for $|z| < R$.

Let us assume that $|\Delta z| < R - |z|$ and form the expression

$$f(\Delta z) = \frac{S(z + \Delta z) - S(z)}{\Delta z} - S_1(z) = \sum_{n=2}^{\infty} c_n \left\{ \frac{(z + \Delta z)^n - z^n}{\Delta z} - nz^{n-1} \right\}.$$

The binomial formula then yields

$$\frac{(z + \Delta z)^n - z^n}{\Delta z} - nz^{n-1}$$

$$= \binom{n}{2} z^{n-2} \Delta z + \binom{n}{3} z^{n-3}(\Delta z)^2 + \cdots + \binom{n}{n} (\Delta z)^{n-1}$$

$$= \frac{n(n-1)}{2} \Delta z \left\{ z^{n-2} + \frac{n-2}{3} z^{n-3} \Delta z + \cdots + \frac{2}{n(n-1)} (\Delta z)^{n-2} \right\}.$$

Since the modulus of the expression in braces is less than or equal to $(|z| + |\Delta z|)^{n-2}$, we have the estimate

$$\left| \frac{(z + \Delta z)^n - z^n}{\Delta z} - nz^{n-1} \right| \leq \frac{|\Delta z|}{2} n(n-1)(|z| + |\Delta z|)^{n-2},$$

from which it follows that

$$|f(\Delta z)| \leq \frac{|\Delta z|}{2} \sum_{n=2}^{\infty} n(n-1)|c_n|(|z| + |\Delta z|)^{n-2}.$$

The series on the right is made up of the moduli of the terms of the series (7.16), taken at the point $|z| + |\Delta z|$. It converges because $|z| + |\Delta z| < R$. If we choose

$$|z| + |\Delta z| \leq R_1 < R,$$

then there exists a finite number M such that

$$\sum_{n=2}^{\infty} n(n-1)|c_n|(|z| + |\Delta z|)^{n-2} < M$$

and therefore

$$|f(\Delta z)| \leq |\Delta z| \frac{M}{2}.$$

From this it follows that

$$\lim_{\Delta z \to 0} f(\Delta z) = 0,$$

and

$$S'(z) = \lim_{\Delta z \to 0} \frac{S(z + \Delta z) - S(z)}{\Delta z} = S_1(z).$$

This reasoning can be applied again to the power series $S_1(z)$, etc. We thus obtain the following general theorem.

Theorem 5. *A power series defines within its circle of convergence a continuous function. This function possesses continuous derivatives of every order, which are obtained by term-by-term differentiation of the original power series. All the power series derived in this fashion have the same radius of convergence as the original series.*

From this we conclude, in particular, that a power series defines within its circle of convergence an *analytic function.*

Later on, in Chapter 9, we shall see that, conversely, every function which is analytic in the neighborhood of a point $z = z_0$ can be represented by a power series. Karl Weierstrass (1815–1897) developed the theory of analytic functions from this property.

7.10. The Power Series Expansions of Elementary Functions

As an application, we shall expand the functions e^z, $\cos z$, and $\sin z$ into power series in z. It follows from the definition of the exponential function that

$$e^z = e^{x+iy} = e^x(\cos y + i \sin y).$$

We employ the power series expansions of these real functions to obtain

$$\cos y + i \sin y = 1 + iy - \frac{y^2}{2!} - i\frac{y^3}{3!} + \frac{y^4}{4!} + \cdots,$$

$$e^x = 1 + x + \frac{x^2}{2!} + \frac{x^3}{3!} + \cdots.$$

Both series are absolutely convergent for all values of x and y. If we now multiply the series according to the Cauchy product rule, we get, as the general term

$$\frac{(x + iy)^n}{n!} = \frac{z^n}{n!},$$

and, therefore, as the complete expansion,

$$e^z = 1 + z + \frac{z^2}{2!} + \cdots + \frac{z^n}{n!} + \cdots. \tag{7.17}$$

This series converges for all z; its sum is e^z.

The functions $\cos z$ and $\sin z$ are defined in terms of the exponential function as

$$\cos z = \frac{e^{iz} + e^{-iz}}{2}, \qquad \sin z = \frac{e^{iz} - e^{-iz}}{2i}.$$

If we now expand the functions e^{iz} and e^{-iz} according to (7.17), we get the series expansions

$$\cos z = 1 - \frac{z^2}{2!} + \frac{z^4}{4!} - \cdots,$$

$$\sin z = z - \frac{z^3}{3!} + \frac{z^5}{5!} - \cdots,$$

which converge for all values of z. They have the same form as in the real case.

EXERCISES ON CHAPTER 7

1. If the series $u_1 + u_2 + \cdots$ is convergent, then there exists a positive number M such that the inequality

$$|u_\nu + u_{\nu+1} + \cdots + u_{\nu+p}| < M$$

holds for all ν and p.

2. Prove the Cauchy product rule (Section 7.3).

3. Prove that a series converges uniformly if and only if the series of real parts and the series of imaginary parts of the terms occurring in the original series converge uniformly.

4. Determine the domain of convergence and the sum of the following geometric series:

a) $\dfrac{1}{z+1} - \dfrac{1}{(z+1)^2} + \dfrac{1}{(z+1)^3} - \cdots,$

b) $\dfrac{z}{z-1} + \left(\dfrac{z}{z-1}\right)^2 + \left(\dfrac{z}{z-1}\right)^3 + \cdots,$

c) $(z^2 - 1) + (z^2 - 1)^2 + (z^2 - 1)^3 + \cdots.$

5. Expand $1/(z + a)$ into increasing powers of $(z - b)$ and of $1/(z - b)$, and determine the domain of convergence of each of the resulting series.

6. Expand the rational function $1/(z^2 + 1)$ into increasing powers of the difference $z - 1$ and determine the domain of convergence of the series. (Expand the function in partial fractions and expand each term individually into a series.)

7. Expand the rational function $1/(z + 1)(z + 2)$ into partial fractions and expand it into a series (a) of positive powers of z, (b) of negative powers of z. (c) Then expand one partial fraction into positive powers of z and the other into negative powers of z.

Determine the domain of validity of the resulting series in each case, and the law governing the formation of the coefficients in the series.

8. Set $z = r(\cos \phi + i \sin \phi)$ in the series

$$\sum_{n=0}^{\infty} z^n,$$

and split each term into its real and imaginary parts. Form the series of real parts and the series of imaginary parts, and find the sum of each when it converges.

9. What can be said about the domain of convergence of the power series

$$\sum_{n=0}^{\infty} \frac{a_n}{(z - z_0)^n} ?$$

10. Show that the power series

$$\sum_{\nu=0}^{\infty} a_\nu z^\nu \qquad \text{and} \qquad \sum_{\nu=n}^{\infty} a_\nu z^{\nu-n}$$

both have the same radius of convergence.

11. Determine the radii of convergence of the following power series:

a) $\sum n^p z^n$, b) $\sum \dfrac{z^n}{n^n}$, c) $\sum q^{n^2} z^n$ $(|q| < 1)$, d) $\sum \left(\dfrac{z}{2 + (-1)^n}\right)^n$.

12. Determine the region of convergence of the following series:

a) $\sum \dfrac{(-1)^n}{z + n}$, b) $\sum \dfrac{z^n}{1 - z^n}$, c) $\sum \dfrac{z^n}{z^{2n} + 1}$.

13. Prove that if R_1 and R_2 are the radii of convergence of the series $\sum a_n z^n$ and $\sum b_n z^n$, then the series $\sum a_n b_n z^n$ has a radius of convergence $R \geq R_1 R_2$.

14. Show (by differentiation of the series $1/(1 - z) = \sum z^n$) that the function $(1 - z)^{-m}$ (m a positive integer) can be represented within the unit circle by the familiar binomial series. Derive the same result by use of the product rule for series.

15. Prove that if $|a_n/a_{n+1}|$ tends to a finite limit ρ as n tends to infinity, then ρ is the radius of convergence of the series $\sum a_n z^n$.

CHAPTER 8

INTEGRATION IN THE
COMPLEX DOMAIN. CAUCHY'S THEOREM

§1. COMPLEX LINE INTEGRALS

8.1. Arcs and Closed Curves

An *arc ab* is defined by a parametric equation

$$z = z(\tau) \qquad (a = z(\alpha), b = z(\beta)) \tag{8.1}$$

in which τ runs through a real interval $\alpha \leq \tau \leq \beta$, and $z(\tau) = x(\tau) + iy(\tau)$ is a continuous function of τ in this interval. The orientation of the arc is fixed by its parametrization: the point z describes the arc in the positive sense as τ increases from α to β. An oriented arc is also called a *path*.

If l is a path (8.1) then the same arc with the opposite orientation is denoted by l^{-1}. The path l^{-1} is thus described when τ decreases from β to α.

If the terminal point of a path l' coincides with the initial point of a path l, then the composite path that is obtained as the point z describes first the path l' and then the path l is denoted by the product ll'.

The arc *ab* is said to be a *Jordan arc* if $z(\tau_1) \neq z(\tau_2)$ for $\alpha \leq \tau_1 < \tau_2 \leq \beta$.

A *Jordan curve* is defined to be a *closed path* $(z(\alpha) = z(\beta))$ with the property that $z(\tau_1) \neq z(\tau_2)$ for $\alpha \leq \tau_1 < \tau_2 < \beta$.

If the function $z(\tau)$ has a continuous derivative $dx/d\tau = \dot{z}(\tau) = \dot{x}(\tau) + i\dot{y}(\tau) \neq 0$ throughout the interval $\alpha \leq \tau \leq \beta$, the arc *ab* has at every point a tangent whose direction varies continuously as the point describes the curve.

Such an arc is said to be *regular* or *smooth*. A curve which consists of a finite number of smooth arcs is said to be *piecewise* regular (or smooth).

From the Heine-Borel theorem (cf. Exercise 26, p. 21) one can show that any arc lying in the domain G can be covered by a finite number of disks belonging entirely to G. Hence, any two points P and Q of the domain can be joined by a finite chain of disks C_ν $(\nu = 1, 2, \ldots, n)$ with the following property: Each disk C_ν is contained in G; the center of the disk C_ν lies in the interior of $C_{\nu-1}$ $(\nu = 2, \ldots, n)$; P is in the disk C_1 and Q is in the disk C_n.

8.2. The Complex Line Integral

Let $w = w(z)$ be a single-valued complex function defined in a domain G in the finite complex plane. We wish to define the complex line integral

$$\int_a^b w(z) \, dz$$

108

extended over the arc (8.1) lying in the domain G. We proceed as one does for real integrals. The parameter-interval (α, β) is divided up into a finite number of subintervals whose end-points form a partition

$$D: \qquad \alpha = \tau_0 < \ldots < \tau_{\nu-1} < \tau_\nu < \ldots < \tau_n = \beta.$$

The corresponding points on the curve (8.1) are

$$z_\nu = z(\tau_\nu) \qquad (\nu = 0, 1, \ldots, n, \; z(\alpha) = a, \; z(\beta) = b).$$

From each interval $(\tau_{\nu-1}, \tau_\nu)$ we choose an arbitrary point $\tau = \sigma_\nu$ $(\tau_{\nu-1} \leqq \sigma_\nu \leqq \tau_\nu)$, and setting $\zeta_\nu = z(\sigma_\nu)$ we form the sum

$$\Sigma_D = \sum_{\nu=1}^{n} w(\zeta_\nu)(z_\nu - z_{\nu-1}).$$

If the curve (8.1) and the function $w(z)$ satisfy additional conditions that we shall give in the next section, it can be shown that Σ_D will tend to a finite limit when the partition D is unrestrictedly refined (i.e., as $n \to \infty$, the length of longest subinterval tends to zero), and the value of this limit will be independent of the way in which the limiting process is carried out. We then define the integral as

$$\int_a^b w(z) \, dz = \lim_{n\to\infty} \sum_{\nu=1}^{n} w(\zeta_\nu)(z_\nu - z_{\nu-1}). \tag{8.2}$$

8.3. Existence Proof

We assert that Σ_D will tend to a finite limit in the manner described if the function $w(z)$ and the arc $l \subset G$ satisfy the following conditions.

1. The function $w(z)$ is continuous throughout the domain G.
2. The length of the polygons $z_0 \ldots z_{\nu-1} z_\nu \ldots z_n$ corresponding to the partitions D is bounded.

Thus, there exists a finite constant L (independent of D) such that

$$L_D = \sum_{1}^{n} |z_\nu - z_{\nu-1}| \leqq L.$$

From a given partition D we can form a refinement D' by introducing a finite number of new points of division. The corresponding sums then satisfy the condition

$$|\Sigma_D - \Sigma_{D'}| \leqq O_D L,$$

where O_D denotes the maximal oscillation† of $w(z)$ on the subarcs of l determined by the partition D.

---

† The oscillation of a function $w(z)$ on a set A is defined by

$$\sup_{a,b \in A} |w(a) - w(b)|.$$

For the proof of the assertion we consider the first subinterval (z_0, z_1) of D and the corresponding term

$$w(\zeta_1)(z_1 - z_0) \tag{8.3}$$

in the sum Σ_D. Suppose that this interval is subdivided by the partition D' into m subintervals with end-points $z_0 = z_0', z_1', \ldots, z_m' = z_1$. Let an intermediate point of the interval $(z_{\mu-1}', z_\mu')$ be denoted by $z = \zeta_\mu'$. The contribution of these intervals to the sum $\Sigma_{D'}$ is

$$\sum_{\mu=1}^{m} w(\zeta_\mu')(z_\mu' - z_{\mu-1}').$$

If we write

$$z_1 - z_0 = \sum_{1}^{m} (z_\mu' - z_{\mu-1}'),$$

then we have

$$\left| w(\zeta_1)(z_1 - z_0) - \sum_{1}^{m} w(\zeta_\mu')(z_\mu' - z_{\mu-1}') \right|$$

$$= \left| \sum_{1}^{m} \left(w(\zeta_1) - w(\zeta_\mu') \right)(z_\mu' - z_{\mu-1}') \right| \leqq O_D \sum_{1}^{m} |z_\mu' - z_{\mu-1}'|.$$

The same reasoning is applied to each subinterval of D, and the n inequalities obtained in this way are added together. The triangle inequality then yields the estimate

$$|\Sigma_D - \Sigma_{D'}| \leqq O_D L_{D'} \leqq O_D L.$$

Now let D_1 and D_2 be two arbitrary partitions and $\Sigma_{D_1}, \Sigma_{D_2}$ the corresponding sums (the intermediate points ζ are chosen arbitrarily). The totality of all the points of subdivision occurring in these partitions determines a new partition D' which is a refinement of both D_1 and D_2. If $\Sigma_{D'}$ is one of the sums corresponding to this new partition, we have, in view of the foregoing inequality, that

$$|\Sigma_{D_1} - \Sigma_{D_2}| \leqq |\Sigma_{D_1} - \Sigma_{D'}| + |\Sigma_{D_2} - \Sigma_{D'}| \leqq L(O_{D_1} + O_{D_2}).$$

Since the function $w(z)$ is continuous on the closed arc l, it is *uniformly* continuous on l (Exercise 1, p. 127). Hence, for any $\epsilon > 0$ there exists a number $\delta_\epsilon > 0$, such that the oscillation O_D of the function $w(z(\tau))$ is less than ϵ for every partition D for which $\tau_\nu - \tau_{\nu-1} < \delta_\epsilon$. From the inequality $O_D < \epsilon$ it follows that for any two sufficiently fine partitions D_1, D_2

$$|\Sigma_{D_1} - \Sigma_{D_2}| \leqq 2L\epsilon. \tag{8.4}$$

The Cauchy convergence criterion now implies that the finite limit (8.2) will exist for every partition D as it becomes progressively finer (i.e., as the length of the maximal subinterval of the partition D tends to zero).

8.4. The Concept of Arc Length

If the arc (8.1) has the property postulated above that the lengths L_D of the inscribed polygons have a finite upper bound L, then the arc is said to be *rectifiable*, and the least upper bound of the set (L_D) (for all partitions D)

$$\sup_{(D)} L_D = s \qquad (8.5)$$

is called the *length* of the arc. We shall prove the following.

As the partition D becomes progressively finer, the length L_D converges to a limit:†

$$s = \lim L_D. \qquad (8.6)$$

In view of (8.5), for every $\epsilon > 0$ there is a partition D_ϵ of the interval (α, β) for which

$$L_{D_\epsilon} > s - \frac{\epsilon}{2}.$$

Let N be the number of the points of division of D_ϵ that lie in the interior of (α, β). Since the function $z(\tau)$ is uniformly continuous in the closed interval (α, β), there exists a number $\delta > 0$ such that

$$|z(\tau) - z(\tau')| < \frac{\epsilon}{4N} \qquad (8.7)$$

whenever $|\tau - \tau'| < \delta$. Now consider an arbitrary partition D of (α, β) whose subintervals are each less than δ in length. For a common refinement D' of D and D_ϵ we have

$$L_{D'} \geqq L_{D_\epsilon} > s - \frac{\epsilon}{2}.$$

The number of subintervals of D' that have an internal division-point of D_ϵ as one of their end-points is at most $2N$. The sum of the corresponding contributions to $L_{D'}$ is at most $2N\epsilon/4N = \epsilon/2$. All the remaining subintervals of D' are also subintervals of D. Hence, the sum of their contributions to $L_{D'}$ is certainly no greater than L_D. We thus obtain for $L_{D'}$ the estimate

$$L_{D'} \leqq L_D + \frac{\epsilon}{2},$$

whence

$$s \geqq L_D \geqq L_{D'} - \frac{\epsilon}{2} > s - \epsilon.$$

The assertion (8.6) is thereby proved.

---

† This limit can be denoted as an integral: $s = \int_l |dz|$.

8.5.

Suppose now that the curve (8.1) *is continuously differentiable*, that is, the derivative

$$\frac{dz}{d\tau} = \dot{z}(\tau) = \dot{x}(\tau) + i\dot{y}(\tau)$$

exists and is continuous. Then the arc length is given by the formula:

$$s = \int_\alpha^\beta |\dot{z}(\tau)|\, d\tau = \int_l |dz|. \tag{8.8}$$

Proof. By the definition of the derivative,

$$z(\tau + \Delta\tau) - z(\tau) = \dot{z}(\tau)\Delta\tau + \Delta\tau(\Delta\tau), \tag{8.9}$$

where $(\Delta\tau) \to 0$ as $\Delta\tau \to 0$. It is a consequence of the continuity of the derivative that the function $(\Delta\tau)$ tends to zero uniformly, i.e., for $\epsilon > 0$ there exists a $\delta_\epsilon > 0$ such that $|(\Delta\tau)| < \epsilon$ for all τ in the interval (α, β), provided that $|\Delta\tau| < \delta_\epsilon$ (cf. Exercise 3, p. 127).

Suppose now that D is a partition of (α, β) for which $\tau_\nu - \tau_{\nu-1} < \delta_\epsilon$. Then for the corresponding polygon we have

$$z_\nu - z_{\nu-1} = \dot{z}(\tau_{\nu-1})(\tau_\nu - \tau_{\nu-1}) + (\tau_\nu - \tau_{\nu-1})\langle\epsilon\rangle,$$

where $\langle\epsilon\rangle$ denotes a number whose modulus is less than ϵ: $|\langle\epsilon\rangle| < \epsilon$. Hence, we have also

$$|z_\nu - z_{\nu-1}| = |\dot{z}(\tau_{\nu-1})|(\tau_\nu - \tau_{\nu-1}) + (\tau_\nu - \tau_{\nu-1})\langle\epsilon\rangle,$$

and so, by summing, we obtain

$$L_D = \sum_1^n |\dot{z}(\tau_{\nu-1})|(\tau_\nu - \tau_{\nu-1}) + r_D, \tag{8.10}$$

where

$$|r_D| \leq \sum_1^n \epsilon(\tau_\nu - \tau_{\nu-1}) = \epsilon(\beta - \alpha). \tag{8.11}$$

Now $|\dot{z}(\tau)|$ is continuous in the interval $\alpha \leq \tau \leq \beta$. By taking D progressively finer, we obtain

$$\lim \sum_1^n |\dot{z}(\tau_{\nu-1})|(\tau_\nu - \tau_{\nu-1}) = \int_\alpha^\beta |\dot{z}(\tau)|\, d\tau.$$

Hence, it follows from (8.11) that L_D tends to the expression in (8.8), and this is what we wanted to prove.

To the interval (α, τ) $(\alpha \leq \tau \leq \beta)$ there thus corresponds the arc length

$$s(\tau) = \int_\alpha^\tau |\dot{z}(\tau)|\, d\tau; \qquad \frac{ds}{d\tau} = \dot{s}(\tau) = |\dot{z}(\tau)|.$$

If in addition the curve is regular:

$$\dot{z}(\tau) = \dot{x}(\tau) + i\dot{y}(\tau) \neq 0,$$

then $ds/d\tau > 0$. The arc length $s(\tau)$ is then a strictly increasing function of τ and thus the same is true for its inverse function $\tau = \tau(s)$, whose derivative is just $d\tau/ds = 1/(ds/d\tau) > 0$. Hence, for a regular curve, one can introduce the arc length as a new parameter: $z = z(\tau) = z(\tau(s)) = z^*(s)$, and this is often useful in the theory of line integrals.

8.6. The Line Integral over a Regular Curve

If the arc (8.1) is continuously differentiable (or, more specially, if it is regular), then, by means of the substitution $z = z(\tau)$, one can reduce the line integral of a continuous complex-valued function $w = w(z)$ to the ordinary integral of a function of τ extended over the parameter-interval (α, β). If, in the sum Σ_D (Section 8.2) we take $\zeta_\nu = z_{\nu-1}$ $(\nu = 1, \ldots, n)$,

$$\Sigma_D = \sum_1^n w(z_{\nu-1})(z_\nu - z_{\nu-1}),$$

and replace the difference $z_\nu - z_{\nu-1}$ by (8.9), we obtain

$$\Sigma_D = \sum_1^n w\big(z(\tau_{\nu-1})\big)\dot{z}(\tau_{\nu-1})(\tau_\nu - \tau_{\nu-1}) + r_D. \tag{8.12}$$

Here

$$r_D = \sum_1^n w\big(z(\tau_{\nu-1})\big)(\tau_\nu - \tau_{\nu-1})\langle\epsilon\rangle,$$

provided that the length $\tau_\nu - \tau_{\nu-1}$ of each subinterval is less than δ_ϵ (Section 8.5). If we denote the maximum of $|w|$ on l by M, we have that

$$|r_D| \leq M(\beta - \alpha)\epsilon.$$

The function $f(\tau) = w(z(\tau))\dot{z}(\tau)$ is continuous in the interval (α, β). Therefore as the partition D becomes progressively finer, the first sum on the right-hand side of (8.12) converges to the integral

$$\int_\alpha^\beta f(\tau)\, d\tau = \int_\alpha^\beta w(z(\tau))\dot{z}(\tau)\, d\tau.$$

Since the remainder term r_D converges to zero, this integral is also the limit of the sum Σ_D, and thus

$$\int_a^b w(z)\, dz = \int_\alpha^\beta w(z(\tau))\dot{z}(\tau)\, d\tau. \tag{8.13}$$

8.7. Rules of Computation

From the definition of the line integral follow these rules of computation:

1)
$$\int Cw(z)\,dz = C\int w(z)\,dz \qquad (C\text{ a constant});$$

$$\int (w_1 + w_2)\,dz = \int w_1\,dz + \int w_2\,dz.$$

2) If the arc $l = ab$ is extended by an arc $l' = bc$, then

$$\int_{abc} w\,dz = \int_{ab} w\,dz + \int_{bc} w\,dz.$$

3)
$$\int_a^b w\,dz = -\int_b^a w\,dz.$$

4) If $M = \max\limits_{z\in l} |w(z)|$ and L is the length of l, then

$$\left|\int_l w\,dz\right| \le M\int_l |dz| = ML.$$

5) For $w = u + iv,\ z = x + iy$ we have

$$\int w\,dz = \int (u\,dx - v\,dy) + i\int (v\,dx + u\,dy).$$

Finally, we mention the following theorem:

If $w_1(z), w_2(z), \ldots$ are continuous functions defined on a rectifiable curve l, and if the series

$$w(z) = \sum_{\nu=1}^{\infty} w_\nu(z)$$

converges uniformly on this curve, then the series can be integrated term by term:

$$\int_l w(z)\,dz = \sum_{\nu=1}^{\infty} \int_l w_\nu(z)\,dz.$$

The proof of this theorem is left as an exercise (Exercise 6, p. 127).

§2. THE PRIMITIVE FUNCTION

8.8. Formulation of the Problem

Let $w(z) = u(z) + iv(z)$ be a continuous single-valued complex function in the domain G of the finite z-plane. Any complex function $W(z) = U(z) + iV(z)$ which is single-valued in G and has the property that

$$W'(z) = w(z)$$

is said to be a *primitive function* of $w(z)$.

Such a primitive function W, if it exists, is an analytic function of z in G. We ask:

1) Under what conditions does $w(z)$ possess a primitive function $W(z)$?

2) What is the totality of all primitive functions $W(z)$?

The theory of integration in the real domain depends in an essential way on the connection between the notions of "primitive function" and "definite integral". This connection is also valid in the complex domain. If $W(z) = U(z) + iV(z)$ is a primitive function of $w(z)$ which is single-valued in G, and if $l = ab$ denotes a continuously differentiable path joining the points $z = a$ and $z = b$ inside of G, then

$$\int_{ab} w(z)\, dz = W(b) - W(a). \qquad (8.14)$$

The proof is obtained from the corresponding theorem for real integrals (the so-called fundamental theorem of the calculus). Let $z = z(\tau)\,(\alpha \leq \tau \leq \beta;$ $z(\alpha) = a, z(\beta) = b)$ be the equation of l. Then

$$\frac{dW(z(\tau))}{d\tau} = w(z(\tau))\dot{z}(\tau),$$

and, hence, $W(z(\tau))$ is a primitive function of $f(\tau) \equiv w(z(\tau))\dot{z}(\tau)$ on the interval $\alpha \leq \tau \leq \beta$. If we decompose f into its real and imaginary parts, we see that the condition (8.14) is indeed a consequence of the fundamental theorem of the calculus.

From (8.14) it follows that the primitive function W of w, when it exists, is uniquely determined up to an additive constant. In fact,

$$W(b) = \int_{ab} w(z)\, dz + C, \qquad (8.15)$$

where $l = ab$ is a path joining the points a and b, and $C = W(a)$. Conversely, if W is a primitive function and C is an arbitrary constant, then $W + C$ is another primitive function. Thus if W is one particular primitive function, all the others are given by the expression $W + C$, where C is an arbitrary constant.

8.9. Conditions of Integrability

We now pass on to question (1) (Section 8.8) and derive a necessary and sufficient condition for the existence of a primitive function. The right-hand side of formula (8.14) depends only on the end-points a and b of the curve l. Hence, the same is true for the left-hand side.

If the function $w(z)$ is integrable in G (that is, if $w(z)$ has a single-valued primitive function in G), then the value of the integral

$$\int_a^b w(z)\, dz \qquad (8.16)$$

is independent of the path of integration joining the points a and b in G.

Suppose now that l is a closed path, i.e., suppose that $a = b$. In this case (8.14) implies the following integrability condition.

If $w(z)$ is integrable in G, then for any continuously differentiable closed curve γ, lying entirely in G,†

$$\int_\gamma w(z)\,dz = 0. \tag{8.17}$$

Remark. If both the arcs l_1 and l_2 join the points a and b, then the path $l_2^{-1} l_1 = l$ is closed. The path l is thus obtained by running first through l_1 and then back through l_2 (i.e., through the arc l_2^{-1}). We have

$$\int_l w\,dz = \int_{l_1} + \int_{l_2^{-1}} = \int_{l_1} - \int_{l_2}.$$

Thus if the integral vanishes over every closed curve, then the integral $\int_a^b$ is independent of the path, and conversely.

8.10. The Sufficiency of the Integrability Condition (8.17)

We assume that the necessary condition (8.17) for integrability is fulfilled, and show conversely that the function $w(z)$ has a primitive function.

We choose in G an arbitrary point z_0, which we take as fixed; we let z be another arbitrary point of G and l a piecewise regular path from z_0 to z. The points of l will be denoted by t.

If $w(z)$ has a primitive function $W(z)$, then we know by (8.14) that

$$W(z) = C + \int_l w(t)\,dt \qquad (C = W(z_0)).$$

Conversely, if we wish to deduce the existence of the primitive function from condition (8.17), we proceed directly from the integral

$$\phi(z) \equiv \int_{z_0}^{z} w(t)\,dt$$

taken over an arbitrary, piecewise regular path $z_0 z = l \subset G$. Since the integrability condition (8.17) is assumed to be fulfilled, the value $\phi(z)$ is independent of the choice of the path $z_0 z$; $\phi(z)$ is thus defined in G as a single-valued function. We have to show that $\phi(z)$ is a primitive function of $w(z)$: $\phi'(z) = w(z)$.

We consider a disk with center $z \in G$ and radius ρ which lies entirely in G. For $|\Delta z| < \rho$ we have

$$\Delta\phi \equiv \phi(z + \Delta z) - \phi(z) = \int_{z_0}^{z+\Delta z} w(t)\,dt - \int_{z_0}^{z} w(t)\,dt = \int_{z}^{z+\Delta z} w(t)\,dt, \tag{8.18}$$

---

† If the path γ is *piecewise* regular, then the integral is the sum of the integrals over the regular subarcs. Hence, the theorems stated above remain valid for piecewise regular curves.

where in the last integral we choose the segment $(z, z + \varDelta z)$ for our path of integration. Since $w(t)$ is continuous at the point $t = z$, we have on this segment

$$w(t) = w(z) + r(t),$$

where $|r(t)|$ is less than ϵ, provided that $|t - z| < \delta_\epsilon$. Hence,

$$\int_z^{z+\varDelta z} w(t)\, dt = \int_z^{z+\varDelta z} w(z)\, dt + \int_z^{z+\varDelta z} r(t)\, dt = w(z)\varDelta z + \int_z^{z+\varDelta z} r(t)\, dt,$$

where the modulus of the last integral does not exceed

$$\int_z^{z+\varDelta z} |r|\, |dt| < \epsilon|\varDelta z|$$

whenever $|\varDelta z| < \delta_\epsilon$. It follows that

$$\phi(z + \varDelta z) - \phi(z) = w(z)\varDelta z + |\varDelta z|(\varDelta z),$$

where $(\varDelta z) \to 0$ as $\varDelta z \to 0$. Then, by the definition of the derivative, we have

$$\phi'(z) = w(z).$$

Thus ϕ is a primitive function of w in the domain G.

The problem of integrability is thus reduced to the necessary and sufficient condition (8.17).

§3. CAUCHY'S THEOREM

8.11. Integrability and Analyticity

In the previous sections it has been proved that the independence of the integral

$$\int_a^b w(z)\, dz$$

of its path of integration constitutes a necessary and sufficient condition for the integrability of the complex-valued function $w(z)$, single-valued and continuous in the domain G. This property can be reduced to a simple local condition.

For the integrability of the function $w(z)$ in the domain G it is necessary that $w(z)$ be analytic at every point of G.

Under an additional assumption on the topological character of the domain G, this condition is also sufficient.

To prove that the condition is necessary we require tools that are not yet at our disposal. For this reason the proof of this part of the assertion will be given in the next chapter (Exercise 6, p. 165). The second part of the assertion will be proved first under the assumption that the domain G is *convex*. This means that if a and b are two arbitrary points of G, then the segment *ab* also lies in *G*. In Section 4 it will be possible to replace this assumption by a weaker one. What we shall prove is:

In a convex domain G every analytic function w = w(z) is integrable.

8.12. Goursat's Proof

We consider the integral

$$I = \int_\gamma w(z)\, dz$$

taken in the positive sense over the boundary γ of a triangle $\varDelta$ in *G*. We decompose $\varDelta$ into four congruent subtriangles $\varDelta_1$ with positively oriented boundaries γ_1. Then we have

$$I = \sum \int_{\gamma_1} w(z)\, dz.$$

In fact, every edge in this partition that is interior to $\varDelta$ is the common edge of two adjoining subtriangles, but with opposite orientation. Thus the contributions of these sides to the integral cancel each other, while the contributions of the outer sides add up to the complete integral over the boundary γ.†

Thus we have

$$|I| \leq \sum \left| \int_{\gamma_1} w(z)\, dz \right| \leq 4|I_1|,$$

where

$$I_1 = \int_{\gamma_1} w\, dz$$

denotes the integral taken over the boundary of whichever of the four triangles $\varDelta_1$ gives it its largest absolute value. (If there are several triangles giving the greatest absolute value, I_1 can be chosen to be the integral over any one of them provided it is fixed.) If $|\varDelta|$ and $|\varDelta_1| = |\varDelta|/4$ denote the areas of the triangles so fixed, we have

$$\frac{|I|}{|\varDelta|} \leq \frac{4}{|\varDelta|}\, |I_1| = \frac{|I_1|}{|\varDelta_1|}.$$

---

† The rigorous proof of these intuitively obvious assertions rests on the definition of orientation of the boundary. The positive orientation of the triangle $P_1P_2P_3$ is fixed in just the same way as for circles in the footnote on p. 46. Let T_1 be the half-plane bounded by the line through P_2 and P_3 and containing P_1. The half-planes T_2 and T_3 are defined similarly. The interior of the triangle $P_1P_2P_3$ is then defined as the intersection of the half-planes T_1, T_2, T_3.

Let *a* be an arbitrary interior point of the triangle. One can show that as *z* traverses the perimeter of the triangle in the sense $P_1P_2P_3P_1$, $d \arg (z - a)$ is either everywhere positive, or everywhere negative independently of the choice of *a*. In the first case we say that the orientation of the boundary is positive with respect to the plane, or with respect to the interior of the triangle; in the second case the orientation is said to be negative.

By repeating this process we obtain a sequence of nested similar triangles $\Delta \supset \Delta_1 \supset \cdots \supset \Delta_n \supset \cdots$ with boundaries $\gamma, \gamma_1, \ldots, \gamma_n, \ldots$ such that

$$\frac{|I|}{|\Delta|} \leq \frac{|I_1|}{|\Delta_1|} \leq \cdots \leq \frac{|I_n|}{|\Delta_n|} \leq \cdots, \tag{8.19}$$

where

$$I_n = \int_{\gamma_n} w(z) \, dz.$$

The length $|\gamma_n| = |\gamma|/2^n$ of the boundary γ_n tends to zero as $n \to \infty$. It follows that the (closed) triangles Δ_n ($n = 1, 2, \ldots$) have exactly *one* common point $z = z_0$ in the (closed) triangle Δ.

Now $w(z)$ is differentiable at the point $z = z_0$, and, hence,

$$w(z) = w(z_0) + w'(z_0)(z - z_0) + |z - z_0|\epsilon(z),$$

where $\epsilon(z) \to 0$ as $z \to z_0$. Hence,

$$\int_{\gamma_n} w(z) \, dz = w(z_0) \int_{\gamma_n} dz + w'(z_0) \int_{\gamma_n} (z - z_0) \, dz + \int_{\gamma_n} |z - z_0|\epsilon(z) \, dz.$$

The primitive functions of the first two integrands on the right-hand side are z and $(z - z_0)^2/2$; thus the integrals over the closed path γ_n are zero. In the third integral $|z - z_0| < |\gamma_n| \to 0$ as $n \to \infty$; that is, for every $\epsilon > 0$ there exists an n_ϵ such that $|\epsilon(z)| < \epsilon$ on γ_n whenever $n > n_\epsilon$. For these values of n we have

$$|I_n| = \left| \int_{\gamma_n} w \, dz \right| = \left| \int_{\gamma_n} |z - z_0|\epsilon(z) \, dz \right| \leq |\gamma_n|\epsilon \int_{\gamma_n} |dz| = \epsilon|\gamma_n|^2,$$

and, hence,

$$\frac{|I_n|}{|\Delta_n|} \leq \epsilon \frac{|\gamma_n|^2}{|\Delta_n|} = \epsilon \frac{|\gamma|^2}{|\Delta|}.$$

Thus, in view of (8.19), $|I| \leq \epsilon|\gamma|^2$ for $n > n_\epsilon$, which is possible only if $I = 0$.

8.13. Cauchy's Theorem

We are now in a position to construct a primitive function for a function $w(z)$, which is analytic in a convex domain G.

Let z_0 be a fixed point of G, and let $z \in G$ be an arbitrary second point. We define in G a single-valued function by the integral

$$\phi(z) = \int_{z_0}^{z} w(t) \, dt,$$

where the integral is taken over the straight-line segment $z_0 z$. If we go from z to the point $z + \Delta z \in G$, we have

$$\Delta\phi = \phi(z + \Delta z) - \phi(z) = \int_{z_0}^{z + \Delta z} w(t) \, dt - \int_{z_0}^{z} w(t) \, dt,$$

where both integrals are taken over straight-line segments. In view of Section 8.12, the integral of w over the boundary of the triangle $z_0, z, z + \Delta z$, vanishes. Hence,

$$\Delta\phi = \int_z^{z+\Delta z} w(t)\, dt.$$

It can now be shown, as in Section 8.10, that $\phi(z)$ is a primitive function of $w(z)$ in G, which was to be proved. Applying the necessary condition of integrability (8.17), one can further conclude that:

For an analytic function $w(z)$, single-valued in the convex domain G, the integral

$$\int_\gamma w(z)\, dz$$

vanishes over any (piecewise) regular closed curve γ contained in G.

This is Cauchy's theorem, the fundamental theorem for the development of the theory of analytic functions. In the next section we shall extend it to more general domains.

Remark 1. The theorem remains valid if the curve γ contains a boundary arc of G on which $w(z)$ is analytic. If we keep in mind the definition of analyticity at a point, we see that the above proof is still valid in this case.

Remark 2. If the path l $(z = z(\tau);\ \alpha \leq \tau \leq \beta;\ z(\alpha) = a,\ z(\beta) = b)$ in G is rectifiable, then the line integral

$$\int_l w(z)\, dz \tag{8.20}$$

is to be understood in the sense of the definition of Section 1. If $w(z)$ now has a single-valued primitive function $W(z)$ in G and if the path of integration is piecewise regular, then

$$\int w(z)\, dz = \int_l dW = W(b) - W(a). \tag{8.21}$$

This formula is valid for an *arbitrary* rectifiable curve, since the integral over a rectifiable curve can be approximated arbitrarily closely by means of integrals over piecewise regular curves (Exercise 14, p. 128).

8.14. Determination of the Primitive Function on Chains of Convex Domains

Let G be an *arbitrary* domain, $w(z)$ an analytic function in G, and $l = ab$ a piecewise regular path in G. We can decompose l into a finite number of subarcs $l_\nu = c_{\nu-1}c_\nu$ $(\nu = 1, 2, \ldots, n;\ c_0 = a,\ c_n = b)$ in such a way that each l_ν belongs to a convex domain $G_\nu \subset G$ (Section 8.1). Then, in view of Section 8.13, there exists in each subdomain G_ν a single-valued primitive function $W_\nu(z)$ of $w(z)$, so that the integral (8.20) can be evaluated by the formula

$$\int_l w(z)\, dz = \sum_{\nu=1}^n \int_{l_\nu} w(z)\, dz = \sum_{\nu=1}^n \left(W_\nu(c_\nu) - W_\nu(c_{\nu-1}) \right). \tag{8.22}$$

These considerations can be extended to the case in which *l* is an *arbitrary* (*continuous*) path. The integral (8.20), which, until now, has been defined only for rectifiable paths *l*, can be *defined* for an arbitrary continuous path by the formula (8.22). This definition is independent of the manner of decomposition (l_ν) (Exercise 15, p. 128).

Cauchy's theorem is valid therefore for arbitrary continuous paths γ which lie in a convex domain *G*.

§4. THE GENERAL FORMULATION OF CAUCHY'S THEOREM

8.15. Winding Number of a Closed Curve

In the previous paragraph we have discussed the integration of analytic functions in a *convex* domain. We now ask ourselves the question: is this special property of the domain *G* essential for the validity of the results of Section 3, in particular, is it essential for the validity of Cauchy's theorem? That the topological nature of the domain has some bearing upon the problems of integrability is evident from the following simple example.

Let $z = c$ be an arbitrary point of the plane and let γ denote a piecewise regular closed path $z = z(\tau)$ ($\alpha \leqq \tau \leqq \beta$) which does not meet the point $z = c$ ($z(\tau) \neq c$). The function $w(z) = 1/(z - c)$ is analytic in the punctured plane $0 < |z - c| < \infty$ where it is the derivative of the function $\log (z - c) = \log |z - c| + i \arg (z - c)$. In view of (8.13) we have

$$u_c = \frac{1}{2\pi i} \int_\gamma \frac{dz}{z - c} = \frac{1}{2\pi i} \int_\alpha^\beta \frac{\dot{z}(\tau)\, d\tau}{z(\tau) - c}$$

$$= \frac{1}{2\pi i} \int_\alpha^\beta \frac{d}{d\tau} \log |z(\tau) - c|\, d\tau + \frac{1}{2\pi} \int_\alpha^\beta \frac{d}{d\tau} \arg (z(\tau) - c)\, d\tau. \quad (8.23)$$

Since the function $\log |z - c|$ is single-valued, the first integral on the right-hand side is zero. The second integral is the increment of $\arg (z - c)$ along γ, and thus it is an integral multiple of 2π. If we write $c = a + ib$ and $z(\tau) = x + iy$, we obtain for the *integer* u_c the following value:

$$\frac{1}{2\pi} \int_\alpha^\beta \frac{d}{d\tau} \arg (z(\tau) - c)\, d\tau = \frac{1}{2\pi} \int_\alpha^\beta \frac{d}{d\tau} \arc\tan \frac{y - b}{x - a}\, d\tau$$

$$= \frac{1}{2\pi} \int_\alpha^\beta \frac{(x - a)\dot{y} - (y - b)\dot{x}}{(x - a)^2 + (y - b)^2}\, d\tau.$$

The integer u_c defined by the integral (8.23) is called the *winding number* of the oriented closed curve γ with respect to the point $z = c$; it gives just the increment of $(1/2\pi) \arg (z(\tau) - c)$ as τ runs through the interval (α, β), and z describes the curve γ (cf. Exercise 10, p. 75).

If, for example, γ is the circle $z = re^{i\tau}$ ($0 \leqq \tau \leqq 2\pi$), then the winding number u_c is zero for $|c| > r$, and is 1 for $|c| < r$.

Thus if γ denotes the circle $z = c + re^{i\tau}$,

$$\int_\gamma \frac{dz}{z - c} = 2\pi i$$

in spite of the fact that the integrand $w = 1/(z - c)$ is analytic in the domain $G: 0 < |z - c| < \infty$. Accordingly, the integral (8.20) which appears in Cauchy's theorem does not vanish for all closed curves γ in G. It is easy to see why the construction that we carried out in Section 8.13 breaks down in this case. In fact, if $z_0 \neq c$ is an arbitrary point of G, then the line segment $z_0 z$, which served in Section 8.13 as the path of integration in obtaining the primitive function, will lie in G only when this segment does not pass through the boundary point $z = c$ of G. If, on the other hand, the point c is on this segment, one cannot reach the point z by means of the construction, since the integrand becomes infinite on the path of integration (at the point $z = c$), and so the construction breaks down.

8.16. Deformation of Paths

We now turn to the problem of integration for a *general domain* G. For this we require some auxiliary topological concepts.

Let l be a *continuous* path,

$$l: \quad z = z(\tau) \qquad (\alpha \leqq \tau \leqq \beta; z(\alpha) = a, z(\beta) = b)$$

lying to G, and let l_1 be a subarc $\left(z = z(\tau), \alpha_1 \leqq \tau \leqq \beta_1; \alpha \leqq \alpha_1 < \beta_1 \leqq \beta\right)$ of l which lies in a convex subdomain G_1 of G.† We leave the initial and terminal positions $(\alpha \leqq \tau \leqq \alpha_1, \beta_1 \leqq \tau \leqq \beta)$ of the curve l fixed, but we replace the middle portion l_1 $(\alpha_1 \leqq \tau \leqq \beta_1)$ by another continuous curve l_1' which joins the point $a_1 = z(\alpha_1)$ to the point $b_1 = z(\beta_1)$ in G_1. We say that the new continuous path l' obtained in this way arises from l by means of an *elementary deformation*.

Now suppose that l and l' are two arbitrary paths in G which join the points a and b. If l' can be obtained from l by means of a finite number of elementary deformations, then l is said to be *homotopic* to l' (with respect to the domain G).

Homotopy is an equivalence relation: it is (1) reflexive: l is homotopic to itself; (2) symmetric: if l is homotopic to l', then l' is homotopic to l; (3) transitive: if l is homotopic to l', and l' is homotopic to l'', then l is homotopic to l''.

---

† This condition is certainly fulfilled if $\beta_1 - \alpha_1$ is chosen sufficiently small; l_1 will then lie in a disk $G_1 \subset G$.

8.17. Remarks

The above definition of homotopy is equivalent to the usual topological definition (cf. Exercise 16, p. 128). The latter is based on the notion of "continuous deformation", whose exact definition is as follows.

Two continuous paths l_ν: $z = z_\nu(\tau)$ $(\alpha \le \tau \le \beta; \nu = 0, 1)$ joining the points a and b in G are homotopic (to each other) if there exists a continuous function $z = z(\sigma, \tau)$ defined in the rectangle ("deformation-rectangle") $\alpha \le \tau \le \beta$, $0 \le \sigma \le 1$, with values belonging to G, such that $z(\sigma, \alpha) = a$, $z(\sigma, \beta) = b$, and $z(0, \tau) = z_0(\tau)$, $z(1, \tau) = z_1(\tau)$.

The continuous family of curves l_σ: $z = z(\sigma, \tau)$ $(\alpha \le \tau \le \beta)$ defined for $0 \le \sigma \le 1$, each joining the points a and b, provides a "continuous deformation" of l_0 into l_1. We base homotopy theory on the notion of elementary deformations because it is particularly convenient to apply: to carry out an elementary deformation on a curve we only need to enclose a portion of the curve by a convex subdomain of the given domain G. This is often simpler to do than to construct a deformation rectangle.

8.18. The Fundamental Group

The concept of homotopy can be applied to the special case of closed paths $l = \gamma$ in G. We fix an arbitrary point $z = a$ in G and we consider the totality of all continuous paths γ for which the point a is both the initial and the terminal point. Since homotopy is an equivalence relation for such paths, the set of all paths can be decomposed into disjoint equivalence classes (H), made up of mutually homotopic paths. These *homotopy classes* form a group (H). The group operation is defined in the following way: If H_1 and H_2 are given classes, and if $\gamma_\nu \in H_\nu$ $(\nu = 1, 2)$, then $H_2 H_1$ is the homotopy class which contains the "product path" $\gamma_2\gamma_1$ (cf. Section 8.1). In view of the equivalence property of homotopy, the definition of the product class $H_2 H_1$ is independent of the choice of the representatives γ_1 and γ_2 of the homotopy classes H_1 and H_2.

Furthermore, the group axioms are satisfied:

1) The product is associative.

2) There exists a well-defined "unit class" H_0 with the property that $H_0 H = H H_0 = H$ for every class H. (H_0 is the class of all null-homotopic paths γ, i.e., the set of all paths homotopic to the "null path" $z = z(\tau) \equiv a$.)

3) Each class H has an inverse class H^{-1} with the property that $H H^{-1} = H^{-1} H = H_0$. (If $\gamma \in H$, then H^{-1} is the class containing the path γ^{-1} with opposite orientation.)

The group (H) is called the *fundamental group* of the domain G.

8.19.

Remark 1. The fundamental group (H) of G has been defined by means of continuous closed paths γ passing through a fixed point $z = a \in G$. It is important to note that the structure of the group does not depend on the choice of the point a: the group is uniquely determined by the domain G up to an isomorphism.†

To prove this assertion we consider on the one hand the paths (γ) with initial point a, and on the other hand the paths (γ') whose initial point is another fixed point $z = a' \in G$. We join a and a' by an arbitrary continuous path $aa' = l \subset G$. The relations

$$\gamma' = l\gamma l^{-1}, \qquad \gamma = l^{-1}\gamma' l$$

define a one-to-one correspondence between the paths γ and the paths γ'. Two homotopic paths γ correspond to two homotopic paths γ', and conversely. Furthermore, the path $\gamma_1\gamma_2$ will correspond to the path $\gamma'_1\gamma'_2$, and conversely. Thus we have established a one-to-one correspondence between the homotopy classes (H) and (H'), and this correspondence is an isomorphism.

The relations between corresponding homotopy classes can be expressed by the formulas

$$H' = lHl^{-1}, \qquad H = l^{-1}H'l;$$

the groups (H) and (H') are said to be conjugate under the transformation by l.

Remark 2. We have used continuous paths l for the definition of homotopy. It can be proved easily that we should have achieved the same results if, instead of allowing general continuous paths, we had restricted our attention to *polygonal paths* with a finite number of edges (cf. Exercise 17, p. 129).

8.20. The General Form of Cauchy's Theorem. Primitive Functions

If the fundamental group (H) of the domain G of the finite z-plane consists of the unit element H_0 alone, then G is said to be *simply connected*. In this case every closed path in G is null-homotopic.

It is a trivial consequence of the definition that every convex domain is simply connected.

We mention without proof that a domain is simply connected if its boundary consists of a single continuum (Section 1.10).

---

† Two groups A and B are *isomorphic* if the following conditions are fulfilled: (1) There is a one-to-one correspondence between the elements a of the group A and the elements b of the group B $(a \leftrightarrow b)$; (2) $a_\nu \leftrightarrow b_\nu$ $(\nu = 1, 2)$ implies that $a_1a_2 \leftrightarrow b_1b_2$.

If the conditions (1) and (2) are valid in one direction only, $a \to b$, $a_\nu \to b_\nu$, $a_1a_2 \to b_1b_2$, the group B is said to be *homomorphic* to the group A. Thus, if B is homomorphic to A and A is homomorphic to B, then A and B are isomorphic.

We can now state the general form of *Cauchy's theorem*:

If $w(z)$ is analytic in a simply connected domain G, then

$$\int_\gamma w(z)\, dz = 0 \qquad (8.24)$$

for every closed path γ in G.

First of all, we note that, in view of Section 8.14, the integral (8.24) is well defined for any path γ. To prove the theorem we shall use the special form of Cauchy's theorem (Section 3) and the properties of the homotopy. Since G is simply connected, the path γ can be deformed into a point-path (null path) z_0 in G by means of a finite number of elementary deformations. It follows from the special form of Cauchy's theorem (compare Sections 8.13 and 8.14) that the value of the integral is *invariant under an elementary deformation*. Since the integral over a null path is zero, the assertion (8.24) is proved.

If we assume that G is simply connected, the integral

$$f(z) = \int_{z_0}^z w(z)\, dz, \qquad (8.25)$$

over an arbitrary piecewise regular path $l = z_0 z$ (or, in particular, over a polygonal path) defines a single-valued primitive function of $w(z)$ in G: $f'(z) = w(z)$. The totality of primitive functions is obtained from $f(z)$ by the addition of a constant.

8.21. The Group of Integral Values

We now abandon the assumption that the domain G is simply connected. If $w(z)$ is analytic in G, we may draw the following conclusion from Section 8.20.

The Cauchy integral

$$\int_\gamma w(z)\, dz$$

taken over a closed curve γ has the same value I_H for all curves γ belonging to the same homotopy class H. If $\gamma = \gamma_1 \gamma_2$ is the "product" of the paths $\gamma_1 \in H_1$, and $\gamma_2 \in H_2$, then

$$I_{H_1 H_2} = \int_{\gamma_1 \gamma_2} w\, dz = \int_{\gamma_1} w\, dz + \int_{\gamma_2} w\, dz = I_{H_1} + I_{H_2}. \qquad (8.26)$$

Thus the values I_H of the integrals form a (commutative) group (I_H) with the addition (of complex numbers) as group operation. The unit element of the group (I_H) is the number zero. The groups (H) and (I_H) are thus related in the following way: To each element H of the fundamental group corresponds a well-defined integral-value I_H, and this correspondence satisfies the relation (8.26). Hence, the group (I_H) is homomorphic to the group (H) (footnote on p. 124). To the unit element H_0 (the class of null-homotopic paths) corresponds the integral-value $I_{H_0} = 0$.

If H is the homotopy class defined by the closed path γ, we have as a generalization of Cauchy's theorem that

$$\int_\gamma w(z)\, dz = I_H.$$

In the special case when γ is null-homotopic in G, this reduces to the original form of Cauchy's theorem.

Finally, we observe that the integral over the closed path $\gamma' = l\gamma l^{-1}$ has the same value as the integral over γ. Thus the group (I_H) is isomorphic to the group $(I_{H'})$, where (H') denotes the group conjugate to (H) under the transformation by l. From this it follows that the group (I_H) is independent of the choice of the initial point a on the closed path γ.

8.22. Modules of Periodicity

If the function $w(z)$ is analytic in the domain G, then the integral of w assumes the same value along every path $l' = ab$ homotopic to $l = ab \subset G$. If l and l' are not homotopic (which happens if and only if the closed path $\gamma = l'l^{-1}$ is not null-homotopic), we have

$$\int_{l'} w\, dz = \int_l w\, dz + \int_\gamma w\, dz.$$

Thus, the integrals over l and l' differ by the value I_H, the *module of periodicity*, which in turn is determined by the class H (containing $\gamma = l'l^{-1}$). Hence:

For fixed z and z_0, the primitive function

$$f(z) = \int_{z_0}^z w(z)\, dz + C \qquad (C = f(z_0))$$

is determined up to an additive term I_H. If the path of integration varies within a fixed homotopy class, then the term I_H (the module of periodicity) remains constant.

8.23. Multiply Connected Domains

If the domain D is multiply connected (i.e., not simply connected), then the fundamental group has other elements H besides the unit H_0 corresponding to paths in G which are not null-homotopic. If there exists a system of finitely many generators $H_0, H_1, \ldots, H_n$ such that every element of the fundamental group can be written as a finite product of the generators and their inverses, then (H) has a *basis*, i.e., a system $H_0, H_1, \ldots, H_{q-1}$ with a minimal number $q \geq 1$ of generators. This number, q, the rank of the fundamental group, is called the *connectivity number* of the domain G. If (H) does not possess a finite system of generators, we say that G has infinite connectivity (cf. Exercise 20, p. 130).

If $w(z)$ is analytic in the q-tuply connected domain G, and if H_ν ($\nu = 0, 1, \ldots, q - 1$) is a basis of G, then every module of periodicity I_H of the primitive function of $w(z)$ can be written in the form

$$I_H = \sum_{\nu=0}^{q-1} m_\nu I_{H_\nu}$$

with *integer* coefficients m_ν.

EXERCISES ON CHAPTER 8

1. Prove that a function $w(z)$ which is continuous on a closed arc l is uniformly continuous on l, i.e., that for every $\epsilon > 0$ there exists a $\rho_\epsilon > 0$, such that $|w(z_1) - w(z_2)| < \epsilon$ whenever z_1 and z_2 are points of the arc l and $|z_1 - z_2| < \rho_\epsilon$.

2. If $w(z)$ is continuous in a domain G, then it is uniformly continuous on every compact (closed and bounded) subset G' of G, i.e., for every $\epsilon > 0$, there is a corresponding $\rho_\epsilon > 0$, such that $|w(z_1) - w(z_2)| < \epsilon$ provided that $|z_1 - z_2| < \rho_\epsilon$ and $z_1, z_2 \in G'$.

3. Show that the function $(\Delta\tau)$ in (8.9) tends to zero uniformly in the interval $\alpha \leq \tau \leq \beta$ as $\Delta\tau \to 0$, i.e., that for every $\epsilon > 0$, there exists a $\delta_\epsilon > 0$ such that for every τ in the interval (α, β), $|(\Delta\tau)| < \epsilon$ whenever $|\Delta\tau| < \delta_\epsilon$.

Hint. Split the function $z(\tau)$ into real and imaginary parts and apply the mean-value theorem.

4. Show that the value of the integral (8.2) is independent of the parametric representation (8.1) of the arc l, provided that the conditions for the existence of the integral are fulfilled.

5. Prove the rules of computation (1) to (5) for line integrals (Section 8.7).

6. Prove the theorem on the term-by-term integration of uniformly convergent series (Section 8.7).

7. Evaluate

$$\int_{-i}^{+i} |z|\, dz$$

for the following paths of integration: (a) a straight-line segment, (b) the arc $|z| = 1$, $\mathrm{Re}\, z \geq 0$, (c) the arc $|z| = 1$, $\mathrm{Re}\, z \leq 0$.

8. Evaluate $\int (\mathrm{Re}\, z)\, dz$ (a) along the segment $z_1 z_2$, (b) along a circle with center z_0 and radius r, described in the positive direction.

9. Let the function $w(z)$ be continuous outside the circle $|z| = r_0$, and let $\lim_{r \to \infty} rM(r) = 0$, where $M(r)$ is the maximum of $|w(z)|$ on K_r: $|z| = r\, (> r_0)$. Show that

$$\lim_{r \to \infty} \int_{K_r} w(z)\, dz = 0.$$

10. Let the function $w(z)$ be continuous for $0 < |z| < r_0$, and let $\lim_{r \to 0} r M(r) = 0$, where $M(r)$ is the maximum of $|w(z)|$ on the circle K_r: $|z| = r$ $(< r_0)$. Show that

$$\lim_{r \to 0} \int_{K_r} w(z)\, dz = 0.$$

11. Evaluate $\int z\, dz$, where γ is a rectifiable closed curve.

12. Evaluate the integral $\int |z - 1||dz|$ along the circle $|z| = 1$ described in the positive direction.

13. Evaluate the integral

$$\int \frac{e^z}{1 + z^2}\, dz$$

along the curve $|z - 1| = 1$ described in the positive direction.

14. Let $w(z)$ be a continuous function in the domain G, and let $l \subset G$ be a rectifiable curve. Prove that for every $\epsilon > 0$ there exists a piecewise regular curve γ with the same end-points as l, such that

$$\left| \int_l w\, dz - \int_\gamma w\, dz \right| < \epsilon.$$

Hint. Let G_1 be a bounded closed subdomain of G containing the curve l, and let L be the length of l. Since $w(z)$ is uniformly continuous in G_1, for every $\epsilon > 0$ there exists a $\delta_\epsilon > 0$ such that $|w(z') - w(z'')| < \epsilon/(2L)$ whenever $z' \in G_1$, $z'' \in G_1$ and $|z' - z''| < \delta_\epsilon$. Divide the curve l into subarcs $z_{\nu-1}z_\nu$ each lying in a disk in G of diameter δ_ϵ. Then γ can be chosen as the polygon with the vertices z_ν ($\nu = 0, 1, \ldots, n$), since

$$\left| \int_l w(z)\, dz - \sum_{\nu=1}^{n} w(z_{\nu-1})(z_\nu - z_{\nu-1}) \right| < L \frac{\epsilon}{2L} = \frac{\epsilon}{2},$$

$$\left| \int_\gamma w(z)\, dz - \sum_{\nu=1}^{n} w(z_{\nu-1})(z_\nu - z_{\nu-1}) \right| < \frac{\epsilon}{2}.$$

15. Show that the generalized definition of the line integral (given in Section 8.14)

$$\int_l w\, dz = \sum_{\nu=1}^{n} \int_{l_\nu} w\, dz$$

is independent of the choice of the partition (l_ν).

16. Prove that the two definitions of homotopy given in Sections 8.16 and 8.17 are equivalent.

Hint. (1) The property in Section 8.17 is a consequence of the definition in Section 8.16. To prove this, it is sufficient to construct a deformation rectangle for an elementary deformation D. If D is effected by means of the curves

$l_\nu: z = z_\nu(\tau)$ $(\alpha \leqq \tau \leqq \beta; z_\nu(\alpha) = a, z_\nu(\beta) = b; \nu = 0, 1)$ lying in the convex domain G, we may define $z(\sigma, \tau)$ by $z(\sigma, \tau) = (1 - \sigma)z_0(\tau) + \sigma z_1(\tau)$ for $0 \leqq \sigma \leqq 1$.

(2) The property in Section 8.16 is a consequence of the definition in Section 8.17. Suppose that the deformation $z = z(\sigma, \tau)$ is given in accordance with Section 8.17. The deformation rectangle can be divided up into small (congruent) rectangles R in such a way that the image of each rectangle will lie in a corresponding convex subdomain of G (since $z(\sigma, \tau)$ is uniformly continuous in the closed deformation rectangle; Exercise 2). The elementary deformations to be constructed can be defined in the following way (Fig. 28). We start with the rectangles adjoining the side $\sigma = 0$. First the subsegments 12, 23, ... of the side $\sigma = 0$, $\alpha \leqq \tau \leqq \beta$ are replaced by the polygons 11'2'2, 22'3'3, ... Each replacement corresponds, by means of the mapping $(\sigma, \tau) \to z$, to an elementary deformation of the corresponding arc of l_0. Next, the twice-described segments 2'22', 3'33' of the paths 11'2'22'3'3 ... are replaced, by means of an elementary deformation, by the point paths 2', 3', ... The curve l_0 is thereby deformed by means of a finite number of elementary deformations into the image of the segment 1'2'3' .... Continuing this process, we finally reach the curve l_1.

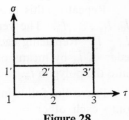

Figure 28

17. Suppose that two continuous paths l and l' which join the points a and b in G are homotopic in the sense of Section 8.16. Then, there exists a sequence of continuous paths $l = l_0, l_1, \ldots, l_m = l'$ such that l_ν is obtained from $l_{\nu-1}$ by means of an elementary deformation D_ν $(\nu = 1, \ldots, m)$. Show that the paths $l_0, l_1, \ldots, l_m$ can be replaced by polygonal paths $\bar{l}_0, \bar{l}_1, \ldots, \bar{l}_m$, which are "polygonally homotopic"; this means they go over into one another by means of a finite number of elementary deformations; here the notion of deformation is restricted to deformations that transform polygonal paths into polygonal paths.

Hint. Suppose that the elementary deformation D_ν, which transforms $l_{\nu-1}$ into l_ν, deforms the arc $a_\nu b_\nu$ of $l_{\nu-1}$ into a subarc of l_ν (with the same endpoints). Divide $l = l_0$ into n_0 small subarcs $c_{\mu-1}^0 c_\mu^0$ $(\mu = 1, \ldots, n_0)$, each subarc belonging to a convex subdomain G_μ of G. By means of n_0 elementary deformations replace each of these arcs by the corresponding *straight-line segment* $c_{\mu-1}^0 c_\mu^0$. In this way one obtains a polygonal path $\bar{l}_0$, homotopic to $l = l_0$. The elementary deformation D_1 transforms l_0 into l_1. If the subarc $a_1 b_1$ (deformed by D_1) contains the j division points $c_i^0, \ldots, c_{i+j-1}^0$, then l_1 will contain the division points $c_0^0 = a, c_1^0, \ldots, c_{i-1}^0, a_1, b_1, c_{i+j}^0, \ldots, c_{no}^0 = b$. We shall denote these division points (in the order in which they occur on l_1) by $c_0^1 = a, c_1^1, \ldots, c_{n1}^1 = b$. If each arc $c_{\mu-1}^1 c_\mu^1$ is deformed into the *segment* $c_{\mu-1}^1 c_\mu^1$

(by means of an elementary deformation), the arc l_1 is transformed into a polygonal path $\bar{l}_1$.

Moreover, l_1 may be obtained from $\bar{l}_0$ by means of "polygonal deformations" in the following way. First subject $\bar{l}_0 = c_0^0 \ldots c_{i-1}^0 c_i^0 \ldots c_{i+j-1}^0 c_{i+j}^0 \ldots c_{n_0}^0$ to three elementary deformations, transforming the subpolygons $c_{i-1}^0 c_i^0$, $c_i^0 \ldots c_{i+j-1}^0$, and $c_{i+j-1}^0 c_{i+j}^0$ into the polygons $c_{i-1}^0 a_1 c_i^0$, $c_i^0 a_1 b_1 c_{i+j-1}^0$, and $c_{i+j-1}^0 b_1 c_{i+j}^0$, respectively. Two further elementary polygonal deformations (replacing the polygon $a_1 c_i^0 a_1$ by the point path a_1 and $b_1 c_{i+j-1}^0 b_1$ by b_1) produce the polygonal path $\bar{l}_1 = c_0^1 \ldots c_{n_1}^1$.

Repeating this process, one obtains the desired sequence of polygons: $\bar{l}_0, \bar{l}_1, \ldots, \bar{l}_m$. The vertices $c_0^m, \ldots, c_{nm}^m$ of $\bar{l}_m$ are all points of the curve $l_m = l'$. Replacing each subarc $c_0^m c_1^m$, $c_1^m c_2^m$, $\ldots$ of l' by the corresponding edge of $\bar{l}_m$ by means of elementary deformations, the arc l' is transformed into the polygon $\bar{l}_m$.

18. Prove the following assertion: If two domains G_1 and G_2 are mapped onto each other by means of a homeomorphism (a one-to-one mapping continuous in both directions), each (closed) null-homotopic path in G corresponds to a null-homotopic path in G_2. Consequently, the homeomorphic image of a simply connected domain is also simply connected.

19. What are the different values of the integral

$$\int_0^1 \frac{dz}{1+z^2}$$

when all possible paths of integration are considered?

20. What is the connectivity number of the domain $z \neq n$ $(n = 1, 2, \ldots)$?

21. Use the formula

$$\log z - \log z_0 = \int_{z_0}^z \frac{dz}{z}$$

to derive properties of the mapping $w = \log z$.

22. Prove that the circular annulus $0 \leq r < |z| < R \leq \infty$ is doubly connected, and determine its fundamental group.

Hint. Let l_z be a path joining z_0 to z inside the annulus. The integral

$$w = u + iv = \int_{l_z} \frac{dz}{z}$$

maps l_z onto a path l_w lying in the strip $\log(r/|z_0|) < u < \log(R/|z_0|)$ and joining the points $w = 0$ and $w = n \cdot 2\pi i$ (n an integer). Such a path l_w can be deformed into the segment $(0, n \cdot 2\pi i)$. This deformation will induce a deformation of l_z onto the circle $|z| = |z_0|$ described n times or (in the case $n = 0$) into the point path $z = z_0$. The class of the null-path $z = z_0$ and the circle $|z| = |z_0|$ therefore form a basis of the fundamental group.

CHAPTER 9

CAUCHY'S INTEGRAL
FORMULA AND ITS APPLICATIONS

§1. CAUCHY'S FORMULA

9.1. Derivation of the Formula for a Disk

Let the function $w = w(z)$ be analytic in the domain G. We consider a closed disk $K \subset G$, along with the positive orientation of its circumference γ. We evaluate the integral

$$I_\gamma = \int_\gamma \frac{w(z)}{z - a}\, dz$$

where $a \notin \gamma$ is an arbitrary point of the complex plane.

First, if a is in the exterior of K, the quotient $f(z) = w(z)/(z - a)$ is analytic in K, so that $I_\gamma = 0$ by Cauchy's theorem.

Now suppose that a is an interior point of the disk K. Then the quotient $f(z)$ is analytic at every point $z \neq a$ of the domain G. In order to calculate the integral we choose three points z_1, z_2, z_3 on the circle γ which have a positive orientation and which are such that the arcs $z_\nu z_{\nu+1}$ $(\nu = 1, 2, 3; z_4 = z_1)$ when viewed from the point a subtend angles less than π. We form a circle γ' $(|z - a| = r)$ lying in K, and denote by $z = z'_\nu$ $(\nu = 1, 2, 3)$ the intersection of the straight line az_ν with the circle γ'.

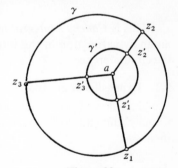

Figure 29

Since the closed path $z'_1 z_1 z_2 z'_2 z_1$ lies in the closed convex sector $az_1 z_2$ in which $f(z) = w(z)/(z - a)$ is analytic (except at $z = a$), we can apply Cauchy's theorem† (Section 8.13) to obtain

$$0 = \int_{z'_1 z_1} + \int_{z_1 z_2} + \int_{z_2 z'_2} + \int_{z'_2 z'_1}.$$

By cyclic permutation of the indices 1, 2, 3, we obtain two similar equalities. If we add these three equations we have

$$I_\gamma = I_{\gamma'}.$$

---

† Note that the sector we are considering can be embedded in a larger convex sector in which $f(z)$ is still analytic.

131

If we substitute $w(z) = w(a) + (w(z) - w(a))$ in the integral on the right, we find that

$$I_{\gamma'} = w(a) \int_{\gamma'} \frac{dz}{z - a} + \int_{\gamma'} \frac{w(z) - w(a)}{z - a}\, dz.$$

To calculate the first integral on the right-hand side, we set $z - a = re^{i\phi}$ and obtain

$$\int_{\gamma'} \frac{dz}{z - a} = \int_{\gamma'} d \log (z - a) = i \int_0^{2\pi} d\phi = 2\pi i.$$

Now the absolute value of the second integral in the expression for $I_{\gamma'}$ is at most

$$\int_{\gamma'} |w(z) - w(a)| \, |d \log (z - a)| = \int_0^{2\pi} |w(z) - w(a)| \, d\phi < 2\pi\epsilon,$$

for, because of the continuity of $w(z)$, we can choose the radius r of γ' so small that $|w(z) - w(a)| < \epsilon$ will hold on γ' for a given $\epsilon > 0$. Hence (using the notation $\langle 2\pi\epsilon \rangle$; cf. Section 8.5)

$$I_\gamma = I_{\gamma'} = 2\pi i w(a) + \langle 2\pi\epsilon \rangle.$$

As $\epsilon \to 0$ we obtain

$$I_\gamma = \int_\gamma \frac{w(z)}{z - a}\, dz = 2\pi i w(a).$$

Thus, we have proved the following theorem:

If γ is the positively oriented circumference of the disk K, then, at every interior point $z = a$ of K

$$w(a) = \frac{1}{2\pi i} \int_\gamma \frac{w(z)}{z - a}\, dz. \tag{9.1}$$

This is *Cauchy's integral formula* for a disk K. It shows that the values of an analytic function in the interior of a disk are determined by its values on the circumference γ.

9.2. Expansion of an Analytic Function into a Power Series

We shall now derive a fundamental expansion for analytic functions from Cauchy's integral formula. If $w(z)$ is analytic on a closed disk $K: |z - a| \leq \rho$, then

$$w(z) = \frac{1}{2\pi i} \int_\gamma \frac{w(\zeta)}{\zeta - z}\, d\zeta \tag{9.2}$$

holds for all values $|z - a| < \rho$; here γ is the positively oriented circumference of K. We expand the factor $1/(\zeta - z)$ of the integrand to a geometric series

$$\frac{1}{\zeta - z} = \frac{1}{(\zeta - a) - (z - a)}$$

$$= \frac{1}{\zeta - a} + \frac{z - a}{(\zeta - a)^2} + \cdots + \frac{(z - a)^{n-1}}{(\zeta - a)^n} + \frac{(z - a)^n}{(\zeta - a)^n(\zeta - z)}.$$

By integration we obtain

$$w(z) = c_0 + c_1(z - a) + \cdots + c_{n-1}(z - a)^{n-1} + R_n(z). \tag{9.3}$$

The coefficients in this expansion are given by

$$c_\nu = \frac{1}{2\pi i} \int_\gamma \frac{w(\zeta)}{(\zeta - a)^{\nu+1}} \, d\zeta \qquad (\nu = 0, \ldots, n-1), \tag{9.3}'$$

and the remainder term is

$$R_n(z) = \frac{(z-a)^n}{2\pi i} \int_\gamma \frac{w(\zeta) \, d\zeta}{(\zeta - a)^n (\zeta - z)}. \tag{9.3}''$$

From (9.3)″ we obtain the estimate

$$|R_n(z)| \leqq \frac{|z-a|^n}{2\pi} \int_\gamma \frac{|w(\zeta)| \, |d\zeta|}{|\zeta - a|^n |\zeta - z|}.$$

Since $|\zeta - z| = |(\zeta - a) - (z - a)| \geqq \rho - |z - a|$ and $|w(\zeta)| \leqq M$ (with a suitable constant M), we have

$$|R_n(z)| \leqq \frac{M}{\rho - |z-a|} \frac{|z-a|^n}{\rho^{n-1}}. \tag{9.3}'''$$

9.3. The General Form of Cauchy's Integral Formula

We consider again a function $w = w(z)$ which is analytic in a domain G of the finite z-plane. Let $z = a$ be an arbitrary point of the domain G. Then the difference quotient

$$f(z) = \frac{w(z) - w(a)}{z - a}$$

is analytic at every point $z \neq a$ of the domain G. We shall show that it is also analytic at the point a. Since the function $w(z)$ is analytic in the domain G by hypothesis, it is differentiable:

$$\frac{w(z) - w(a)}{z - a} \to w'(a) \qquad \text{as} \qquad z \to a.$$

Hence, if we define the value of $f(z)$ at a to be $f(a) = w'(a)$, then $f(z)$ is continuous at the point $z = a$. By means of the expansion (9.3) we may conclude that $f(z)$ is even differentiable at the point $z = a \in G$. In fact, if we apply this expansion for a disk $|z - a| \leqq \rho$ lying in G, we find first of all that $c_0 = w(a)$. For $n = 2$ we find that

$$f(z) = \frac{w(z) - c_0}{z - a} = c_1 + \frac{R_2(z)}{z - a}.$$

It follows from the estimate $(9.3)'''$ that the quotient $R_2(z)/(z-a)$ tends to zero as $z \to a$. Hence, $c_1 = w'(a) = f(a)$. We now apply (9.3) for $n = 3$. We find that

$$f(z) = \frac{w(z) - c_0}{z - a} = f(a) + c_2(z - a) + \frac{R_3(z)}{z - a},$$

and, hence,

$$\frac{f(z) - f(a)}{z - a} = c_2 + \frac{R_3(z)}{(z - a)^2}.$$

In view of $(9.3)'''$ the second term tends to zero as $z \to a$, and we conclude that the limit

$$\lim_{z \to a} \frac{f(z) - f(a)}{z - a} = f'(a) = c_2$$

exists.

Thus we have shown that the quotient $f(z)$ is an analytic function of z in the *whole domain D*. Using Cauchy's theorem, we obtain the result that *for every null-homotopic path γ in G*

$$\int_\gamma f(z)\, dz = 0.$$

If γ does not pass through a, we have

$$0 = \int_\gamma \frac{w(z) - w(a)}{z - a}\, dz = \int_\gamma \frac{w(z)}{z - a}\, dz - w(a) \int_\gamma \frac{dz}{z - a}.$$

The value of the second integral is $2\pi i u_a$, where u_a is the winding number of the path γ with respect to the point a. Thus we have derived the following theorem.

Let the function $w(z)$ be analytic in G, and let γ be a null-homotopic closed path in G. Then, for every point $z \in G, z \notin \gamma$,

$$u_z w(z) = \frac{1}{2\pi i} \int_\gamma \frac{w(\zeta)}{\zeta - z}\, d\zeta, \tag{9.4}$$

where u_z is the winding number of γ with respect to the point z.

In a *simply connected domain* every closed path γ is null-homotopic, and (9.4) holds therefore for any closed path γ in G not passing through z. If the winding number u_z of γ is 1, Cauchy's integral formula (9.4) takes the simpler form:

$$w(z) = \frac{1}{2\pi i} \int_\gamma \frac{w(\zeta)}{\zeta - z}\, d\zeta. \tag{9.4'}$$

This is the case, in particular, if γ is a positively oriented circle which is null-homotopic with respect to G (compare with Eq. 9.1).

Remark. Cauchy expounded his integral theory in an extensive series of papers, the first of which was published in 1814. Even earlier, however, some knowledge existed concerning complex integration and complex functions. The most important forerunners of Cauchy in complex function theory were Leonhard Euler (1707–1783) and Carl Friedrich Gauss (1777–1855).

§2. THE TAYLOR EXPANSION OF AN ANALYTIC FUNCTION

9.4. Taylor Expansion

Once more, we consider a fixed disk $|z - a| \leq \rho$ contained in a domain G in which we have an analytic function $w(z)$. If the positively oriented circle $|z - a| = \rho$ is denoted by γ, the expansion (9.3) is valid for every $n \geq 0$. The coefficients c_ν do not depend on z, and have the values (9.3)′, while the remainder term satisfies the inequality

$$|R_n(z)| \leq M \frac{|z - a|}{\rho - |z - a|} \left(\frac{|z - a|}{\rho} \right)^{n-1},$$

where M is the maximum of $|w(z)|$ on the circle $|z - a| = \rho$. We now consider a, ρ, and z fixed ($|z - a| < \rho$), and let n tend to infinity. Then

$$\left(\frac{|z - a|}{\rho} \right)^{n-1} \to 0$$

and therefore the remainder term $R_n(z)$ tends to the limit zero. Thus we have proved that in the disk $|z - a| < \rho$ the function $w(z)$ has the convergent power series representation

$$w(z) = \sum_0^\infty c_n(z - a)^n$$

with coefficients

$$c_n = \frac{1}{2\pi i} \int_\gamma \frac{w(z)}{(z - a)^{n+1}} \, dz \qquad (n = 0, 1, \ldots).$$

In view of Section 7.9, the sum of a convergent power series has derivatives of all orders, which can be found by term-by-term differentiation. The values of the derivatives at the point $z = a$ are given by

$$w^{(n)}(a) = n! \, c_n = \frac{n!}{2\pi i} \int_\gamma \frac{w(z)}{(z - a)^{n+1}} \, dz.$$

Thus we have proved the following theorem.

A function analytic in a domain G has derivatives of all orders. In the neighborhood of a point $z = a \in G$, it has the Taylor expansion

$$w(z) = \sum_0^\infty \frac{w^{(n)}(a)}{n!} (z - a)^n, \tag{9.5}$$

which converges at least in the disk $|z - a| < \rho$ whose radius ρ is the shortest distance of the point a from the boundary of the domain G.

The derivatives have the integral representation

$$w^{(n)}(z) = \frac{n!}{2\pi i} \int_\gamma \frac{w(\zeta)}{(\zeta - z)^{n+1}} \, d\zeta, \tag{9.6}$$

where γ is the circumference of a disk $|\zeta - z| \leq \rho$ lying in the domain G. We can deduce this result directly from Cauchy's integral formula (9.1) if we differentiate with respect to the parameter a (Exercise 1, p. 165). The same argument shows that (9.6) is valid for an arbitrary null-homotopic closed curve in G whose winding number with respect to the point z is 1. If the winding number is not 1, the value of the right-hand side of (9.6) is $u_z w^{(n)}(z)$.

9.5. Expansion of the Elementary Functions

It follows from the theorem proved above that the Taylor expansion of an *entire* function (i.e., a function analytic everywhere in the finite z-plane) converges for every finite value of z. As was shown directly in Section 7.10, this holds in particular for the functions e^z, $\sin z$, and $\cos z$.

The branch of the function $\log (1 + z)$ which vanishes for $z = 0$ and which is analytic in the disk $|z| < 1$ can be expanded into a convergent power series in z. This series is the same as it is for real values of the argument, i.e.,

$$\log (1 + z) = z - \frac{z^2}{2} + \frac{z^3}{3} - \cdots.$$

Similarly, for the function

$$(1 + z)^\mu = e^{\mu \log (1+z)}$$

we obtain the binomial series

$$(1 + z)^\mu = \sum_{n=0}^\infty \binom{\mu}{n} z^n,$$

which converges in the disk $|z| < 1$ whenever we choose that branch of the logarithm which takes the value 1 when $z = 0$.

9.6. The Function Defined by the Cauchy Integral

Let us now investigate what can be said about the function defined by (9.4)′ if on the right-hand side $w(\zeta)$ is replaced by an *arbitrary* function $\psi(\zeta)$ which is continuous on the rectifiable arc γ. We shall prove that the function

$$w(z) = \frac{1}{2\pi i} \int_\gamma \frac{\psi(\zeta)}{\zeta - z} \, d\zeta \tag{9.7}$$

defined in this way is analytic for every z not lying on γ. Suppose that a is an arbitrary point not lying on γ. We expand the function $w(z)$ in powers of $z - a$ as in Section 9.2. We conclude from this, as in Section 9.4, that the function (9.7) is analytic at $z = a$. Its derivatives are given by

$$w^{(n)}(a) = \frac{n!}{2\pi i} \int_\gamma \frac{\psi(\zeta)}{(\zeta - a)^{n+1}} \, d\zeta \qquad (n = 1, 2, \ldots).$$

If z approaches some point $\zeta \in \gamma$, $w(z)$ will *not*, in general, converge to the value $\psi(\zeta)$ (cf. Exercise 5, p. 165).

In the special case when γ is a closed curve, e.g. a circle, (9.7) defines an analytic function in the interior of γ and another analytic function in its exterior.

9.7. Integrals Depending upon a Parameter

As a generalization of the above results we shall prove the following theorem.

Let γ be a rectifiable arc and G a domain. Let $f(t, z)$ be a single-valued function defined for $t \in \gamma$, $z \in G$, which is continuous and has a derivative $f_z(t, z)$ continuous in t and z. Then the integral

$$w(z) = \int_\gamma f(t, z) \, dt$$

defines an analytic function $w(z)$ in the domain G, whose derivative is

$$w'(z) = \frac{d}{dz} \int_\gamma f(t, z) \, dt = \int_\gamma f_z(t, z) \, dt. \qquad (9.8)$$

To prove this theorem it is sufficient to show that for $z \in G$

$$I = \int_\gamma \left(\frac{f(t, z + \Delta z) - f(t, z)}{\Delta z} - f_z(t, z) \right) dt \to 0 \qquad (9.9)$$

as $\Delta z \to 0$.

Suppose that the disk $|\zeta - z| \leq \rho$ is contained in G, and that $|\Delta z| < \rho$. Since $f(t, z)$ is an analytic function of z for every fixed $t \in \gamma$, we have, in view of Sections 9.2 and 9.3, that

$$f(t, z + \Delta z) - f(t, z) = f_z(t, z)\Delta z + R_2(t, z, \Delta z), \qquad (9.10)$$

where R_2 is the integral

$$R_2(t, z, \Delta z) = \frac{(\Delta z)^2}{2\pi i} \int_K \frac{f(t, \zeta)}{(\zeta - z)^2(\zeta - z - \Delta z)} \, d\zeta$$

taken over the circle $K: |\zeta - z| = \rho$. Since $f(t, \zeta)$ is continuous, there exists a constant M such that $|f(t, z)| \leq M$ for every $t \in \gamma$ and $\zeta \in K$. Therefore

$$|R_2(t, z, \Delta z)| \leq \frac{|\Delta z|^2}{2\pi} \int_K \frac{M}{\rho^2(\rho - |\Delta z|)} \, |d\zeta| = \frac{M}{\rho(\rho - |\Delta z|)} \, |\Delta z|^2$$

independently of $t \in \gamma$.

In view of (9.10), we obtain the following estimate for the integral (9.9):

$$|I| = \left| \int_\gamma \frac{R_2(t, z, \Delta z)}{\Delta z} \, dt \right| \leqq \frac{M |\Delta z|}{\rho(\rho - |\Delta z|)} \int_\gamma |dt| \to 0 \qquad \text{as} \qquad \Delta z \to 0.$$

Thus we have proved that $w(z)$ has the derivative (9.8). Therefore $w(z)$ is analytic.

§3. CONSEQUENCES OF CAUCHY'S INTEGRAL FORMULA

9.8. Limit of a Sequence of Analytic Functions

As an application of Cauchy's integral formula we shall prove the following *theorem of Weierstrass.*

> *If $w_1(z), w_2(z), \ldots$ is a sequence of functions analytic in G, and if this sequence converges uniformly on every compact subset of G to a finite limit function,*

$$\lim_{n \to \infty} w_n(z) = w(z), \tag{9.11}$$

then $w(z)$ is analytic in G and its derivative is

$$w'(z) = \lim_{n \to \infty} w'_n(z).$$

Let z be an arbitrary point of G, and let γ be a circle in G, containing z in its interior. By Cauchy's integral formula, we have

$$w_n(z) = \frac{1}{2\pi i} \int_\gamma \frac{w_n(\zeta)}{\zeta - z} \, d\zeta \qquad (n = 1, 2, \ldots). \tag{9.12}$$

Since the convergence in (9.11) is uniform on the circle γ, we have

$$|w_n(\zeta) - w(\zeta)| < \epsilon \qquad \text{for} \qquad n \geqq n_\epsilon.$$

Hence,

$$\left| \frac{1}{2\pi i} \int_\gamma \frac{w_n(\zeta)}{\zeta - z} \, d\zeta - \frac{1}{2\pi i} \int_\gamma \frac{w(\zeta)}{\zeta - z} \, d\zeta \right| \leqq \frac{1}{2\pi} \int_\gamma \frac{|w_n(\zeta) - w(\zeta)|}{|\zeta - z|} \, |d\zeta| < \frac{\epsilon L}{2\pi \rho},$$

where ρ is the shortest distance of the point z from γ and L is the length of γ. It follows from this estimate that the right-hand side of (9.12) has the limit

$$\frac{1}{2\pi i} \int_\gamma \frac{w(\zeta)}{\zeta - z} \, d\zeta.$$

Since the limit of the left-hand side is $w(z)$, we have

$$w(z) = \frac{1}{2\pi i} \int_\gamma \frac{w(\zeta)}{\zeta - z} \, d\zeta.$$

The function $w(z)$ can therefore be represented by a Cauchy integral; hence, it is analytic in G.

Starting from the formula

$$w'_n(z) = \frac{1}{2\pi i} \int_\gamma \frac{w_n(\zeta)}{(\zeta - z)^2} \, d\zeta$$

and repeating the above argument, we see that

$$\lim_{n \to \infty} w'_n(z) = w'(z).$$

We can formulate our result in another form:

If $w_1(z)$, $w_2(z)$, ... is a sequence of functions, analytic in G, and if the series

$$\sum_{\nu=1}^\infty w_\nu(z)$$

converges uniformly on every compact subset of G, then the sum $w(z)$ of the series is analytic in G. Its derivative can be calculated by differentiating the series term by term.

9.9. Uniqueness Theorem for Analytic Functions

We shall prove the following fundamental theorem.

If a function $w(z)$ is analytic in a domain G and if $w(z) = 0$ on a set of points (z) having a limit point a in G, then $w(z)$ vanishes identically in G.

Proof. Let C_0 be a disk $|z - a| < r$ which lies in G. By assumption, there exists in C_0 a sequence of points $a_1, a_2, \ldots, a_n, \ldots$ ($a_n \neq a$, $a_n \to a$) such that $w(a_n) = 0$ ($n = 1, 2, \ldots$). We shall show that all coefficients vanish in the Taylor expansion

$$w(z) = c_0 + c_1(z - a) + \cdots + c_\nu(z - a)^\nu + \cdots$$

which converges in $|z - a| < r$.

By assumption, we have for $z = a_n$ ($n = 1, 2, \ldots$)

$$-c_0 = c_1(a_n - a) + \cdots + c_\nu(a_n - a)^\nu + \cdots.$$

As $n \to \infty$, the right-hand side of this identity tends to zero; hence, $c_0 = 0$. We now assume that we have already proved that $c_0 = c_1 = \cdots = c_{\nu-1} = 0$. Then

$$0 = w(a_n) = (a_n - a)^\nu [c_\nu + c_{\nu+1}(a_n - a) + \cdots].$$

Since $a_n \neq a$, the sum in the bracket must vanish. From this it follows as above that $c_\nu = 0$. Since all the coefficients c_ν vanish, $w(z) = 0$ in the whole disk C_0.

To show now that $w(z_0) = 0$ for any point z_0 of G, we join the point $z = a$ and the point $z = z_0$ by a finite chain of disks in G (cf. Section 8.1). If we apply the result just proved to these disks, we have that $w(z)$ vanishes in each of these disks, and, hence, vanishes at $z = z_0$.

From the theorem just proved we obtain immediately the following result.

If $w_1(z)$ and $w_2(z)$ are analytic in a domain G, and if $w_1(z) = w_2(z)$ on a set of points (z) having a limit point in G, then $w_1(z) \equiv w_2(z)$ identically in G.

9.10. Gauss's Mean-Value Theorem

Suppose that $w(z)$ is analytic in a neighborhood K: $|z - a| < R$ of the point $z = a$. We expand $w(z)$ into the power series

$$w(z) = \sum_0^\infty c_n(z - a)^n.$$

The coefficients are

$$c_n = \frac{1}{2\pi i} \int_\gamma \frac{w(z)}{(z - a)^{n+1}} \, dz,$$

where γ is a closed path in K with winding number 1 with respect to a. If we choose the circle $|z - a| = r$ as γ and write $z = a + re^{i\phi}$, we have

$$\frac{dz}{(z - a)^{n+1}} = \frac{i}{r^n} e^{-in\phi} \, d\phi$$

so that

$$c_n = \frac{w^{(n)}(a)}{n!} = \frac{1}{2\pi r^n} \int_0^{2\pi} w(a + re^{i\phi})e^{-in\phi} \, d\phi. \tag{9.13}$$

For $n = 0$ we obtain the so-called *mean-value theorem of Gauss*:

$$w(a) = \frac{1}{2\pi} \int_0^{2\pi} w(a + re^{i\phi}) \, d\phi. \tag{9.14}$$

This theorem asserts that the value of an analytic function at the center of a circle is equal to the arithmetic mean of its values on the circle.

9.11. Liouville's Theorem

With the help of formula (9.13) one can prove *Liouville's theorem*.

If $w(z)$ is an entire function (that is, analytic in the finite z-plane) and is bounded (that is, there exists a finite constant M such that $|w(z)| \leq M$ for every value $z \neq \infty$), then $w(z)$ reduces to a constant.

Proof.   It follows from (9.13) that

$$|c_n| \leq \frac{1}{2\pi r^n} \int_0^{2\pi} |w(a + re^{i\phi})| \, d\phi \leq \frac{M}{r^n}. \tag{9.15}$$

If we let $r \to \infty$, the right-hand side tends to zero for $n \geq 1$.   Hence, $c_1 = c_2 = \ldots = 0$, and $w(z) = \text{const.} = c_0 = w(a)$.

In the same way we can prove the following more general theorem.

If the absolute value of an entire function $w(z)$ increases more slowly than the m-th power of r, where m is a positive integer, that is, if

$$M(r) = \max_{|z|=r} |w(z)| \tag{9.16}$$

satisfies the condition

$$\frac{M(r)}{r^m} \to 0 \qquad as \qquad r \to \infty,$$

then $w(z)$ is a polynomial of degree less than m.

In fact, if we apply (9.15) with $a = 0$, we have

$$|c_n| \leqq \frac{M(r)}{r^n} = \frac{M(r)}{r^m} \frac{1}{r^{n-m}}.$$

The right-hand side tends to zero for every $n \geqq m$ as $r \to \infty$; hence, $c_m = c_{m+1} = \ldots = 0$, and

$$w(z) = c_0 + c_1 z + \cdots + c_{m-1} z^{m-1}.$$

9.12. The Maximum Principle

Let $w(z)$ be analytic in a domain G. We denote the least upper bound of its modulus by

$$g = \sup_G |w(z)|. \tag{9.17}$$

Then for every $z \in G$ we have $|w(z)| \leqq g$. We shall prove the following theorem.

If $|w(z)|$ attains its least upper bound g in G then $w(z)$ is a constant (of modulus g).

Suppose that $|w(a)| = g \ (< \infty)$ for some $a \in G$. Let r be a positive number less than the shortest distance ρ of the point a from the boundary of G. By the mean-value theorem of Gauss,

$$0 = |w(a)| - g = \left| \frac{1}{2\pi} \int_0^{2\pi} w(a + re^{i\phi}) \, d\phi \right| - g$$

$$\leqq \frac{1}{2\pi} \int_0^{2\pi} |w(a + re^{i\phi})| \, d\phi - g \leqq \frac{1}{2\pi} \int_0^{2\pi} g \, d\phi - g = 0,$$

whence

$$0 = g - \frac{1}{2\pi} \int_0^{2\pi} |w(a + re^{i\phi})| \, d\phi = \frac{1}{2\pi} \int_0^{2\pi} (g - |w(a + re^{i\phi})|) \, d\phi.$$

The integrand of the last integral is a non-negative continuous function of ϕ, so that the integral can vanish only if the integrand is identically zero (Exercise

9, p. 165). Hence, $|w(a + re^{i\phi})| = g$ everywhere on the circle $|z - a| = r$, and, since r can be chosen arbitrarily in the interval $0 < r < \rho$, $|w(z)| = g$ holds everywhere in the disk $|z - a| < \rho$. But an analytic function whose modulus is constant is itself a constant (Exercise 10, p. 165). Thus $w(z)$ is constant in the disk $|z - a| < \rho$ and, by the uniqueness theorem of Section 9.9, in the whole domain G.

Consequently, if $w(z)$ is not constant, $|w(z)| < g$ holds at every point of G. From this *maximum principle* we can deduce the following theorem.

Let Γ be the boundary of G. Suppose that the function $w(z)$ is analytic in G, and satisfies at every boundary point $\zeta \in \Gamma$ the condition

$$\limsup_{z \to \zeta} |w(z)| \leq M, \tag{9.18}$$

where M is a constant. Then $|w(z)| \leq M$ in the whole domain G. If $|w(z)| = M$ at a point $z \in G$, then $w(z)$ reduces to a constant.

To prove this theorem it is sufficient to show that $g = \sup_G |w(z)| \leq M$.

By the definition of the least upper bound there exists a sequence of points a_n $(n = 1, 2, \ldots)$ in the domain G and a point $a \in G \cup \Gamma$ such that

$$\lim a_n = a \quad \text{and} \quad \lim |w(a_n)| = g \quad \text{as} \quad n \to \infty.$$

To begin with if $a \in G$, it follows from the continuity of w at the point a that $|w(a)| = \lim |w(a_n)| = g$. Thus $|w(z)|$ attains its least upper bound in the domain G and therefore, by the last theorem, $|w(z)| \equiv g$. The assumption (9.18) now implies that $g \leq M$.

On the other hand, suppose that a is a point of the boundary Γ. Then

$$g = \lim |w(a_n)| \leq \limsup_{z \to a} |w(z)| = M,$$

and the proof is complete.

9.13. The Fundamental Theorem of Algebra

As an application of the maximum principle we shall prove the *fundamental theorem of algebra* (see Section 2.6).

We consider a polynomial of degree n

$$P(z) = a_0 z^n + a_1 z^{n-1} + \cdots + a_n \quad (n \geq 1, a_0 \neq 0).$$

We fix an arbitrary point $z_0 \neq \infty$, and subsequently a positive number

$$M > |P(z_0)|. \tag{9.19}$$

Since $|P(z)| \to \infty$ as $z \to \infty$, there exists a number $R > |z_0|$ such that $|P(z)| > M$ for $|z| \geq R$. Assume that $P(z) \neq 0$ for every z. Then by the maximum principle we must have $|1/P(z)| < 1/M$, or $|P(z)| > M$, for

$|z| < R$. This implies that $|P(z_0)| > M$, which contradicts (9.19). Thus $P(z)$ has at least one zero, which was to be proved.

9.14. Schwarz's Lemma

Next we shall apply the maximum principle to prove *Schwarz's lemma*.

Let $w = w(z)$ be a bounded analytic function in the unit disk $|z| < 1$,

$$|w(z)| \leqq 1 \quad for \quad |z| < 1, \tag{9.20}$$

which vanishes at the origin:

$$w(z) = c_1 z + c_2 z^2 + \cdots. \tag{9.20$'$}$$

Then

$$|w(z)| \leqq |z| \tag{9.21}$$

for every z ($|z| < 1$). If equality $|w(z)| = |z|$ holds for some value z ($0 < |z| < 1$), then $w(z)$ is a linear transformation $w = e^{i\alpha}z$, where α is a real constant.

Proof. In the unit disk $|z| < 1$

$$f(z) = \frac{w(z)}{z} = c_1 + c_2 z + \cdots$$

is analytic (if we set $f(0) = c_1$). Let $z = a$ be an arbitrary point of the unit disk. We choose an r such that $|a| < r < 1$. On the circle $|z| = r$ we have

$$|f(z)| = \frac{|w(z)|}{|z|} \leqq \frac{1}{r}.$$

By the maximum principle this inequality also holds in the disk $|z| \leqq r$, and therefore

$$|f(a)| = \left| \frac{w(a)}{a} \right| \leqq \frac{1}{r}.$$

If we let r tend to 1, we have that

$$|f(a)| = \left| \frac{w(a)}{a} \right| \leqq 1.$$

Thus $|f(a)| = 1$ can hold only in the case $f(z) = w(z)/z = e^{i\alpha}$, where α is a real constant. This proves our assertion. The name "Schwarz's lemma" and the above proof are due to C. Carathéodory (1904).

9.15. Generalization of Schwarz's Lemma

We now drop the special assumption that $w(0) = 0$ but we keep the assumption that $|w(z)| < 1$. We write $b = w(a)$ ($|a| < 1$, $|b| < 1$). We consider the linear transformations (cf. Section 3.10)

$$\zeta = \frac{z - a}{1 - \bar{a}z}, \qquad \omega = \frac{w - b}{1 - \bar{b}w},$$

which map the unit disks $|z| < 1$ and $|w| < 1$ onto themselves in such a way that the points $z = a$ and $w = b$ are taken into the origin. Applying the reasoning of the last section to the quotient

$$\frac{\omega}{\zeta} = \frac{[w(z) - b]/[1 - \bar{b}w(z)]}{(z - a)/(1 - \bar{a}z)}, \qquad (9.22)$$

we find that

$$\left|\frac{\omega}{\zeta}\right| \leqq 1. \qquad (9.23)$$

Equality holds only if $\omega = e^{i\alpha}\zeta$, i.e., if $w(z)$ is a linear transformation of the unit disk onto itself which carries the point $z = a$ into the point $z = b$.

This result, which contains Schwarz's lemma as a special case, has the following geometric interpretation (cf. Chapter 3).

Let us consider the Steiner circles of the first kind with limiting points $z = a$, $1/\bar{a}$ and $w = b$, $1/\bar{b}$ in the z-plane and the w-plane. If $w = w(z)$ is a linear transformation which maps the disk $|z| < 1$ onto $|w| < 1$ in such a way that $w(a) = b$, then the circles

$$\left|\frac{z - a}{1 - \bar{a}z}\right| = \lambda, \qquad \left|\frac{w - b}{1 - \bar{b}w}\right| = \lambda \qquad (9.24)$$

will map onto each other. The theorem just proved can now be stated in the following way. If $w = w(z)$ is an analytic function in $|z| < 1$ which satisfies there the conditions $|w(z)| < 1$ and $w(a) = b$, and if the point z is in the interior or on the circumference of the first circle of (9.24), then the corresponding value of the function $w(z)$ lies in the interior or on the circumference of the second circle of (9.24) with the same value λ (< 1). The point can lie on the boundary only if $w(z)$ is the *linear* transformation considered above.

In particular, if we set $z = a$, $w(a) = b$, it follows from (9.22) and (9.23) that

$$|w'(a)| \frac{1 - |a|^2}{1 - |b|^2} \leqq 1,$$

or, if we set $a = z$,

$$\frac{|dw(z)|}{1 - |w(z)|^2} \leqq \frac{|dz|}{1 - |z|^2}. \qquad (9.25)$$

In view of Section 3.11, we can formulate this result as follows†:

If $w = w(z)$ is analytic in the disk $|z| < 1$ and is bounded there, $|w(z)| < 1$, then the hyperbolic length of the image $dw = w'(z)dz$ of an element of arc dz cannot exceed the hyperbolic length of dz.

---

† This generalization of Schwarz's lemma was given by G. Pick in 1916.

If l_z is a rectifiable arc lying in the unit disk which is mapped by $w = w(z)$ onto the arc l_w, then by integrating the inequality (9.25) over l_z we obtain

$$\int_{l_w} \frac{|dw|}{1 - |w|^2} \leq \int_{l_z} \frac{|dz|}{1 - |z|^2}.$$

Hence, the mapping $w = w(z)$ *diminishes* non-Euclidean arc length. Equality holds in the above inequality only if the mapping $w = w(z)$ is a "non-Euclidean motion."

9.16. Conformal Mapping of a Disk onto a Disk

We give one more application of the maximum principle by proving the following theorem.

An analytic function $w(z)$ which maps the unit disk $|z| < 1$ homeomorphically (i.e., in a one-to-one and bicontinuous manner) onto itself and which leaves the origin $z = 0$ invariant is of the form $w(z) = e^{i\alpha}z$, where α is a real constant.

Proof. Let ρ_0 be an arbitrary number in the interval $0 < \rho_0 < 1$. Under the mapping $w(z)$ the disk $|w| \leq \rho_0$ corresponds to a closed set (z) in the disk $|z| < 1$. On this set $|z|$ attains a well-defined maximum $r_0 < 1$. By the one-to-one property of the mapping, we have

$$\rho_0 \leq |w(z)| < 1 \qquad \text{for} \qquad r_0 \leq |z| < 1. \tag{9.26}$$

The zero of the function $w(z)$ at $z = 0$ has a finite order $\nu \geq 1$. The quotient $f(z) = w(z)/z^\nu$ is analytic in $|z| < 1$ and is non-zero. In view of $|f(z)| = |w(z)| \, |z|^{-\nu}$ and the relation (9.26) we have for $|z| = r$ ($r_0 < r < 1$) the inequalities

$$\rho_0 r^{-\nu} \leq |f(z)| \leq r^{-\nu}. \tag{9.27}$$

If we apply the maximum principle to the analytic functions f and $1/f$ in the disk $|z| \leq r$, we see that (9.27) is valid for every $|z| \leq r$. Let us now fix a point z ($|z| < 1$) and choose $r \geq \max(|z|, r_0)$. If we first let $r \to 1$ and then let $\rho_0 \to 1$, we obtain $|f(z)| = 1$.

Since this equality holds for all $|z| < 1$, it follows that $f(z)$ is a unimodular constant $e^{i\alpha}$, so that $w(z) = e^{i\alpha}z^\nu$. Since the mapping is one-to-one, we must have $\nu = 1$, and the theorem is proved.

From this result we deduce the following more general theorem (compare Section 3.8).

An analytic function $w = f(z)$ which maps a disk K_z of the z-plane homeomorphically onto a disk K_w of the w-plane is a linear transformation.

Proof. Let $\zeta = \zeta(z)$, $z = z(\zeta)$, be the linear transformation which maps K_z onto the disk $|\zeta| < 1$ and takes a fixed point z_0 of K_z into the origin $\zeta = 0$, and let $\omega = \omega(w)$, $w = w(\omega)$ be the transformation which maps the disk K_w onto the disk $|\omega| < 1$ and takes the point $w_0 = w(z_0)$ into the origin $\omega = 0$. Then the function

$$\omega = \omega(f(z(\zeta))) = \omega^*(\zeta) \qquad (9.28)$$

maps the unit disk onto itself in a one-to-one manner and leaves the origin invariant. By the theorem proved at the beginning of this section, $\omega^*(\zeta)$ is then a linear transformation. Hence, in view of (9.28),

$$\omega = f(z) = f(\omega^*(\zeta(z)))$$

is therefore a linear transformation, as asserted.

§4. THE LAURENT EXPANSION

9.17. Derivation of the Expansion

Let the function $w(z)$ be analytic in the annulus $G: r_0 < |z - a| < R_0$. Let z be an arbitrary point of G which, for the time being, we shall consider as fixed. Further, let r and R be two numbers such that $r_0 < r < |z - a| < R < R_0$. We denote γ_r and γ_R the positively oriented circles $|z - a| = r$ and $|z - a| = R$, respectively, and we choose two points $z_1 \in \gamma_r$ and $z_2 \in \gamma_R$ in such a way that the straight-line segment $z_1 z_2$ lies in $r < |z - a| < R$ and does not pass through the point z. We denote by Γ the closed path describing the paths $z_2 z_1$, γ_r^{-1}, $z_1 z_2$, and γ_R in succession. The winding number of the curve Γ with respect to z is

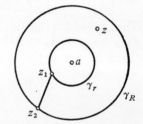

Figure 30

$$\frac{1}{2\pi i} \int_\Gamma \frac{d\zeta}{\zeta - z}$$

$$= \frac{1}{2\pi i} \left(\int_{z_2 z_1} - \int_{\gamma_r} + \int_{z_1 z_2} + \int_{\gamma_R} \right) = 1,$$

since the first and third integrals cancel each other, the second integral vanishes, and the fourth integral is equal to $2\pi i$.

Applying Cauchy's integral formula to the function $w(z)$, we obtain

$$w(z) = \frac{1}{2\pi i} \int_\Gamma \frac{w(\zeta)}{\zeta - z} \, d\zeta = w_1(z) + w_2(z), \qquad (9.29)$$

where

$$w_1(z) = \frac{1}{2\pi i} \int_{\gamma_R} \frac{w(\zeta)}{\zeta - z} \, d\zeta, \qquad w_2(z) = -\frac{1}{2\pi i} \int_{\gamma_r} \frac{w(\zeta)}{\zeta - z} \, d\zeta, \qquad (9.30)$$

since the integrals taken over the segments $z_2 z_1$ and $z_1 z_2$ cancel.

The function $w_1(z)$ is analytic in the *whole disk* $|z - a| < R$ (Section 9.6). It possesses a Taylor expansion about the point a:

$$w_1(z) = \sum_{\nu=0}^{\infty} c_\nu (z - a)^\nu, \tag{9.31}$$

with

$$c_\nu = \frac{1}{2\pi i} \int_{\gamma_R} \frac{w(\zeta)}{(\zeta - a)^{\nu+1}} \, d\zeta \qquad (\nu = 0, 1, \ldots). \tag{9.32}$$

The series converges in the disk $|z - a| < R$.

The integral $w_2(z)$ defines a function analytic in the domain $|z - a| > r$ (cf. Section 9.6). Let us expand it into a series of powers of $1/(z - a)$.

First we expand the expression $1/(\zeta - z)$ into a geometric series:

$$-\frac{1}{\zeta - z} = \frac{1}{z - a} \frac{1}{1 - \dfrac{\zeta - a}{z - a}} = \sum_{\nu=1}^{n} \frac{(\zeta - a)^{\nu-1}}{(z - a)^\nu} + \frac{(\zeta - a)^n}{(z - a)^n(z - \zeta)}.$$

By integration we obtain

$$w_2(z) = \sum_{\nu=1}^{n} \frac{c_{-\nu}}{(z - a)^\nu} + R_n(z),$$

where the coefficients are given by

$$c_{-\nu} = \frac{1}{2\pi i} \int_{\gamma_r} w(\zeta)(\zeta - a)^{\nu-1} \, d\zeta \qquad (\nu = 1, 2, \ldots), \tag{9.33}$$

and where

$$R_n(z) = \frac{1}{2\pi i} \int_{\gamma_r} w(\zeta) \frac{(\zeta - a)^n}{(z - a)^n(z - \zeta)} \, d\zeta.$$

In the domain $|z - a| > r$ we have the bound

$$|R_n(z)| \leq \frac{1}{2\pi} \int_{\gamma_r} \frac{|w(\zeta)|}{|z - a| - r} \left(\frac{r}{|z - a|} \right)^n |d\zeta| \leq \frac{rM_r}{|z - a| - r} \left(\frac{r}{|z - a|} \right)^n,$$

where

$$M_r = \max_{|\zeta - a| = r} |w(\zeta)|.$$

Hence, $R_n(z)$ tends to zero as $n \to \infty$. Thus we obtain the following expansion for $w_2(z)$:

$$w_2(z) = \sum_{\nu=1}^{\infty} \frac{c_{-\nu}}{(z - a)^\nu}. \tag{9.34}$$

Both expansions (9.31) and (9.34) hold in the annulus $r < |z - a| < R$. Since the values of the integrals (9.32) and (9.33) are independent of the radius

ρ $(r \leqq \rho \leqq R)$ of the circle γ along which we integrate, we may combine (9.31) and (9.34) to give

$$w(z) = \sum_{-\infty}^{+\infty} c_\nu (z - a)^\nu, \tag{9.35}$$

where the coefficients are given by

$$c_\nu = \frac{1}{2\pi i} \int_\gamma \frac{w(\zeta)}{(\zeta - a)^{\nu+1}} \, d\zeta \qquad (\nu = 0, \pm 1, \pm 2, \ldots).$$

The expansion (9.35) converges in the annulus $r < |z - a| < R$. But, since r and R are arbitrary numbers $(r_0 < r < R < R_0)$, the expression (9.35) converges in fact in the whole annulus $r_0 < |z - a| < R_0$. This expansion is called the *Laurent expansion* of the function $w(z)$.

If the function $w(z)$ is analytic in the domain G except at the point a and if R_0 is the shortest distance of a from the boundary of G, then r and R can be chosen arbitrarily, provided only that $R < R_0$. The values of the functions $w_1(z)$ and $w_2(z)$ at the point z do not depend on the choice of r and R so long as $r < |z - a| < R$. Hence, $w_2(z)$ is analytic in the whole domain G except for the point $z = a$, and the expansion (9.34) for $w_2(z)$ is valid. Thus we have proved the following theorem.

A function $w(z)$ which is analytic and single-valued in the domain G with the exception of a point a can be expanded into a series (9.35) which converges in the greatest annulus $0 < |z - a| < R_0$ lying entirely in G.

The coefficients of the series are given by the expression (9.32), where γ_R is any arbitrary positively oriented circle $|\zeta - a| = R$ $(0 < R < R_0)$.

As a power series, the Laurent series converges uniformly on every compact subset in its domain of convergence.

9.18. Uniqueness Theorem

Suppose that in some way we obtain for the function $w(z)$ a second expansion of the form

$$w(z) = \sum_{\nu=-\infty}^{+\infty} b_\nu (z - a)^\nu \tag{9.36}$$

valid in the annulus $(0 \leqq) r < |z - a| < R$. Then $b_\nu = c_\nu$ $(\nu = 0, \pm 1, \pm 2, \ldots)$. To prove this uniqueness theorem we note that the series

$$\frac{w(z)}{(z - a)^{n+1}} = \sum_{\nu=-\infty}^{+\infty} b_\nu (z - a)^{\nu-n-1}$$

converges uniformly on every closed subset of the annulus. If we integrate this series term by term over a circle γ with center at a and with radius ρ $(r < \rho < R)$, we obtain

$$\int_\gamma \frac{w(\zeta)}{(\zeta - a)^{n+1}} \, d\zeta = \sum_{\nu=-\infty}^{+\infty} \int_\gamma b_\nu(\zeta - a)^{\nu-n-1} \, d\zeta. \qquad (9.37)$$

For $\nu \neq n$ we have

$$\int_\gamma (\zeta - a)^{\nu-n-1} \, d\zeta = 0.$$

On the other hand, if $\nu = n$ we obtain

$$\int_\gamma b_n(\zeta - a)^{-1} \, d\zeta = b_n \int_\gamma d \log (\zeta - a) = b_n \cdot 2\pi i.$$

Hence, it follows from (9.37) that

$$b_n = \frac{1}{2\pi i} \int_\gamma \frac{w(\zeta)}{(\zeta - a)^{n+1}} \, d\zeta = c_n \qquad (n = 0, \pm 1, \ldots).$$

This proves the uniqueness theorem.

§5. ISOLATED SINGULARITIES OF AN ANALYTIC FUNCTION

9.19. Poles

Let the function $w = w(z)$ be analytic (and single-valued) for $0 < |z - a| \leq R_0$. We have shown in the previous section that $w(z)$ can be expanded into a Laurent series (9.35).

We write

$$M_r = \max_{|z-a|=r} |w(z)|$$

and we assume that as z tends to the point a (at which $w(z)$ is not defined) $w(z)$ increases more slowly than a certain power of $1/|z - a|$, so that for some integer $n \geq 0$

$$M_r|z - a|^{n+1} \to 0 \qquad \text{as} \qquad r = |z - a| \to 0. \qquad (9.38)$$

Using the formula (9.32) we obtain for the absolute values of the coefficients the estimates

$$|c_{-m}| \leq \frac{1}{2\pi} \int_{\gamma_r} |w(\zeta)| \, |\zeta - a|^{m-1}|d\zeta| \leq M_r r^m.$$

If $m \geq n + 1$, then by (9.38), $M_r r^m$ tends to zero as $r \to 0$, and, since the coefficient c_{-m} does not depend upon r, it follows that $c_{-n-1} = c_{-n-2} = \ldots = 0$. Thus the Laurent expansion of the function $w(z)$,

$$w(z) = \frac{c_{-n}}{(z - a)^n} + \cdots + \frac{c_{-1}}{(z - a)} + c_0 + c_1(z - a) + c_2(z - a)^2 + \cdots, \qquad (9.39)$$

contains only a *finite number* of terms (at most n), which become infinite as $z \rightarrow a$.

If we further assume that $c_{-n} \neq 0$, we see that

$$w(z)(z - a)^n \rightarrow c_{-n} \neq 0 \qquad \text{as} \qquad z \rightarrow a. \qquad (9.40)$$

In this case we say (if $n > 0$) that the function $w(z)$ has a *pole of order n* at the point $z = a$.

If (9.38) is already satisfied for $n = 0$, the expansion of $w(z)$ contains no negative powers of $z - a$:

$$w(z) = c_0 + c_1(z - a) + \cdots.$$

If we extend the definition of $w(z)$ to the point $z = a$ by setting $w(a) = c_0$, $w(z)$ becomes continuous, indeed analytic at this point. Accordingly, the point a is called a *removable* singularity.

Conversely, if condition (9.40) is satisfied for $n \geq 0$, $M_r|z - a|^{n+1}$ tends to zero as $z \rightarrow a$, and the Laurent expansion of the function is of the form (9.39).

Hence, (9.38) is the necessary and sufficient condition that the function have a pole of order $\leq n$ or a removable singularity at the point $z = a$.

If the function $w(z)$ is analytic in a domain G with the exception of certain singularities, we say that $w(z)$ is *regular* at all the remaining points of G.

9.20. Essential Singularities

If (9.38) is not satisfied for any finite n, the maximum of $|w(z)|$ increases faster than any power of $|z - a|$. In view of what we have shown in Section 9.19 this is the case if and only if the Laurent expansion (9.35) of the function contains *infinitely many* terms with negative powers of $z - a$. Such a point $z = a$ is said to be an *essential* singularity of $w(z)$.

If the singularity $z = a$ of $w(z)$ is a removable singularity or a pole, then $w(z)$ tends to a *definite limit* (finite or infinite) as $z \rightarrow a$. On the other hand, the behavior of an analytic function is highly discontinuous in the neighborhood of an *essential* singularity, as is shown by the following *theorem of Weierstrass.*

If $z = a$ is an essential singularity of an analytic function $w(z)$, then the values taken by $w = w(z)$ in every neighborhood $0 < |z - a| \leq r$ of a come arbitrarily close to every complex number w.

Thus for every $c \neq \infty$ and for every $\epsilon > 0$ there exists a point z ($\neq a$) in the neighborhood $0 < |z - a| < r$ such that $|w(z) - c| < \epsilon$. If the values of $w = w(z)$ are treated as points of the w-plane, then the points $w(z)$ which correspond to the domain $0 < |z - a| < r$ are "everywhere dense", i.e., no disk of the w-plane (however small its radius) is free of the points $w(z)$ (see the examples in Section 9.22).

We shall prove Weierstrass's theorem by contradiction. If the theorem were false, then there would exist $\epsilon > 0$, $r > 0$ and a complex number $c \neq \infty$ such that $|w(z) - c| \geq \epsilon$ for every point of the disk $|z - a| < r$, and, hence,

$$\left| \frac{1}{w(z) - c} \right| \leq \frac{1}{\epsilon}.$$

The function $1/(w(z) - c)$ is then regular for $0 < |z - a| < r$, and must then (by Section 9.19) have a removable singularity at the point a. Therefore we must have

$$\frac{1}{w(z) - c} = c_n(z - a)^n + c_{n+1}(z - a)^{n+1} + \cdots,$$

where $n \geq 0$ and $c_n \neq 0$. It would follow that

$$w(z) - c = \frac{1}{(z - a)^n} \frac{1}{c_n + c_{n+1}(z - a) + \cdots} = \frac{1}{(z - a)^n} f(z).$$

The function $f(z)$ would be regular in the neighborhood of the point $z = a$, and $f(a) = 1/c_n \neq 0$. Hence, either $w(z)$ would have a pole of order n at $z = a$, or else (if $n = 0$) $w(z)$ would be regular at this point. This contradicts our assumption, and consequently the theorem is true.

9.21. Behavior of a Function in the Neighborhood of the Point ∞

If a function $w(z)$ is analytic in a domain $R < |z| < \infty$, its behavior near the point $z = \infty$ can be investigated by means of the Laurent expansion. Let $M_r = \max |w(z)|$ for $|z| = r$.

1) If there exists an integer n (≥ 0) such that

$$\frac{M_r}{r^{n+1}} \to 0 \qquad \text{as} \qquad r = |z| \to \infty,$$

then it follows from (9.32) (with $a = 0$) that at most n positive powers of z appear in the Laurent expansion

$$\sum_{-\infty}^{+\infty} c_n z^n. \tag{9.41}$$

In fact, we have

$$|c_m| \leq \frac{M_r}{r^m},$$

and for $m \geq n + 1$ the right-hand side tends to zero as $r \to \infty$. Hence, $c_{n+1} = c_{n+2} = \ldots = 0$ and

$$w(z) = c_n z^n + \cdots + c_1 z + c_0 + \frac{c_{-1}}{z} + \frac{c_{-2}}{z^2} + \cdots. \tag{9.42}$$

It follows that

$$\frac{w(z)}{z^n} \to c_n \qquad \text{as} \qquad z \to \infty.$$

If $c_n \neq 0$, the point $z = \infty$ is said to be a *pole of order n* of the function $w(z)$.

In particular, if $w(z)$ is an entire function, that is, a function analytic in the whole finite z-plane, its Laurent expansion does not contain any negative powers of z, and the Laurent expansion reduces to the Taylor expansion of the function about the point $z = 0$. Thus we arrive once again at the following conclusion (already proved in Section 9.11).

If the modulus of an entire function $w(z)$ increases more slowly than a power of r, so that

$$\frac{M_r}{r^{n+1}} \to 0 \qquad \text{as} \qquad r \to \infty,$$

then $w(z)$ reduces to a polynomial of degree at most n. For $n = 0$ we obtain a sharper form of Liouville's theorem (Section 9.11).

If the maximum modulus M_r of an entire function increases more slowly than r,

$$\frac{M_r}{r} \to 0 \qquad \text{as} \qquad r \to \infty,$$

the function reduces to a constant.

2) If the maximum of $|w(z)|$ increases faster than any power of r,

$$\frac{M_r}{r^n} \to \infty \qquad \text{as} \qquad r \to \infty$$

for any choice of n, then the Laurent expansion (9.41) of $w(z)$ contains infinitely many positive powers of z. In this case the point $z = \infty$ is an essential singularity of the function $w(z)$. In the neighborhood of such a point there are values of the function $w(z)$ as close to any prescribed complex number c as one pleases. This can be proved as in Section 9.20 by considering the function $w(z) - c$ (Exercise 14, p. 166).

One can also investigate the behavior of a function $w(z)$ in the neighborhood of the point $z = \infty$ by transforming it by means of the inversion $z = 1/\zeta$ into a function $w(1/\zeta) = w^*(\zeta)$ of ζ, which will have the same kind of singularity (a pole or an essential singularity) at the point $\zeta = 0$ as $w(z)$ has at the point $z = \infty$. In particular, if $n = 0$ in the expansion (9.42), $w^*(\zeta)$ will be regular at the point $\zeta = 0$ if we set $w^*(0) = c_0$. For this reason we say that the function $w(z)$ is regular at the point $z = \infty$ and set $w(\infty) = c_0$.

Remark. A remarkable sharpening of Weierstrass's theorem was obtained by Émile Picard in 1879: He proved that an entire function which is not a polynomial actually assumes *every* complex value $c \neq \infty$ in the neighborhood of the essential singularity $z = \infty$ with at most *one* exception. An exceptional value can in fact occur: e.g., the exponential function $w = e^z$ omits the value $c = 0$. The proof of Picard's theorem requires deeper methods, and will be given only in the last chapter of this book (Section 17.36).

9.22. Examples

As an illustration we shall consider the singularities of the single-valued elementary functions. The exponential function $w = e^z$ has only one singularity, $z = \infty$, and this is an essential singularity. The inversion $1/z = \zeta$ transforms e^z into the function $e^{1/\zeta}$ which has an essential singularity at $\zeta = 0$ and no other singularities. In the neighborhood of $\zeta = 0$ this function takes every non-zero value infinitely often. The inversion maps the period strips of the exponential function onto regions bounded by circles which are tangent to the real axis at the origin.

Similarly, $z = \infty$ is the only singularity of the functions $\sin z$ and $\cos z$. It is an essential singularity for both functions.

The function $\tan z = \sin z/\cos z$ is regular everywhere except at the points

$$z_k = \frac{\pi}{2} + k\pi \qquad (k = 0, \pm 1, \ldots), \tag{9.43}$$

which are the zeros of the function $\cos z$. In the neighborhood of the points (9.43) we have†

$$\tan z = \frac{\sin z}{\cos z} = \frac{(-1)^k + [z - z_k]}{(-1)^{k+1}(z - z_k) + [(z - z_k)^2]}$$

$$= -\frac{1}{z - z_k}\frac{1 + [z - z_k]}{1 + [z - z_k]}.$$

The second factor is regular both at the point z_k and in a neighborhood of z_k. Therefore we can expand it into a series of positive powers of $z - z_k$, which implies that it is of the form $1 + [z - z_k]$. We obtain

$$\tan z = -\frac{1}{z - z_k}(1 + [z - z_k]) = -\frac{1}{z - z_k} + \mathfrak{P}(z - z_k),$$

where $\mathfrak{P}(z - z_k)$ denotes a power series in positive powers of $z - z_k$. We shall also use this notation in the sequel. This expansion shows us that $\tan z$ has simple poles (poles of order one) at the points (9.43).

The point $z = \infty$ is a limit point of the poles of $\tan z$. In every neighborhood of $z = \infty$ the function $\tan z$ assumes every complex value with the exception of the values $\pm i$.

It can be shown in the same way that the points $z = k\pi$ ($k = 0, \pm 1, \ldots$)

---

† Henceforth $[(z - z_k)^n]$ will denote a function which has the property that when it is divided by the expression $(z - z_k)^n$ the quotient remains bounded as $z - z_k \to 0$.

are simple poles of the function $\cot z = \cos z/\sin z$; the point $z = \infty$ is a limit point of these poles.

The functions $\tan z$ and $\cot z$ are therefore *meromorphic* functions (cf. Section 6.4).

9.23. Analytic Functions whose only Singularities are Poles

We saw in Chapter 2 that the only singularities of a rational function are poles, and that the number of poles is finite. We now prove the converse theorem.

An analytic function which has no singularities in the extended plane other than poles is a rational function.

Proof. The number of poles must be finite, otherwise they would have a limit point in the extended plane and this point would be neither a pole nor a point of regularity of the function.

Let $b_1, b_2, \ldots, b_k$, and possibly $z = \infty$, be the poles of the function $w(z)$. At the pole b_i $(i = 1, 2, \ldots, k)$ of order n_i the function $w(z)$ has the Laurent expansion

$$w(z) = \frac{c_{-n_i}}{(z - b_i)^{n_i}} + \frac{c_{-n_i+1}}{(z - b_i)^{n_i-1}} + \cdots + c_0 + c_1(z - b_i) + \cdots. \qquad (9.44)$$

This expansion is valid in the largest disk with center b_i which is free of other poles. We may write (9.44) in the form

$$w(z) = G_{n_i}\left(\frac{1}{z - b_i}\right) + \mathfrak{P}(z - b_i), \qquad (9.45)$$

where G_{n_i} denotes the sum of those terms which become infinite at the point $z = b_i$. We form a circle about the origin containing all the finite poles b_i; then outside this circle the function $w(z)$ has the expansion

$$w(z) = c_m z^m + c_{m-1} z^{m-1} + \cdots + c_0 + \frac{c_{-1}}{z} + \cdots \qquad (m \geq 0),$$

which we may write, as in (9.45), in the form

$$w(z) = G_m(z) + \mathfrak{P}\left(\frac{1}{z}\right), \qquad (9.46)$$

where $G_m(z)$ is a polynomial in z and $\mathfrak{P}(1/z)$ is a power series in $1/z$.

The function

$$R(z) = \sum_{i=1}^{k} G_{n_i}\left(\frac{1}{z - b_i}\right) + G_m(z)$$

is rational and has the same poles as $w(z)$. The function

$$(z) = w(z) - R(z)$$

is certainly regular everywhere with the possible exception of the points $z = b_i$ and $z = \infty$. If we write $f(z)$ in the form

$$f(z) = \left\{ w(z) - G_{n_i}\left(\frac{1}{z - b_i}\right) \right\} - \sum_{\substack{j=1 \\ j \neq i}}^{k} G_{n_j}\left(\frac{1}{z - b_j}\right) - G_m(z),$$

we see that $f(z)$ is bounded in the neighborhood of the point b_i, and therefore is regular at the point b_i. From the representation

$$f(z) = \{w(z) - G_m(z)\} - \sum_{j=1}^{k} G_{n_j}\left(\frac{1}{z - b_j}\right)$$

we also see that $f(z)$ is regular at infinity. Hence, $f(z)$ is regular in the extended plane and thus, by Liouville's theorem, it is a constant. The function $w(z) = R(z) + f(z)$ is therefore rational.

We have used a similar argument already in Sections 2.12–2.13 to derive the partial-fraction expansion of rational functions. From the theorem we have just proved it follows that a meromorphic function which is regular at $z = \infty$, or has a pole there, is rational.

§6. THE INVERSE OF AN ANALYTIC FUNCTION

9.24. The Inverse of a Function in the Neighborhood of a Point at which the Derivative does not Vanish

Let us now consider an analytic function

$$f(z) = a_0 + a_1 z + a_2 z^2 + \cdots$$

defined in a neighborhood $|z| < R$ of the origin and let us assume that $f'(0) = a_1 \neq 0$. We shall prove that the function $w = f(z)$ is uniquely invertible for sufficiently small values of $|w - a_0|$:

In a certain disk $|w - a_0| < \rho_0$ ($\rho_0 > 0$) there exists a well-defined single-valued function

$$z = g(w) = b_1(w - a_0) + b_2(w - a_0)^2 + \cdots \quad \left(b_1 = \frac{1}{a_1}\right),$$

such that the identity $f(g(w)) \equiv w$ holds throughout the disk $|w - a_0| < \rho_0$.

By replacing f by $(f - a_0)/a_1$ we can restrict ourselves to the case $a_0 = 0$, $a_1 = 1$. Under this assumption $f'(z) \to 1$ as $z \to 0$. If Θ is a fixed number in the interval $0 < \Theta < 1$ we can choose a positive number $r_0 < R$ such that

$$|f'(z) - 1| \leqq \Theta \qquad \text{for} \qquad |z| \leqq r_0. \tag{9.47}$$

First of all we shall prove:

1) The mapping of the disk $|z| \leq r_0$ by the function $f(z)$ is schlicht, i.e., it has the property that

$$f(a) \neq f(b) \qquad \text{for} \qquad a \neq b.$$

To prove this assertion we write

$$f(z) = z + \phi(z), \tag{9.48}$$

where $\phi(0) = \phi'(0) = 0$. If a and b are points of the disk $|z| \leq r_0$, we have

$$\phi(b) - \phi(a) = \int_a^b \phi'(z) \, dz,$$

and if we integrate along the straight line segment ab, we find that

$$|\phi(b) - \phi(a)| \leq \int_a^b |\phi'(z)| \, |dz| \leq \Theta \int_a^b |dz| = \Theta |b - a|. \tag{9.49}$$

Hence,

$$\begin{aligned} |f(b) - f(a)| &= |(b - a) + (\phi(b) - \phi(a))| \geq |b - a| - \Theta|b - a| \\ &= |b - a|(1 - \Theta) > 0, \end{aligned}$$

and our assertion is proved.

Now we proceed to the construction of the inverse function. To solve the equation $f(z) = w$ for z we may consider the equivalent equation (see Eq. 9.48)

$$z = w - \phi(z) \tag{9.50}$$

and solve it by means of Picard's method of *successive approximation*. We set $z_0 = 0$ and define the sequence $z_1, z_2, \ldots$ by means of the recursion formula

$$z_{n+1} = w - \phi(z_n) \qquad (n = 0, 1, \ldots). \tag{9.50'}$$

We now prove the following assertions:

2) If w is chosen from the disk

$$|w| \leq \rho_0 = r_0(1 - \Theta),$$

then the points z_n $(n = 0, 1, \ldots)$ all lie in the disk $|z| \leq r_0$.

3) The sequence z_n converges uniformly in the disk $|w| \leq r_0$ to a limit $z = g(w)$.

Proof of assertion (2). For $n = 0$ we have $|z_0| = 0 < r_0$. If we assume that $|z_\nu| \leq r_0$ holds for $\nu = 0, 1, \ldots, n$ we can show that $|z_{n+1}| \leq r_0$. In fact, if we use the recursion formula (9.50)', we have

$$|z_{n+1}| \leq |w| + |\phi(z_n)|,$$

whence it follows from the inequality (9.49) with $a = 0$, $b = z_n$ ($\phi(a) = \phi(0) = 0$) that

$$|z_{n+1}| \leqq |w| + \Theta|z_n| < |w| + \Theta r_0.$$

Now if $|w| \leqq \rho_0 = r_0(1 - \Theta)$, then $|z_{n+1}| \leqq r_0$, so that this proves (2) by induction.

Proof of assertion (3). By applying the inequality (9.49) we obtain for the modulus of the difference $z_{n+1} - z_n = -(\phi(z_n) - \phi(z_{n-1}))$ the following estimate:

$$|z_{n+1} - z_n| = |\phi(z_n) - \phi(z_{n-1})| \leqq \Theta|z_n - z_{n-1}| \leqq \Theta^n|z_1|$$
$$= \Theta^n|w| \leqq \Theta^n\rho_0.$$

Hence,

$$|z_{n+p} - z_n| = \left| \sum_{\nu=n}^{n+p-1} (z_{\nu+1} - z_\nu) \right| \leqq \sum_{n}^{n+p-1} |z_{\nu+1} - z_\nu|$$

$$\leqq \rho_0 \sum_{n}^{n+p-1} \Theta^\nu < \Theta^n \frac{\rho_0}{1 - \Theta}.$$

The last expression tends to zero as $n \to \infty$. The uniform convergence of the sequence z_n follows from the Cauchy criterion.

It can be easily seen that $g(w) = \lim z_n$ is the inverse function we were looking for. $g(w)$ is the limit of a uniformly convergent sequence of analytic functions $z_n = z_n(w)$ in $|w| \leqq \rho_0$, and, hence, it is itself an analytic function of w for $|w| < \rho_0$ (cf. Section 9.8). Further, in view of the continuity of $\phi(z)$, it follows from (9.50)' that

$$g(w) = \lim z_{n+1} = w - \lim \phi(z_n) = w - \phi(g(w)).$$

Thus, in view of (9.48), we have

$$f(g(w)) = g(w) + \phi(g(w)) = w.$$

Hence, $g(w)$ is the inverse function of $f(z)$. By the chain rule (Section 1.15) $(df/dz) \cdot (dg/dw) = 1$ and, hence, $g'(w) = 1/f'(z)$.

We conclude now from these results that the function $z = g(w)$ maps the disk $|w| < \rho_0$ onto some domain G_0 of the z-plane which lies in the disk $|z| < r_0$. Its boundary Γ_0 is the one-to-one image of the circle $|w| = \rho_0$. The mapping is conformal everywhere since $f'(z) \neq 0$ in the disk $|z| \leqq r_0$ (cf. Section 1.16).

9.25. The Nature of the Mapping in the Neighborhood of a Zero of the Derivative

Suppose that $w = f(z)$ is analytic in the disk $|z| \leq R$ and that its derivative is zero at the origin. Let us assume that $f(z)$ does not vanish identically and that $f(0) = 0$. Then the function has an expansion

$$w = f(z) = a_n z^n + a_{n+1} z^{n+1} + \cdots \qquad (a_n \neq 0, n \geq 2).$$

To investigate the mapping effected by this function, we write

$$w = a_n z^n (1 + \phi(z))$$

and choose an $r_0 > 0$ so small that

$$|\phi(z)| = \left| \frac{a_{n+1}}{a_n} z + \cdots \right| < 1$$

whenever $|z| \leq r_0$.

We now introduce a new variable

$$w = \zeta^n, \qquad \zeta = \sqrt[n]{w},$$

and obtain

$$\zeta = \sqrt[n]{a_n}\, z (1 + \phi(z))^{1/n}. \tag{9.51}$$

We fix the values of the roots on the right-hand side in the following way. If $a_n = |a_n| e^{i\alpha_n}$ $(0 \leq \alpha_n < 2\pi)$ we define the constant $\sqrt[n]{a_n}$ by putting $\sqrt[n]{a_n} = \sqrt[n]{|a_n|}\, e^{i\alpha_n/n}$, where $\sqrt[n]{|a_n|} > 0$. Since $|\phi| < 1$ for $|z| \leq r_0$, we have $1 + \phi \neq 0$. If we choose that branch of $\log(1 + \phi(z))$ which vanishes for $z = 0$, $\phi(0) = 0$, then

$$\log(1 + \phi(z)) = \int_0^z \frac{\phi'(z)}{1 + \phi(z)}\, dz$$

is single-valued in $|z| \leq r_0$. This then determines a branch of the function

$$(1 + \phi(z))^{1/n} = e^{(1/n)\,\log\,(1+\phi(z))}$$

which is single-valued in $|z| \leq r_0$.

Thus the function ζ in (9.51) is a single-valued analytic function in the disk $|z| < r_0$; its Taylor expansion is of the form

$$\zeta = b_1 z + b_2 z^2 + \cdots,$$

where $b_1 = \sqrt[n]{a_n} \neq 0$. In view of the results of the preceding section, this function has a single-valued inverse in a neighborhood $|\zeta| \leq \rho_0$ of the origin, where it has the expansion

$$z = \frac{\zeta}{b_1} + \cdots.$$

This function gives a one-to-one conformal mapping of the disk $|\zeta| < \rho_0$

onto a certain domain G_0 lying in the disk $|z| < r_0$. The boundary Γ_0 of G_0 is the one-to-one image of the circle $|\zeta| = \rho_0$.

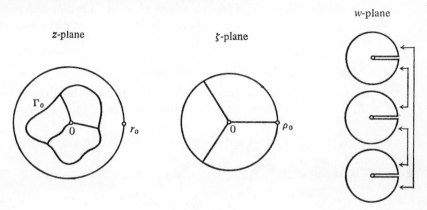

Figure 31

The substitution $w = \zeta^n$ takes us back to the function $w(z)$. We know that the transformation $w = \zeta^n$ (Sections 2.3–2.4) maps the schlicht disk $|\zeta| \leq \rho_0$ onto part of an n-sheeted Riemann surface R_w covering the disk $|w| \leq \rho_0^n$ n times and having the point $w = 0$ as a branch point of order $n - 1$. The mapping is not conformal at this point: the angles at the origin $z = 0$ are multiplied by n under this mapping. To each region

$$\nu \frac{2\pi}{n} \leq \arg \zeta < (\nu + 1)\frac{2\pi}{n}, \qquad |\zeta| \leq \rho_0$$

corresponds a disk $|w| \leq \rho_0^n$ slit along the positive real axis. We can construct the Riemann surface R_w from these disks by pasting the edges of the slits together (as indicated in Section 2.4). In the z-plane these slits correspond to n arcs joining the origin to the boundary Γ_0. Two successive arcs intersect at the origin at an angle of $2\pi/n$. Therefore, the function $w = f(z)$ maps the schlicht domain G_0 in a one-to-one way onto a Riemann surface R_w in such a way that the origin corresponds to the origin. At the origin (and only at this point) the mapping fails to be conformal: An angle α with vertex at the origin goes into an angle $n\alpha$ with vertex at $w = 0$. Therefore, the *inverse function* $z = z(w)$ of $w = f(z)$ is *multiple-valued* in the neighborhood of the branch point $w = 0$. It has n different branches in the disk $|w| \leq \rho_0^n$ which go over into one another as w circumscribes the origin. Only after n such revolutions will the image curve in the z-plane be closed.

Let us sum up our results.

If the function $w(z)$ is analytic in the neighborhood of the point z_0 and if $w'(z_0) \neq 0$, then $w = w(z)$ maps a neighborhood of z_0 one-to-one conformally onto a neighborhood of the point $w_0 = w(z_0)$.

6*

If, however, z_0 is a zero of the derivative $w'(z)$ of order $n - 1$ $(n > 1)$, the function $w = w(z)$ maps some neighborhood of z_0 in a one-to-one way onto an n-sheeted Riemann surface for which $w_0 = w(z_0)$ is a branch-point of order $n - 1$. The mapping is conformal in this neighborhood except at the point z_0.

9.26. The Mapping in the Neighborhood of a Pole

Let the function $w = f(z)$ be single-valued and regular in the region $0 < |z| \leqq R$, and let $z = 0$ be a pole of $f(z)$ of order n $(n \geqq 1)$:

$$w = f(z) = \frac{b_{-n}}{z^n} + \cdots + \frac{b_{-1}}{z} + b_0 + b_1 z + \cdots \qquad (b_{-n} \neq 0).$$

We define the function

$$\omega = \frac{1}{f} = z^n \frac{1}{b_{-n} + b_{-n+1}z + \cdots},$$

where the denominator is a non-zero regular function of z in some disk $|z| < r_0 \leqq R$. Hence, $\omega = 1/f$ is regular for $|z| < r_0$, and $z = 0$ is a zero of ω of order n. We can therefore apply to ω the results obtained in the preceding section.

If $n = 1$, then $d\omega/dz \neq 0$ at the point $z = 0$, and z is a single-valued regular function of ω in a disk $|\omega| < \rho_0$. This disk corresponds to the exterior of the circle $|w| = 1/\rho_0$ in the w-plane. Thus the region $|w| > 1/\rho_0$ is mapped one-to-one conformally onto a neighborhood G_0 of $z = 0$.

On the other hand, if $n > 1$, it follows from Section 9.25 that $w = f(z)$ maps a neighborhood of the point $z = 0$ onto a Riemann surface consisting of n disks $|w| > (1/\rho_0)^n$, which form an n-sheeted surface with the branch point $w = \infty$. The inverse function $z = z(w)$ of $f(z)$ has n branches which go over into one another as w makes a circuit of the branch point $w = \infty$ of the surface.

We note finally that if we wish to investigate the mapping of a neighborhood of the point $z = \infty$ by a function $w = f(z)$ which is single-valued and regular in this neighborhood, the inversion $z \to 1/z$ (which transforms the point ∞ into the origin) will reduce to the case already discussed.

9.27. The Image of a Domain is a Domain

The results proved above contain the following theorem.

A non-constant analytic function maps a domain onto a domain.

To prove this result we assume that $w(z)$ is analytic in a domain G, and we denote by E the set of values in the w-plane assumed by the function $w(z)$. If w_0 $(\neq \infty)$ is an arbitrary point of the set E, there exists a point z_0 in G such that $w(z_0) = w_0$. In view of the results proved above, the function $w(z)$

assumes in a neighborhood of z_0 in G every complex value belonging to some disk with center w_0. If $w = \infty$ belongs to E, then $w(z)$ takes every complex value outside some circle. Thus the image of G is open and one can see easily that it is also connected (since $w(z)$ is continuous in G).

In general the image domain is not schlicht. For example, the function $w = z^2$ maps the domain $|z| < 1$ onto the domain $|w| < 1$, but each point of $|w| < 1$ is covered twice by the image.

9.28. The Limit of a Sequence of Schlicht Functions

We shall use the foregoing results concerning the mapping properties of an analytic function to prove an important theorem about the limit of a sequence of schlicht functions.

Suppose that
$$w = f_n(z) \qquad (n = 1, 2, \ldots)$$

is a sequence of analytic functions regular in a domain G of the finite z-plane and having the following properties:

1) *The mapping of the domain G given by the function $w = f_n(z)$ is schlicht, i.e., at distinct points of G the function $f_n(z)$ takes distinct values:*
$$f_n(z_1) \neq f_n(z_2) \qquad for \qquad z_1 \neq z_2.$$

2) *The sequence $f_n(z)$ converges uniformly on every compact subset of G. Then there are only two possibilities: The limit function $w = f(z)$ is either a constant or else it defines a schlicht mapping of the domain G.*

Proof. In view of Weierstrass's theorem (Section 9.8) the function $f(z)$ is analytic in the domain G. We assume that it is not a constant, and we prove that it is schlicht:
$$f(z) - f(z_0) \neq 0 \qquad for \qquad z - z_0 \neq 0.$$

Since the difference $f(z) - f(z_0)$ does not vanish identically, it has a zero of finite order m ($1 \leq m < \infty$) at the point $z = z_0$. By the theorem in Section 9.25 there exists a small $\rho > 0$ such that the inverse function of $f(z)$ maps an m-sheeted disk $|w - w_0| \leq \rho_0$ with branch point at $w_0 = f(z_0)$ onto a closed schlicht subdomain G_ρ of G. Hence, $f(z) \neq f(z_0)$ on G_ρ if $z \neq z_0$ and $|f(z) - w_0| = \rho$ if z belongs to Γ_ρ, the boundary of G_ρ. Since the sequence f_n converges uniformly on G_ρ, there exists an integer n_0 such that for every $z \in G_\rho$
$$|f_n(z) - f(z)| < \frac{\rho}{4} \qquad for \qquad n \geq n_0. \tag{9.52}$$

We now assert that if $n \geq n_0$ the function $w = f_n(z)$ assumes in G_ρ every complex value w satisfying the condition

$$|w - w_0| \leq \frac{\rho}{2}.$$

If $w = w_1$ is such a value, then on the boundary Γ_ρ we have

$$|f_n(z) - w_1| = |(f(z) - w_1) + (f_n(z) - f(z))|$$
$$\geq |f(z) - w_1| - |f_n(z) - f(z)| > \frac{\rho}{2} - \frac{\rho}{4} = \frac{\rho}{4}.$$

Now if $f_n(z) - w_1 \neq 0$ in G_ρ, then we could apply the maximum principle to the function $1/(f_n(z) - w_1)$ and conclude that the inequality

$$|f_n(z) - w_1| > \frac{\rho}{4} \tag{9.53}$$

holds at every point of the domain G_ρ. However, $f(z)$ assumes in G_ρ every value w in $|w - w_0| \leq \rho$. Let $z_1 \in G_\rho$ be a point such that $f(z_1) = w_1$. Then, in view of (9.52), $|f_n(z_1) - w_1| < \rho/4$, which contradicts (9.53). This contradiction shows that the set of values assumed by the function $w = f_n(z)$ ($n \geq n_0$) in the domain G_ρ covers the whole disk $|w - w_0| \leq \rho/2$.

Since the function $w = f_n(z)$ is schlicht in the domain G, it follows that $|f_n(z) - w_0| > \rho/2$ at every point z of G outside G_ρ. If we let $n \to \infty$, we may also conclude that $|f(z) - w_0| \geq \rho/2$. Thus $f(z) \neq f(z_0) = w_0$ for $z \in G$ outside G_ρ. On the other hand, in the domain G_ρ, $z = z_0$ is the *only* point where $f(z)$ assumes the value w_0. Thus we have proved that $f(z) - f(z_0) \neq 0$ for $z - z_0 \neq 0$. Further, since the mapping $w = f(z)$ is schlicht, it follows that $m = 1$ and, hence, $f'(z_0) \neq 0$. The mapping is therefore *conformal* throughout the domain G.

§7. MAPPING BY A RATIONAL FUNCTION

9.29.

As an application of Section 6 we investigate the mapping effected by a rational function of order n (≥ 1):

$$w = w(z) = \frac{P(z)}{Q(z)} = \frac{a_0 z^n + \cdots + a_n}{b_0 z^n + \cdots + b_n}, \tag{9.54}$$

where at least one of the coefficients a_0, b_0 is not zero, and where $P(z)$ and $Q(z)$ have no common zeros.

We have seen in Section 2.10 that such a rational function has exactly n zeros and n poles provided that each zero and pole is counted according to its multiplicity, and provided that the point $z = \infty$ is also taken into account.

More generally (cf. Section 2.11), $w(z)$ assumes every value n times; hence, it maps the closed schlicht z-plane onto the closed w-plane covered n times. We shall now examine more closely the structure of this n-sheeted Riemann surface R_w.

9.30. The Branch Points of the Surface

To begin with, consider a point $z_0 \neq \infty$ at which $w'(z_0) \neq 0$. By Section 9.24 the function $w(z)$ maps a neighborhood of z_0 one-to-one conformally onto a schlicht neighborhood of the point $w_0 = w(z_0)$. Thus, any branch points of the Riemann surface can be images of only those points at which the derivative vanishes. The point $w = \infty$ and the image of the point $z = \infty$ are also possible branch points.

If $z_0 \neq \infty$ is a zero of $w'(z)$ of order $\mu - 1$ ($\mu > 1$), then $w(z)$ maps a certain neighborhood of z_0 onto part of a μ-sheeted Riemann surface with a branch point of order $\mu - 1$ at the point $w_0 = w(z_0)$.

On the other hand, if $z_0 \neq \infty$ is a pole of $w(z)$ of order ν, the function $w = w(z)$ maps some neighborhood of the point z_0 onto part of a ν-sheeted Riemann surface with a branch point of order $\nu - 1$ at infinity (for $\nu = 1$ the mapping is schlicht). The derivative of $w(z)$ has a pole of order $\nu + 1$ at the point z_0, as can be seen immediately from the partial-fraction expansion of $w(z)$.

We must still examine the mapping of a neighborhood of the point $z = \infty$. Here we may assume without loss of generality that the function $w(z)$ vanishes at the point $z = \infty$ (this means that $b_0 \neq 0$ but $a_0 = 0$ in Eq. 9.54). For if $b_0 = 0$, then $a_0 \neq 0$, and we can reduce this situation to the case $b_0 \neq 0$, $a_0 = 0$ by means of the linear transformation $1/w$. If, on the other hand, $a_0 \neq 0$ and $b_0 \neq 0$, then $w(z) \to w_\infty = a_0/b_0$ as $z \to \infty$ and the function $w(z) - w_\infty$ vanishes at the point $z = \infty$.

If $a_0 = \ldots = a_{\mu-1} = 0$, $a_\mu \neq 0$ ($1 \leqq \mu \leqq n$), then the function $w(z)$ has a zero of order μ at the point $z = \infty$ and thus has an expansion of the form

$$w(z) = \frac{1}{z^\mu} \left\{ \frac{a_\mu}{b_0} + \epsilon(z) \right\},$$

where $\epsilon(z)$ is a rational function which tends to zero as $z \to \infty$. For the derivative we obtain the expression

$$w'(z) = \frac{1}{z^{\mu+1}} \left\{ -\mu \frac{a_\mu}{b_0} + \epsilon_1(z) \right\}, \tag{9.55}$$

where $\epsilon_1(z) \to 0$ as $z \to \infty$ (cf. Exercise 18, p. 166). Therefore, if $z = \infty$ is a zero of $w(z)$ of order μ, the derivative has a zero of order $\mu + 1$ at $z = \infty$.

The inversion $\zeta = 1/z$ transforms $w(z)$ into the function $w(1/\zeta)$, which has a zero of order μ at the point $\zeta = 0$. This function maps a neighborhood of the point $\zeta = 0$ either onto a schlicht neighborhood of the point $w = 0$

(if $\mu = 1$) or onto a μ-sheeted Riemann surface with a branch point of order $\mu - 1$ at $w = 0$ (if $\mu > 1$). Thus the original function $w(z)$ maps the neighborhood of the point $z = \infty$ in a corresponding manner.

9.31. Riemann's Formula

There exists a remarkable connection between the number of sheets of the Riemann surface R_w of a rational function $w(z)$ and the number of its branch points. We now examine this connection.

We assume, as above, that the point $z = \infty$ is a zero of $w(z)$ of order μ_∞ $(1 \leqq \mu_\infty \leqq n)$.

As we saw in the last section, the derivative $w'(z)$ has exactly the same poles as $w(z)$, and a pole $z = \beta \neq \infty$ of $w(z)$ of order ν is a pole of $w'(z)$ of order $\nu + 1$. Each such pole corresponds to a branch point of order $\nu - 1$ of the Riemann surface R_w at the point $w = \infty$. The sum of the orders of the poles of $w'(z)$ is given by

$$N = \sum (\nu + 1) = 2 \sum \nu - \sum (\nu - 1) = 2n - \sum (\nu - 1), \qquad (9.56)$$

where the sum is extended over all the poles; it is equal to the order of the derivative $w'(z)$. The last term $\sum (\nu - 1)$ is the sum of the orders of branch points of the Riemann surface R_w over the point $w = \infty$.

Since $w'(z)$ is of order N, the sum of the orders of its zeros is also equal to N. If $z = \alpha \neq \infty$ is a zero of order μ of $w(z)$ and if $w(\alpha) \neq \infty$, then $z = \alpha$ is a zero of $w'(z)$ of order $\mu - 1$. The sum of the orders of these zeros,

$$\sum (\mu - 1),$$

is the sum of the orders of the *finite* branch points of R_w corresponding to finite points of the z-plane.

The derivative $w'(z)$ also has a zero of order $\mu_\infty + 1$ at the point $z = \infty$. This corresponds to a branch point of the surface R_w (over the point $w = 0$) of order $\mu_\infty - 1$. Hence, the total number of zeros of the derivative (each zero counted according to multiplicity) is

$$N = \sum (\mu - 1) + \mu_\infty + 1 = \sum (\mu - 1) + (\mu_\infty - 1) + 2. \qquad (9.57)$$

Comparing the values (9.56) and (9.57), we obtain

$$2n - 2 = \sum (\mu - 1) + \sum (\nu - 1) + (\mu_\infty - 1).$$

The sum of the orders $r - 1$ of all the branch points is therefore

$$\sum (r - 1) = 2n - 2. \qquad (9.58)$$

This is *Riemann's formula*.

This result we derived under the assumption that the point $z = \infty$ is a zero of $w(z)$. As we have seen in Section 9.30, this assumption does not result in any loss of generality, so that (9.58) is valid in general.

EXERCISES ON CHAPTER 9

1. Derive the expression (9.6) for $w'(z)$ $(n = 1)$ directly by applying the definition of the derivative to the expression (9.1) and prove the continuity of $w'(z)$, by using the definition of continuity.

2. Derive the formula (9.6) for the derivative $w^{(n)}(z)$ of an analytic function $w(z)$ directly from Cauchy's integral formula by applying the theorem on the differentiation of parametric integrals (cf. Section 9.7).

3. Prove that the power-series expansions of the functions arc tan z and arc sin z are valid in the disk $|z| < 1$.

4. Starting from the power-series expansion of the derivative of $\log (z + \sqrt{a^2 + z^2})$ $(a \neq 0)$, expand the function into a power series in z (take that branch of $\sqrt{a^2 + z^2}$ which is equal to a at $z = 0$, and take the principal value of the logarithm). Where is the expansion valid?

5. Let the boundary of the domain G be a rectifiable Jordan curve γ, and let the function $\psi(\zeta)$ be continuous on γ. By Section 9.6, the function $w(z)$ defined by the formula (9.7) is analytic in the domain G. Show that if G is the unit disk $|z| < 1$, γ its boundary $|z| = 1$ and $\psi(\zeta) = 1/\zeta$, then $w(z)$ does not tend to $\psi(\zeta)$ as $z \to \zeta \in \gamma$.

6. Suppose that the function $w(z)$ is continuous in a simply connected domain G and that $\int_\gamma w(z)\, dz = 0$ for every closed curve γ in G. Prove that $w(z)$ is analytic in G. (*Morera's theorem.*)

Hint. It follows from the assumption that $w(z)$ has a single-valued primitive function $W(z)$ in the domain G. Its derivative $w(z)$ is analytic.

Thus we have established that the analyticity of $w(z)$ is a necessary condition for the integrability condition (8.17) (cf. Section 8.11).

7. Prove Liouville's theorem by using Cauchy's integral formula to show that the derivative of the function in question vanishes identically.

8. Prove the fundamental theorem of algebra by applying Liouville's theorem to the reciprocal of the polynomial.

9. Let $f(x)$ be a continuous real function in the interval $\alpha \leq x \leq \beta$ and let $f(x) \geq 0$. Show that if

$$\int_\alpha^\beta f(x)\, dx = 0,$$

then $f(x) \equiv 0$ in the whole interval $\alpha \leq x \leq \beta$.

10. An analytic function $w(z)$ whose modulus $|w(z)|$ is constant in a domain G is itself constant.

Hint. From the assumption $u^2 + v^2 = \text{const.}$ $(w = u + iv)$ it follows that $uu_x + vv_x = uu_y + vv_y = 0$, and from the Cauchy-Riemann differential equations that $(u^2 + v^2)(u_x^2 + u_y^2) = 0$. If $w(z) \not\equiv 0$, then $u = v = 0$ holds only at individual points, so that $u_x = u_y = 0$ must hold everywhere and therefore also $v_x = v_y = 0$.

11. Let $w(z)$ be analytic for $|z| < 1$, with $|w(z)| \leq 1$ and $w(0) = 0$. Show that $|w'(0)| \leq 1$. When does equality hold?

12. Prove the following generalization of Schwarz's lemma: If $w(z)$ is analytic and $|w| \leq 1$ for $|z| < 1$, then

$$\frac{|w(0)| - |z|}{1 - |w(0)| \, |z|} \leq |w(z)| \leq \frac{|w(0)| + |z|}{1 + |w(0)| \, |z|}.$$

13. The functions $f(z)$ and $g(z)$ have poles of orders m and n, respectively, at the point $z = a$. What can one say about the functions $f(z) + g(z)$, $f(z)g(z)$, and $f(z)/g(z)$ at this point?

14. Prove the theorem of Weierstrass when the essential singularity is at infinity (cf. Section 9.21).

15. Investigate the zeros and singularities of the function $e^{-1/z^2} \sin (1/z)$.

16. Let the function $w(z)$ be analytic on the closed domain $R \leq |z| \leq \infty$. Show that

$$w(z) - w(\infty) = -\frac{1}{2\pi i} \int_\gamma \frac{w(\zeta)}{\zeta - z} \, d\zeta \qquad (|z| > R),$$

where γ denotes the circle $|z| = R$.

17. Prove the maximum principle by using the fact that an analytic function maps a domain onto a domain (cf. Section 9.27).

18. Show that in formula (9.55) $\epsilon_1(z) \to 0$ as $z \to 0$.

19. Investigate the mapping effected by the function

$$w = \frac{z^4 + 2z^2 + 1}{z^4 - 2z^2 + 1}.$$

20. Investigate the mapping by the function $w = z^3 + 3z$.

21. A triangle with three right angles bounded by congruent circular arcs in the z-plane is mapped conformally onto the unit disk of the w-plane in such a way that the center O of the triangle is mapped into the center of the disk and the vertices are mapped into the points: $w = 1$, $w = -\frac{1}{2} \pm i\sqrt{3}/2$. Show that the whole z-plane is mapped onto a 4-sheeted Riemann surface and examine precisely the correspondence between this surface and the z-plane.

Solution. Assuming that O is the origin, that the distance of the centers of the boundary arcs from O is one, and that the straight line determined by O and one of these centers is the positive real axis, then the mapping function has the form

$$w = \frac{4z(1 - z^3)}{1 + 8z^3}.$$

CHAPTER 10

THE RESIDUE
THEOREM AND ITS APPLICATIONS

§1. THE RESIDUE THEOREM

10.1. Formulation of the Problem

This chapter is devoted to an important generalization of Cauchy's theorem.

We consider an analytic function $w(z)$ which is single-valued in a simply connected domain G of the finite z-plane and which is regular there except for a finite number of singularities $z = z_\nu$ $(\nu = 1, \ldots, n)$. Let γ be a continuous, oriented, closed path lying entirely in G and not passing through any of the points $z_1, \ldots, z_n$. We wish to evaluate the integral

$$\int_\gamma w(z) \, dz. \tag{10.1}$$

10.2. Derivation of the Residue Theorem

In order to evaluate the integral (10.1) we expand $w(z)$ into a Laurent series in the neighborhood of $z = z_1$:

$$w(z) = f_1(z) + g_1(z),$$

where

$$f_1(z) = a_0 + a_1(z - z_1) + \cdots$$

is regular in a disk $|z - z_1| \leq r_1$ lying in the domain G and

$$g_1(z) = \frac{a_{-1}}{z - z_1} + \frac{a_{-2}}{(z - z_1)^2} + \cdots \tag{10.2}$$

is regular everywhere except at $z = z_1$.

Similarly, we form in the neighborhood of each of the remaining points $z_2, \ldots, z_n$ the Laurent expansions

$$w(z) = f_\nu(z) + g_\nu(z) \qquad (\nu = 2, \ldots, n).$$

The difference

$$F(z) = w(z) - \sum_{\nu=1}^{n} g_\nu(z)$$

167

is regular in the whole domain G. Since this domain is simply connected, it follows from Cauchy's theorem that

$$0 = \int_\gamma F(z)\, dz = \int_\gamma w(z)\, dz - \sum_1^n \int_\gamma g_\nu(z)\, dz.$$

However, the series (10.2) for $g_1(z)$ converges uniformly on the curve γ. Therefore we can compute its integral by term-by-term integration of the expansion (10.2). For all $m \geqq 2$ we have

$$\int_\gamma \frac{dz}{(z - z_1)^m} = \frac{1}{1 - m} \int_\gamma d\left(\frac{1}{z - z_1}\right)^{m-1} = 0.$$

For the integral of the first term of the series we obtain

$$a_{-1} \int_\gamma \frac{dz}{z - z_1} = a_{-1} \cdot 2\pi i u_{z_1},$$

where u_{z_1} is the winding number of the path γ with respect to z_1. The coefficient a_{-1} of the power $(z - z_1)^{-1}$ in the Laurent expansion of $w(z)$ appears as a factor, and this factor is called the *residue of the function $w(z)$ at the point* $z = z_1$. Henceforth it will be denoted by $R_{z_1} = a_{-1}$. By repeating the process of evaluating the integrals of the functions g_ν ($\nu = 2, \ldots, n$), we obtain the residue theorem.

> Let $w(z)$ be single-valued and analytic in a simply connected domain G *except at the points* $z_1, \ldots, z_n$. *If γ is a closed path in G not passing through the singularities* $z_1, \ldots, z_n$, *then*
>
> $$\frac{1}{2\pi i} \int_\gamma w(z)\, dz = \sum_{\nu=1}^n u_{z_\nu} R_{z_\nu},$$
>
> *where u_{z_ν} is the winding number of γ with respect to z_ν and R_{z_ν} is the residue of $w(z)$ at z_ν.*

This theorem contains Cauchy's integral formula as a special case. To show this we assume that $f(z)$ is regular in the whole domain G. Then for $a \in G$ the function

$$w(z) = \frac{f(z)}{z - a}$$

is regular in G except at the point $z = a$, where its residue is $f(a)$. Thus, by the residue theorem

$$\frac{1}{2\pi i} \int_\gamma \frac{f(z)}{z - a}\, dz = u_a f(a),$$

which is Cauchy's integral formula.

§2. APPLICATION OF THE RESIDUE
THEOREM TO THE EVALUATION OF DEFINITE INTEGRALS

10.3.

We shall show through some examples how the residue theorem can be applied to the evaluation of definite integrals. First we shall verify by this method the elementary identity

$$\int_{-\infty}^{+\infty} \frac{dx}{1 + x^2} = \pi. \tag{10.3}$$

The analytic function

$$w(z) = \frac{1}{1 + z^2}$$

is regular everywhere except at the points $z = \pm i$. From its partial-fraction expansion

$$w(z) = \frac{1}{2i} \left(\frac{1}{z - i} - \frac{1}{z + i} \right)$$

we see that the residue R_i at the point i is $1/2i$. We now draw a circle of radius $R > 1$ about the origin and integrate the function $w(z)$ along the curve consisting of the semicircle K_R which lies in the half-plane Im $z > 0$ together with the segment $(-R, R)$ of the real axis. The winding number of γ with respect to i is 1, with respect to $-i$ is 0. Hence, by the residue theorem,

$$\int_\gamma \frac{dz}{1 + z^2} = 2\pi i R_i = \pi. \tag{10.4}$$

We now split the integral into two parts

$$\int_\gamma \frac{dz}{1 + z^2} = \int_{-R}^{R} \frac{dz}{1 + z^2} + \int_{K_R} \frac{dz}{1 + z^2}$$

and let R tend to infinity. The first integral tends to the integral (10.3) to be evaluated, while the second integral tends to zero, since

$$\left| \int_{K_R} \frac{dz}{1 + z^2} \right| \leq \frac{\pi R}{R^2 - 1} \to 0 \quad \text{as} \quad R \to \infty.$$

The formula (10.3) is therefore established.

10.4.

As a second example, we evaluate the integral

$$\int_0^\infty \frac{x^{\lambda-1}}{1 + x} dx,$$

where λ is a real parameter in the interval $0 < \lambda < 1$; this implies the convergence of the integral. We consider the complex function

$$w(z) = \frac{z^{\lambda-1}}{1+z}.$$

Each branch of $w(z)$ is single-valued in the plane slit along the positive real axis. We select that branch which is real on the upper edge of the slit. We

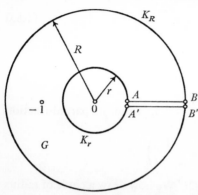

Figure 32

integrate $w(z)$ along the curve γ consisting of the circles K_R: $|z| = R > 1$, K_r: $|z| = r < 1$, and the two segments AB and $B'A'$ which form the two edges of the slit along the real axis (Figure 32). The curve γ is so oriented that K_R is traversed in the positive direction relative to its interior.

   The only singularity of the function $w(z)$ in G is at the point $z = -1$. The residue at this point is the value of the function

$$z^{\lambda-1} = e^{(\lambda-1)\log z}$$

at the point $z = -1$. Here we must choose that branch of the logarithm which is real on the segment AB. Therefore the residue of the function at the point $z = -1$ is

$$R_{-1} = (-1)^{\lambda-1} = e^{(\lambda-1)\pi i} = e^{\lambda\pi i} e^{-\pi i} = -e^{\lambda\pi i}.$$

The winding number of γ with respect to $z = -1$ is 1. Hence, by the residue theorem,

$$\int_\gamma \frac{z^{\lambda-1}}{1+z}\, dz = -2\pi i\, e^{\lambda\pi i}. \tag{10.5}$$

We split the integral (10.5) into four parts:

$$\int_\gamma = \int_{AB} + \int_{K_R} + \int_{B'A'} + \int_{K_r^{-1}}. \tag{10.6}$$

For the second integral on the right-hand side we obtain the estimate

$$\left| \int_{K_R} \frac{z^{\lambda-1}}{1+z}\, dz \right| \leq \frac{2\pi R^\lambda}{R-1}. \tag{10.7}$$

Since λ is less than 1, this expression tends to zero as $R \to \infty$.

   The last integral in (10.6) can be estimated in a similar way:

$$\left| \int_{K_r^{-1}} \frac{z^{\lambda-1}}{1+z}\, dz \right| \leq \frac{2\pi r^\lambda}{1-r}. \tag{10.8}$$

Since λ is positive this integral also tends to zero as $r \to 0$.

The integrals

$$\int_{AB} w(z)\, dz \quad \text{and} \quad \int_{B'A'} w(z)\, dz = -\int_{A'B'} w(z)\, dz$$

on the right-hand side of (10.6) do not cancel, since $w(z)$ has different values on the two edges of the slit. In the first integral $z^{\lambda-1}$ is real, and we can write

$$\int_{AB} \frac{z^{\lambda-1}}{1+z}\, dz = \int_r^R \frac{x^{\lambda-1}}{1+x}\, dx. \tag{10.9}$$

On the other hand, $\arg z = 2\pi$ on the segment $A'B'$ and hence we have

$$z^{\lambda-1} = e^{(\lambda-1)\log z} = e^{(\lambda-1)(\log x + 2\pi i)} = x^{\lambda-1} e^{(\lambda-1)2\pi i} = x^{\lambda-1} e^{2\pi i\lambda},$$

where $z = x + iy$. Thus, for the third integral on the right-hand side of (10.6) we obtain the expression

$$\int_{B'A'} \frac{z^{\lambda-1}}{1+z}\, dz = -e^{2\pi i\lambda} \int_r^R \frac{x^{\lambda-1}}{1+x}\, dx,$$

from which it follows that

$$\int_{AB} + \int_{B'A'} = (1 - e^{2\pi i\lambda}) \int_r^R \frac{x^{\lambda-1}}{1+x}\, dx. \tag{10.10}$$

If we let R tend to infinity and r tend to zero, we obtain from (10.5)–(10.10) the result

$$\int_0^\infty \frac{x^{\lambda-1}}{1+x}\, dx = \frac{-2\pi i\, e^{\lambda\pi i}}{1 - e^{2\pi i\lambda}} = \pi \frac{2i}{e^{\lambda\pi i} - e^{-\lambda\pi i}} = \frac{\pi}{\sin\lambda\pi}.$$

This formula

$$\int_0^\infty \frac{x^{\lambda-1}}{1+x}\, dx = \frac{\pi}{\sin\lambda\pi} \qquad (0 < \lambda < 1) \tag{10.11}$$

is important in the theory of the Γ-function (Chapter 15).

10.5. Laplace Integrals

As a last example we shall evaluate the integrals

$$\int_{-\infty}^{+\infty} \frac{e^{ix}}{x - ia}\, dx \quad \text{and} \quad \int_{-\infty}^{+\infty} \frac{e^{ix}}{x + ia}\, dx, \tag{10.12}$$

where a is a positive real number and the integration is along the real axis. We integrate the analytic functions $e^{iz}/(z - ia)$ and $e^{iz}/(z + ia)$ over a path γ consisting of a semicircle K_R in the upper half-plane of radius $R > a$ with center at the origin and the segment $(-R, +R)$ of the real axis.

The function $e^{iz}/(z - ia)$ is regular everywhere except at the point $z = ia$.

The residue of the function at this point is $R_{ia} = e^{-a}$. Applying the residue theorem, we obtain

$$\int_{\gamma} \frac{e^{iz}}{z - ia} \, dz = 2\pi i \, e^{-a}. \tag{10.13}$$

Since the second function $e^{iz}/(z + ia)$ is regular everywhere in the half-plane $\text{Im } z \geqq 0$, we have

$$\int_{\gamma} \frac{e^{iz}}{z + ia} \, dz = 0. \tag{10.14}$$

We break the integral (10.13) into two parts:

$$\int_{\gamma} \frac{e^{iz}}{z - ia} \, dz = \int_{-R}^{+R} \frac{e^{ix}}{x - ia} \, dx + \int_{K_R} \frac{e^{iz}}{z - ia} \, dz, \tag{10.15}$$

and estimate the second integral by

$$\left| \int_{K_R} \frac{e^{iz}}{z - ia} \, dz \right| \leqq \frac{1}{R - a} \int_{K_R} |e^{iz}| \, |dz|.$$

If we substitute $z = R \, e^{i\phi}$, we obtain

$$\left| \int_{K_R} \frac{e^{iz}}{z - ia} \, dz \right| \leqq \frac{R}{R - a} \int_0^{\pi} e^{-R \sin \phi} \, d\phi = \frac{2R}{R - a} \int_0^{\pi/2} e^{-R \sin \phi} \, d\phi.$$

We choose a positive $\epsilon < \pi/2$ and write

$$\int_0^{\pi/2} e^{-R \sin \phi} \, d\phi = \int_0^{\epsilon} e^{-R \sin \phi} \, d\phi + \int_{\epsilon}^{\pi/2} e^{-R \sin \phi} \, d\phi.$$

We have, independently of R, that

$$0 < \int_0^{\epsilon} e^{-R \sin \phi} \, d\phi < \epsilon.$$

Since

$$0 < \int_{\epsilon}^{\pi/2} e^{-R \sin \phi} \, d\phi < e^{-R \sin \epsilon} \frac{\pi}{2} < \epsilon$$

for sufficiently large R, we obtain

$$\lim_{R \to \infty} \int_0^{\pi/2} e^{-R \sin \phi} \, d\phi = 0.$$

It now follows from (10.13) and (10.15) that

$$\int_{-\infty}^{+\infty} \frac{e^{ix}}{x - ia} \, dx = 2\pi i \, e^{-a}. \tag{10.16}$$

Starting from (10.14) we find in an analogous way that

$$\int_{-\infty}^{+\infty} \frac{e^{ix}}{x + ia} \, dx = 0. \tag{10.17}$$

By adding and subtracting formulae (10.16) and (10.17) and by decomposing the integrals into real and imaginary parts, we obtain the following formulas for the so-called *Laplace integrals*:

$$\int_{-\infty}^{+\infty} \frac{x \sin x}{x^2 + a^2}\, dx = \pi\, e^{-a}, \qquad \int_{-\infty}^{+\infty} \frac{a \cos x}{x^2 + a^2}\, dx = \pi\, e^{-a}. \qquad (10.18)$$

If we let $a \to 0$, we obtain from the first of these formulas that

$$\int_{-\infty}^{+\infty} \frac{\sin x}{x}\, dx = \pi,$$

since

$$\left| \int_{-\infty}^{+\infty} \frac{x \sin x}{x^2 + a^2}\, dx - \int_{-\infty}^{+\infty} \frac{\sin x}{x}\, dx \right| = \left| \int_{-\infty}^{+\infty} \frac{-a^2 \sin x}{x(x^2 + a^2)}\, dx \right|$$

$$\leq \int_{-\infty}^{+\infty} \frac{a^2}{x^2 + a^2}\, dx = \pi a,$$

and this tends to zero as $a \to 0$.

§3. THE PARTIAL-FRACTION EXPANSION OF cot πz

10.6.

Earlier we derived a partial-fraction decomposition for rational functions (Sections 2.12–2.13). The terms in this decomposition are of the form $c_{ik}/(z - a_i)^k$, where the numbers a_i are the poles of the function, the numbers k are positive integers, and the c_{ik} are constants. A corresponding representation holds in general for *meromorphic* functions (Section 6.4). Instead of proving this general result here, we shall restrict ourselves to discussing an important example, the function cot πz.

The function cot πz has period 1, and has simple poles at the points $z = \nu$ $(\nu = 0, \pm1, \ldots)$. We form the integral

$$\frac{1}{2\pi i} \int_K \frac{\cot \pi z}{z - a}\, dz,$$

where $a \neq \nu$ $(\nu = 0, \pm1, \ldots)$, and integrate over the circle K: $|z| = \rho_n = n + \frac{1}{2} > |a|$. In the interior of K the integrand has poles at the points $0, \pm1, \ldots, \pm n$ and at the point a whenever $a \neq \nu + \frac{1}{2}$ $(\nu = 0, \pm1, \ldots)$. The residue at the point $z = a$ is $R_a = \cot \pi a$. In the neighborhood of the point $z = \nu$ we have

$$\cot \pi z = \frac{\cos \pi z}{\sin \pi z} = \frac{\cos \pi \nu + [z - \nu]}{\pi \cos \pi \nu \cdot (z - \nu) + [(z - \nu)^2]} = \frac{1}{\pi(z - \nu)} + \mathfrak{P}(z - \nu)$$

and

$$\frac{1}{z - a} = \frac{1}{\nu - a} + [z - \nu],$$

so that

$$\frac{\cot \pi z}{z - a} = \frac{1}{\pi(v - a)} \frac{1}{z - v} + \mathfrak{P}(z - v).$$

Hence, the residue at the point $z = v$ is $R_v = 1/\pi(v - a)$, and by the residue theorem we have

$$\frac{1}{2\pi i} \int_K \frac{\cot \pi z}{z - a} \, dz = \cot \pi a + \frac{1}{\pi} \sum_{v=-n}^{n} \frac{1}{v - a}$$

$$= \cot \pi a - \frac{1}{\pi} \sum_{v=-n}^{n} \frac{1}{a - v}. \qquad (10.19)$$

This formula is also valid for $a = v + \frac{1}{2}$. In fact, in this case $\cot \pi a = 0$, and $z = a$ is not a pole of the integrand.

10.7.

We write the integral on the left-hand side of (10.19) as

$$\int_K \frac{\cot \pi z}{z - a} \, dz = \int_{K_1} \frac{\cot \pi z}{z - a} \, dz + \int_{K_2} \frac{\cot \pi z}{z - a} \, dz,$$

where K_1 and K_2 denote the upper and lower semicircles of K, respectively. In the last integral we substitute $z = -t$. If z describes the arc K_2 in the positive sense, then t describes the arc K_1 in the positive sense. Hence,

$$\int_K \frac{\cot \pi z}{z - a} \, dz = \int_{K_1} \frac{\cot \pi z}{z - a} \, dz - \int_{K_1} \frac{\cot \pi t}{t + a} \, dt = 2a \int_{K_1} \frac{\cot \pi z}{z^2 - a^2} \, dz. \qquad (10.20)$$

We now let n tend to ∞, whereby the radius ρ_n of K also tends to infinity, and show that the integral (10.20) tends to the limit zero. To estimate the function $\cot \pi z$ we exclude its poles by the disks $C_v: |z - v| < r < \frac{1}{2} \ (v = 0, \pm 1, \ldots)$. Since $\cot \pi z$ tends to $\pm i$ uniformly as $|\text{Im } z| \to \infty$, $|\cot \pi z|$ is bounded by a constant M in that part of the period strip lying outside the disk C_v. Because of the periodicity, $|\cot \pi z| < M$ everywhere outside the disks C_v. Hence, it follows that

$$\left| \int_{K_1} \frac{\cot \pi z}{z^2 - a^2} \, dz \right| \leq \frac{\pi M \rho_n}{\rho_n^2 - |a|^2}.$$

As $\rho_n \to \infty$ this expression tends to zero. Thus it follows from (10.19) that

$$\pi \cot \pi a = \lim_{n \to \infty} \sum_{v=-n}^{n} \frac{1}{a - v}. \qquad (10.21)$$

If we combine the terms which correspond to the values $\pm\nu$, we have

$$\frac{1}{a-\nu} + \frac{1}{a+\nu} = \frac{2a}{a^2-\nu^2} \qquad (\nu = 1, 2, \ldots).$$

Replacing a by z and writing the term which corresponds to $\nu = 0$ separately, we obtain from (10.21) the expansion

$$\pi \cot \pi z = \frac{1}{z} + \sum_{\nu=1}^{\infty} \frac{2z}{z^2 - \nu^2}. \qquad (10.22)$$

This series converges absolutely and uniformly on every compact set which does not contain any of the points $\pm 1, \pm 2, \ldots.$ The expansion (10.22) is valid for every $z \neq \nu$ $(\nu = 0, \pm 1, \ldots)$. It converges uniformly on an arbitrary compact set if we omit a finite number of terms, those which become infinite on the given set. When we approach one of the points $z = 0, \pm 1, \ldots$ both sides of (10.22) become infinite.

§4. THE ARGUMENT PRINCIPLE

10.8.

Suppose that the function $w = w(z)$ is single-valued and, apart from a finite number of poles $b_1, b_2, \ldots, b_n$, regular in a simply connected domain G. Suppose further that $w(z)$ has a finite number of zeros $a_1, a_2, \ldots, a_m$ in G, and that the orders of the poles are $\nu_1, \nu_2, \ldots, \nu_n$ and the orders of the zeros are $\mu_1, \mu_2, \ldots, \mu_m$.

Let us apply the residue theorem to the logarithmic derivative

$$f(z) = \frac{d \log w(z)}{dz} = \frac{w'(z)}{w(z)}$$

of the function $w(z)$; $f(z)$ is regular in the domain G, except at the points a_i $(i = 1, \ldots, m)$ and b_i $(i = 1, \ldots, n)$. In the neighborhood of a zero a_i, $w(z)$ has the expansion

$$w(z) = A_{\mu_i}(z - a_i)^{\mu_i} + A_{\mu_i+1}(z - a_i)^{\mu_i+1} + \cdots \qquad (A_{\mu_i} \neq 0),$$

whence

$$w'(z) = \mu_i A_{\mu_i}(z - a_i)^{\mu_i-1} + [(z - a_i)^{\mu_i}].$$

Thus, for the function $f(z)$ we obtain the expression

$$f(z) = \frac{\mu_i + [z - a_i]}{(z - a_i)\{1 + [z - a_i]\}} = \frac{\mu_i}{z - a_i} + \mathfrak{P}(z - a_i).$$

Hence, the function $f(z)$ has a simple pole with residue $R_{a_i} = \mu_i$ at the point a_i. Similarly, in the neighborhood of a pole b_i of $w(z)$ we have

$$w(z) = \frac{B_{-\nu_i}}{(z - b_i)^{\nu_i}} + \cdots + B_0 + B_1(z - b_i) + \cdots \qquad (B_{-\nu_i} \neq 0),$$

$$w'(z) = -\frac{\nu_i B_{-\nu_i}}{(z - b_i)^{\nu_i+1}} - \cdots - \frac{B_{-1}}{(z - b_i)^2} + B_1 + [z - b_i],$$

and, hence,

$$f(z) = \frac{-\dfrac{\nu_i}{z - b_i}\{1 + [z - b_i]\}}{1 + [z - b_i]} = -\frac{\nu_i}{z - b_i} + \mathfrak{P}(z - b_i).$$

Therefore the function $f(z)$ again has a simple pole with residue $-\nu_i$ at the point b_i.

The zeros $a_1, \ldots, a_m$ and the poles $b_1, \ldots, b_n$ of the function $w(z)$ are thus simple poles of the function $f(z) = w'(z)/w(z)$. The corresponding residues are $\mu_1, \ldots, \mu_m$ and $-\nu_1, \ldots, -\nu_n$, respectively.

If γ is an oriented closed path in G not passing through the points a_i and b_i, it follows from the residue theorem that

$$\int_\gamma \frac{w'(z)}{w(z)}\, dz = 2\pi i \left\{ \sum_{i=1}^m u_{a_i}\mu_i - \sum_{i=1}^n u_{b_i}\nu_i \right\}. \qquad (10.23)$$

On the other hand,

$$\int_\gamma \frac{w'(z)}{w(z)}\, dz = \int_\gamma d\log w(z) = i\Delta_\gamma \arg w(z), \qquad (10.24)$$

where $\Delta_\gamma \arg w(z)$ is the increment of $\arg w(z)$ along the curve γ. It follows now from (10.23) and (10.24) that

$$\Delta_\gamma \arg w(z) = 2\pi \left\{ \sum_{i=1}^m u_{a_i}\mu_i - \sum_{i=1}^n u_{b_i}\nu_i \right\}. \qquad (10.25)$$

We have thus proved the *argument principle*:

Let the function $w(z)$ be analytic in a simply connected domain G, apart from a finite number of poles, and let $w(z)$ have at most a finite number of zeros in G. If γ is an oriented path in G not passing through any of the zeros or poles of $w(z)$, then the increment of $\arg w(z)$, as z describes the curve γ, is given by formula (10.25).

If the function $w(z)$ is regular everywhere in G, the second sum on the right-hand side of (10.25) vanishes.

If $w(z)$ has no zeros in G, the first sum on the right-hand side of (10.25) vanishes. For this special case we have the following theorem.

If $w(z)$ is regular and non-zero in a simply connected domain G, then the variation of the argument of $w(z)$ along a closed curve in G is zero.

In this simplest case the argument principle is still valid if it is assumed only that $w(z)$ is single-valued, continuous and non-zero in the domain G (Exercise 14, p. 183).

If the boundary of G is, in particular, a Jordan curve whose winding number is 1 with respect to every point of G,† we may formulate the argument principle in the following way.

If $w(z)$ is analytic, apart from a finite number of poles, in the closure of the domain G bounded by a simple closed Jordan curve γ and if $w \neq 0$, ∞ on γ, then the increment of the argument of w along γ is equal to the difference of the total number of zeros and the total number of poles G multiplied by 2π.

§5. APPLICATIONS OF THE ARGUMENT PRINCIPLE

10.9. The Fundamental Theorem of Algebra

As a first application we give a new proof of the fundamental theorem of algebra (cf. Sections 2.6 and 9.13). We write the polynomial

$$P(z) = a_0 z^n + a_1 z^{n-1} + \cdots + a_n \qquad (n \geq 1, a_0 \neq 0) \qquad (10.26)$$

in the form

$$P(z) = a_0 z^n \{1 + f(z)\}, \qquad (10.27)$$

where

$$f(z) = \frac{a_1}{a_0} \frac{1}{z} + \frac{a_2}{a_0} \frac{1}{z^2} + \cdots + \frac{a_n}{a_0} \frac{1}{z^n}$$

tends to zero as $z \to \infty$. Therefore there exists an $R > 0$ such that

$$|f(z)| < 1 \qquad \text{for} \qquad |z| \geq R. \qquad (10.28)$$

Since, in view of (10.27) and (10.28), $P(z) \neq 0$ outside and on the circle K_R: $|z| = R$, all the zeros of $P(z)$ (if any) lie in the interior of K_R. By the argument principle, the number of zeros of $P(z)$ multiplied by 2π is equal to $\Delta_{K_R} \arg P(z)$, since the winding number of K_R with respect to each zero is 1. We can calculate the expression $\Delta_{K_R} \arg P(z)$ by using (10.27):

$$\Delta_{K_R} \arg P(z) = \Delta_{K_R} \arg z^n + \Delta_{K_R} \arg \{1 + f(z)\}$$
$$= n \cdot 2\pi + \Delta_{K_R} \arg \{1 + f(z)\}.$$

From (10.28) it follows that the point $\zeta = 1 + f(z)$ lies in the disk $|\zeta - 1| < 1$. As z describes K_R, ζ describes a closed curve in the disk $|\zeta - 1| < 1$. The

---

† We may restrict ourselves to the assumption that G is bounded and that its boundary is a positively oriented Jordan curve (cf. Section 10.11).

increment of its argument is therefore a multiple of 2π. On the other hand, since arg ζ is restricted to lie between $-\pi/2$ and $+\pi/2$, the increment can only be zero,

$$\Delta_{K_R} \arg \{1 + f(z)\} = 0,$$

whence $\Delta_{K_R} \arg P(z) = n \cdot 2\pi$ (cf. Section 9.25). Therefore, the total number of zeros of $P(z)$ is equal to n. We have thus proved the following sharper form of the fundamental theorem of algebra.

Every polynomial of degree n has n zeros (where each zero is counted according to multiplicity).

10.10. Rouché's Theorem

We make the following assumptions:

1) *The domain G is bounded by a Jordan curve γ, whose winding number is 1 with respect to every point of G (cf. footnote on p. 177).*
2) *$w(z)$ and $f(z)$ are analytic in G and on its boundary.*
3) *$|w(z) - f(z)| < |f(z)|$ on γ.*

Then the functions $w(z)$ and $f(z)$ have the same number of zeros in G (where the zeros are counted according to multiplicity).

Proof. It follows from assumption (3) that $f(z) \neq 0$ and $w(z) \neq 0$ on the curve γ. Hence, we can apply the argument principle to the function

$$w(z) = f(z) + \{w(z) - f(z)\} = f(z) \left\{1 + \frac{w(z) - f(z)}{f(z)}\right\}.$$

The increment of the argument along γ is

$$\Delta_\gamma \arg w(z) = \Delta_\gamma \arg f(z) + \Delta_\gamma \arg \left\{1 + \frac{w(z) - f(z)}{f(z)}\right\}. \tag{10.29}$$

By assumption (3) the point $\zeta = 1 + (w(z) - f(z))/f(z)$ lies in the circle $|\zeta - 1| < 1$ for every $z \in \gamma$. It follows from this, exactly as in Section 10.9, that the last term in (10.29) is zero. Hence,

$$\Delta_\gamma \arg w(z) = \Delta_\gamma \arg f(z).$$

The result now follows from the argument principle.

10.11. The Jordan Curve Theorem

In employing assumption (1) of Rouché's theorem we assumed that the closed Jordan curve γ has winding number 1 relative to every point $z \in G$ in its interior. This is part of the content of the Jordan curve theorem.†

---

† We shall not prove this theorem here; for a proof, we refer the reader to textbooks on topology. See, for example, M. H. A. Newman, *Elements of the Topology of Plane Sets of Points*, 4th edition, Cambridge, 1961.

A Jordan curve γ separates the (finite) plane into two domains G_1 and G_2, both of which are bounded by γ. One of the domains, G_1, is bounded and the other, G_2, is unbounded.

The winding number of the curve γ is zero with respect to each point of G_2, and is 1 or -1 with respect to each point of G_1, depending on the direction in which γ is described. (We say that the orientation is positive in the first case and negative in the second; cf. Sections 3.8 and 8.12.)

The domain G_1 is simply connected.

10.12. The Inverse Function

With the help of Rouché's theorem, we shall now give a new proof of the inverse-function theorem (first proved in Section 9.24).

If the function $w = w(z)$ is regular in the neighborhood of a point z_0 and $w'(z_0) \neq 0$, then in a certain neighborhood of the point $w_0 = w(z_0)$ one can define z as a single-valued function of w, $z = z(w)$, $w\big(z(w)\big) \equiv w$.

By assumption we have

$$w(z) - w_0 = (z - z_0) f(z),$$

where $f(z_0) \neq 0, \infty$. Since z_0 cannot be a limit point of zeros of $w(z) - w_0$, there exists a number $\rho_z > 0$ such that

$$w(z) \neq w_0 \qquad \text{for} \qquad 0 < |z - z_0| \leq \rho_z.$$

Therefore, $|w(z) - w_0|$ has a positive minimum on the circle $|z - z_0| = \rho_z$. Let

$$0 < \rho_w < \min_{|z - z_0| = \rho_z} |w(z) - w_0|. \tag{10.30}$$

We shall now show that the function $w(z)$ assumes exactly once in the disk $|z - z_0| < \rho_z$ every value w_1 in the disk $|w_1 - w_0| < \rho_w$. To show this, we apply Rouché's theorem to the functions $w(z) - w_1$ and $w(z) - w_0$. In view of (10.30), the assumptions of that theorem are fulfilled, since $|w_1 - w_0| < \rho_w$. In this way we conclude that in the disk $|z - z_0| < \rho_z$ the function $w(z) - w_1$ assumes the value 0 exactly as many times as the function $w(z) - w_0$ does, that is, exactly once. This proves the theorem.

10.13. A Theorem on the Conformal
Mapping of Domains Bounded by Jordan Curves

As a further application of the argument principle we shall prove the following theorem:

Suppose that the domains G_z and G_w are bounded by Jordan curves γ_z and γ_w. If $w(z)$ is analytic on the closed domain $G_z \cup \gamma_z$ and maps the curve γ_z in a one-to-one manner onto the curve γ_w, then $w(z)$ maps the domain G_z one-to-one conformally onto the domain G_w.

Proof. Let z_1 be an arbitrary point in G_z. Its image $w_1 = w(z_1)$ cannot lie on γ_w, since the points of γ_z and γ_w are in one-to-one correspondence. The function

$$f(z) = \frac{w(z) - w_1}{z - z_1}$$

does not vanish on γ_z and is regular everywhere in G_z, except possibly at z_1. If we set

$$f(z_1) = \lim_{z \to z_1} \frac{w(z) - w_1}{z - z_1} = w'(z_1),$$

then $f(z)$ will be regular at z_1. By the argument principle we have

$$\Delta_{\gamma_z} \arg f(z) = \Delta_{\gamma_z} \arg (w(z) - w_1) - \Delta_{\gamma_z} \arg (z - z_1)$$
$$= n \cdot 2\pi \geqq 0, \tag{10.31}$$

where n is the total number of zeros of $f(z)$ in G_z. If z makes a complete circuit of γ_z in the positive direction, then, by assumption (cf. Section 10.11),

$$\Delta_{\gamma_z} \arg (z - z_1) = 2\pi,$$

whence it follows from (10.31) that

$$\Delta_{\gamma_z} \arg (w(z) - w_1) \geqq 2\pi. \tag{10.32}$$

On the other hand, if z describes the curve γ_z once, the point w describes the curve γ_w once, so that, by Section 10.11, the left-hand side of (10.32) is less than or equal to 2π. Hence,

$$\Delta_{\gamma_z} \arg (w(z) - w_1) = 2\pi.$$

By Section 10.11 the point w_1 lies in G_w and the positive orientation on γ_z corresponds to the positive orientation on γ_w, and vice versa.

In order to show, conversely, that to each point w_1 in G_w corresponds a well-defined point of G_z, we start from the equation

$$\Delta_{\gamma_w} \arg (w - w_1) = 2\pi.$$

If w makes a circuit of the curve γ_w, z describes the curve γ_z in the same direction. Therefore

$$\Delta_{\gamma_z} \arg (w(z) - w_1) = 2\pi.$$

It follows from the argument principle that $w(z)$ assumes the value w_1 at one and only one point of the domain G_z. The one-to-one character of the mapping is thereby proved.

Since the mapping is one-to-one, we have

$$w'(z) \neq 0 \tag{10.33}$$

in the entire domain G_z. For otherwise, if there were a point z_0 in G_z such that $w'(z_0) = 0$, the function $w(z)$ would assume at least twice in a neighborhood of z_0 certain values in a neighborhood of $w(z_0)$. It follows from (10.33) that the mapping is conformal at each point of G_z.

If we make a linear transformation of the z-plane or w-plane which takes a point of γ_z or γ_w to the point ∞, these results can be extended to the case that at least one of γ_z and γ_w passes through the point ∞.

EXERCISES ON CHAPTER 10

1. The function arc tan z can be defined by the integral.

$$\text{arc tan } z = \int_0^z \frac{dz}{1 + z^2}.$$

Using this definition discuss the properties of the function: its multi-valued character and modules of periodicity, singularities, and limiting values as $z \to \pm i$.

2. Using the residue theorem evaluate the following integrals:

a)
$$\int_\gamma \frac{e^z}{z}\, dz,$$

where γ is the circle $|z| = 1$,

b)
$$\int_\gamma \tan \pi z\, dz,$$

where γ is the circle $|z| = n$ and n is a positive integer.

3. Evaluate the integral

$$\int_\gamma \frac{e^{iz}}{z}\, dz,$$

where γ is the curve consisting of the semicircles $|z| = R$, $\text{Im } z > 0$ and $|z| = r$ $(< R)$, $\text{Im } z > 0$, together with the segments $r \leqq z \leqq R$ and $-R \leqq z \leqq -r$. Let $R \to \infty$ and $r \to 0$, and find the value of

$$\int_0^\infty \frac{\sin x}{x}\, dx.$$

4. By using the well-known formula of integral calculus,

$$\int_0^\infty e^{-x^2}\, dx = \frac{\sqrt{\pi}}{2},$$

evaluate the so-called *Fresnel integrals*

$$\int_0^\infty \cos x^2\, dx = \int_0^\infty \sin x^2\, dx = \frac{1}{2\sqrt{2}}\sqrt{\pi}.$$

Hint. Integrate the function e^{-z^2} along a closed curve consisting of the two segments joining the origin to the points R and $R\,e^{i\pi/4}$ and of the minor arc of the circle $|z| = R$ between these points. Then let R tend to infinity.

5. Derive the formula

$$\int_{-\infty}^{+\infty} \frac{dx}{(1 + x^2)^{n+1}} = \frac{1 \cdot 3 \cdot 5 \cdots (2n - 1)}{2 \cdot 4 \cdot 6 \cdots (2n)} \qquad (n \geq 1).$$

6. Derive the formula

$$\int_0^\infty \frac{\cos mx}{1 + x^2}\, dx = \frac{\pi}{2}\, e^{-m} \qquad (m > 0).$$

7. Evaluate the integral

$$\int_{-\infty}^{+\infty} \frac{\cos x\, dx}{(x^2 + 1)(x^2 + 4)}.$$

Answer.

$$\frac{\pi}{6}\, \frac{2e - 1}{e^2}.$$

8. Let the functions $f(z)$ and $w(z)$ be analytic in the simply connected domain G, and let $w(z)$ have in G the zeros $a_1, a_2, \ldots, a_n$ (a zero of order ν is written ν times). Let γ be a closed curve in G not passing through the points a_ν ($\nu = 1, 2, \ldots, n$). Derive the formula

$$\int_\gamma f(z)\, \frac{w'(z)}{w(z)}\, dz = 2\pi i \sum_{\nu=1}^n u_{a_\nu} f(a_\nu),$$

where u_{a_ν} is the winding number of γ with respect to a_ν ($\nu = 1, 2, \ldots, n$). What happens to this formula if $f(z)$ has a finite number of poles in G?

9. Apply the formula derived in Exercise 8 to calculate

$$\sum_{\nu=1}^\infty \frac{1}{\nu^{2k}} \quad \text{for} \quad \text{a) } k = 1, \quad \text{b) } k = 2.$$

Answers.

$$\text{a) } \frac{\pi^2}{6}, \quad \text{b) } \frac{\pi^4}{90}.$$

10. Generalize the preceding exercise to an arbitrary positive integer k.

Hint. The exercise leads to the *Bernoulli numbers* B_k which are defined by the following recursion formula:

$$-\frac{1}{2}(2k - 1) + \binom{2k + 1}{2} B_1 - \binom{2k + 1}{4} B_2 + \cdots$$

$$+ (-1)^{k+1} \binom{2k + 1}{2k} B_k = 0 \qquad (k = 1, 2, \ldots).$$

11. Prove that the partial-fraction expansion (10.22) of the function $\pi \cot \pi z$ converges uniformly on every compact set that does not contain any of the points $z = n$ $(n = 0, \pm1, \pm2, \ldots)$.

12. Using the partial-fraction expansion of $\cot \pi z$, evaluate

$$\sum_{n=0}^{\infty} \frac{1}{n^2 + 1}.$$

13. Expand the function $1/\sin^2 \pi z$ into partial fractions.

14. Prove the argument principle in the following form: If the function $w(z)$ is single-valued, continuous, and non-zero on a Jordan curve γ and in its interior, then

$$\Delta_\gamma \arg w(z) = 0.$$

Hint. Partition the interior G of γ into subdomains G_ν $(\nu = 1, 2, \ldots, n)$ and show that $\Delta \arg w(z) = 0$ along the boundary of each G_ν $(\nu = 1, \ldots, n)$ whenever the partition is sufficiently fine.

15. Find the image of the half-plane $\operatorname{Im} z > 0$ under the mapping $w = z + k \log z$, where k is a positive constant.

16. Let the analytic function $w(z)$ map a domain G_z one-to-one conformally onto a domain G_w; both domains have a well-defined area. Show that the area A of G_w is given by the double integral

$$A = \iint_{G_z} |w'(z)|^2 \, dx \, dy.$$

17. *The Bieberbach area theorem.* If

$$w(z) = \sum_{n=0}^{\infty} c_n z^n$$

is analytic and schlicht in the disk $|z| \leq r$, then the area of the image domain is given by

$$A = \pi \sum_{n=1}^{\infty} n|c_n|^2 r^{2n}.$$

Hint. Apply the formula given in Exercise 16 and use polar coordinates.

18. In addition to the assumptions made in the preceding exercise we assume that $w'(0) = 1$. Show that the area of the image domain is then greater than or equal to the area of the disk $|z| \leq r$. Under what condition does equality hold?

19. Suppose that $w(z)$ is analytic in a domain G, that γ_z is a piecewise regular curve in G, and that $w'(z) \neq 0$ for $z \in \gamma_z$. Show that the length of the image curve γ_w of γ_z is

$$L = \int_{\gamma_z} |w'(z)| \, |dz|.$$

7

CHAPTER 11

HARMONIC FUNCTIONS

§1. PRELIMINARY CONSIDERATIONS

11.1. Definition

The real and imaginary parts of an analytic function satisfy Laplace's differential equation (Section 1.14) and are therefore harmonic functions. In this chapter we shall treat the theory of these functions in detail. We make the following definition:

If a real function $u(x, y)$ of two real variables has differentiable partial derivatives u_x and u_y in a domain G and satisfies Laplace's differential equation

$$\Delta u \equiv \frac{\partial^2 u}{\partial x^2} + \frac{\partial^2 u}{\partial y^2} = 0, \tag{11.1}$$

then it is said to be harmonic in G.

In order to discuss rigorously the theory of harmonic functions, we shall first recall certain fundamental properties of real line integrals.

11.2. Integration of a Differential Form

In Chapter 8 we formulated the problem of determining the primitive function of an analytic function. This problem may be considered as a special case of the so-called fundamental problem of the integral calculus of functions of two real variables:

Let $M(x, y)$ and $N(x, y)$ be single-valued real functions defined in a domain G. Find all functions $f(x, y)$ which are single-valued in G and whose total differential is

$$df = M \, dx + N \, dy. \tag{11.2}$$

In particular, the statement that $f_x = M, f_y = N$ is contained in (11.2). We can solve this problem by the same method which we used earlier to find the primitive function of an analytic function. We shall proceed to do so, under the following assumption:

1) *The functions $M(x, y)$ and $N(x, y)$ are differentiable in the domain G.*

11.3. A Lemma

The solution of the foregoing problem depends on an important lemma concerning the line integral of the differential form $M\,dx + N\,dy$. Let Δ be a triangle $P_1P_2P_3$ which is contained in the domain G together with its (positively oriented) boundary $\partial\Delta = P_1P_2P_3P_1$, and let P_0 denote a point of this closed triangle. We shall discuss the integral

$$\int_{\partial\Delta} (M\,dx + N\,dy).$$

We denote the coordinates of P_ν (in a given cartesian coordinate system) by $x = x_\nu$, $y = y_\nu$ ($\nu = 0, 1, 2, 3$). Since $M(x, y)$ is differentiable in G, we have, in some neighborhood of (x_0, y_0),

$$M(x, y) = M(x_0, y_0) + M_x(x_0, y_0)(x - x_0) + M_y(x_0, y_0)(y - y_0) + r(r),$$

where $r = \sqrt{(x - x_0)^2 + (y - y_0)^2}$ and (r) is a number which tends to zero as $r \to 0$. We substitute this expression into the integral $\int M\,dx$. Since $M(x_0, y_0) + M_x(x_0, y_0)(x - x_0)$ is the derivative of the *single-valued* function $M(x_0, y_0)x + M_x(x_0, y_0)(x - x_0)^2/2$, that part of the integral corresponding to it vanishes over $\partial\Delta$.

To find the value of the integral

$$\int_{\partial\Delta} (y - y_0)\,dx$$

we write the equation of the segment P_1P_2 in the form

$$x = x_1 + \tau(x_2 - x_1), \qquad y = y_1 + \tau(y_2 - y_1) \qquad (0 \leq \tau \leq 1).$$

Since $dx = (x_2 - x_1)\,d\tau$, we obtain

$$\int_{P_1P_2} (y - y_0)\,dx = \tfrac{1}{2}(y_1 + y_2 - 2y_0)(x_2 - x_1).$$

The integrals over P_2P_3 and P_3P_1 are obtained by cyclic permutation. Adding these integrals, we obtain for the whole integral the value

$$\int_{\partial\Delta} (y - y_0)\,dx = -|\Delta| = -\frac{1}{2}\left(\begin{vmatrix} x_1 & x_2 \\ y_1 & y_2 \end{vmatrix} + \begin{vmatrix} x_2 & x_3 \\ y_2 & y_3 \end{vmatrix} + \begin{vmatrix} x_3 & x_1 \\ y_3 & y_1 \end{vmatrix} \right).$$

Taken with opposite sign, this expression represents the area $|\Delta|$ of the triangle Δ.

If $\max |(r)| = m$ on $\partial\Delta$, we can estimate the integral of the remainder term by

$$\left| \int_{\partial\Delta} r(r)\,dx \right| \leq \delta m \cdot 3\delta = \delta^2(\delta),$$

where δ is the length of the longest side of the triangle, and $(\delta) \to 0$ as $\delta \to 0$ (i.e., when the triangle shrinks to the fixed point P_0).

Altogether we have

$$\int_{\partial\Delta} M(x, y)\,dx = -M_y(x_0, y_0)|\Delta| + \delta^2(\delta).$$

In the same way we obtain

$$\int_{\partial \Delta} N(x, y) \, dy = N_x(x_0, y_0)|\Delta| + \delta^2(\delta),$$

where $(\delta) \to 0$ as $\delta \to 0$. We have thus proved the following result. If the functions $M(x, y)$ and $N(x, y)$ are differentiable in the domain G, then the line integral taken over the positively oriented boundary $\partial \Delta$ of a triangle $\Delta \subset G$ can be expressed by the formula

$$\int_{\partial \Delta} (M \, dx + N \, dy) = \big(N_x(x_0, y_0) - M_y(x_0, y_0)\big)|\Delta| + \delta^2(\delta), \quad (11.3)$$

where (x_0, y_0) is an arbitrary point of the domain G, Δ is a triangle $(\subset G)$ containing (x_0, y_0), and δ is the longest side of the triangle; further $(\delta) \to 0$ as the triangle Δ shrinks to the point (x_0, y_0) $(\delta \to 0)$.

One should note that in the proof of this lemma we have not used the full strength of condition (1), but only the following, weaker, condition.

The functions M and N are continuous in the domain G and differentiable at the point $(x_0, y_0) \in G$.

This condition implies the existence of the partial derivatives M_x, M_y, N_x, N_y at the point (x_0, y_0).

11.4. Interchangeability of the Order of Differentiation

Let us apply Eq. (11.3) to a function $f(x, y)$ which is single-valued in the domain G and whose partial derivatives f_x and f_y are continuous in G and differentiable at the point (x_0, y_0). If we write $f_x = M$, $f_y = N$, then $df = M \, dx + N \, dy$, with $M_y = f_{xy}$ and $N_x = f_{yx}$.

Then

$$\int_{\partial \Delta} (M \, dx + N \, dy) = \int_{\partial \Delta} df = f(x_1, y_1) - f(x_1, y_1) = 0$$

and we obtain from (11.3) that

$$f_{yx}(x_0, y_0) - f_{xy}(x_0, y_0) = \frac{\delta^2}{|\Delta|} (\delta).$$

If the triangle shrinks to the point (x_0, y_0) while retaining its shape, then $\delta^2/|\Delta|$ is a constant, δ tends to zero, and so does (δ). Thus the right-hand side of the last formula tends to zero and, hence, the constant on the left-hand side must be zero. Therefore,

$$f_{xy}(x_0, y_0) = f_{yx}(x_0, y_0). \quad (11.4)$$

This result contains the fundamental theorem of the differential calculus concerning the interchangeability of the order of differentiation. We have proved it under rather weak assumptions which differ from those upon which the usual† proofs of this theorem are based.

11.5. The Integrability Condition

We now return to the problem formulated in Section 11.2 and assume to begin with that

> 1) *The functions $M(x, y)$ and $N(x, y)$ are differentiable at every point of the domain G.*

If $f(x, y)$ is a solution of the problem, then $f_x = M$, $f_y = N$ in G, and hence, as we have shown in Section 11.4,

$$N_x(x, y) - M_y(x, y) = 0. \tag{11.5}$$

The vector (M, N), whose components are $f_x = M$, $f_y = N$, is the gradient, grad f, of the function f. The left-hand side of formula (11.5) is the *curl* or *rotation* of this vector:

$$\text{curl grad } f = \text{curl } (M, N) = N_x - M_y.$$

For the existence of the integral $f(x, y)$ in G it is thus necessary that

> 2) *The condition*
> $$\text{curl } (M, N) = N_x - M_y = 0$$
> *is satisfied at every point of G.*

11.6. Sufficiency of the Integrability Condition

We assume now that M and N satisfy the two conditions (1) and (2). If we assume, moreover, that G is *convex*, then the solution $f(x, y)$ can be constructed by the method of Goursat, which led us in Chapter 8 to the construction of the primitive function of an analytic function. In order to show this, we choose two arbitrary points (x_0, y_0) and (x_1, y_1) in G and join them by a straight-line segment; this segment lies in G. If we assume for a moment that $f(x, y)$ is a solution of our problem, then

$$f(x_1, y_1) = f(x_0, y_0) + \int_{(x_0, y_0)}^{(x_1, y_1)} df = f(x_0, y_0) + \int_{(x_0, y_0)}^{(x_1, y_1)} (M\, dx + N\, dy),$$

---

† If it is assumed that f_x and f_y are continuously differentiable at the point (x_0, y_0), then (11.4) is a simple consequence of the mean-value theorem. The so-called *Schwarz Theorem* contains the following refinement: If f_x, f_y, and f_{xy} are *continuous* at the point (x_0, y_0), then $f_{yx}(x_0, y_0)$ exists and is equal to $f_{xy}(x_0, y_0)$. Our derivation of (11.4), however, is based upon different assumptions: we assumed that the partial derivatives are differentiable at the point (x_0, y_0), but we have made no assumption about the continuity of the derivatives f_{xy} and f_{yx}.

where the path of integration is the segment joining the two points. From this it follows that for a given initial value $f(x_0, y_0)$ the problem *can have no other solution* than

$$C + \int_{(x_0, y_0)}^{(x, y)} (M\, dx + N\, dy),$$

where $C = f(x_0, y_0)$.

Conversely, we shall now prove that the *single-valued* function $f(x, y)$ defined by the integral

$$\int_{(x_0, y_0)}^{(x, y)} (M\, dx + N\, dy), \tag{11.6}$$

where the path of integration is the segment joining the points (x_0, y_0) and (x, y), is a solution of our problem.

First of all we shall show the following: If

$$\int_{\partial\Delta} (M\, dx + N\, dy) = 0 \tag{11.7}$$

for every triangle $\Delta \subset G$, then (11.6) is the solution of our problem.

Proof. If the points $P_\nu(x_\nu, y_\nu)$ $(\nu = 0, 1)$ are given, we apply (11.7) to the triangle $P_0 P_1 P P_0$, where the point $P \in G$ is chosen on the line parallel to the x-axis passing through P_1 $(P = (x_1 + \Delta x, y_1))$. By (11.7) we obtain for the increment of the function

$$f(x, y) = \int_{(x_0, y_0)}^{(x, y)} (M\, dx + N\, dy)$$

the expression

$$\Delta f = f(x_1 + \Delta x, y_1) - f(x_1, y_1)$$

$$= \int_{(x_0, y_0)}^{(x_1 + \Delta x, y_1)} - \int_{(x_0, y_0)}^{(x_1, y_1)} = \int_{(x_1, y_1)}^{(x_1 + \Delta x, y_1)}.$$

Here all integrals are taken over straight-line segments. The last integral, however, can be written as

$$\Delta f = \int_{(x_1, y_1)}^{(x_1 + \Delta x, y_1)} M(x, y_1)\, dx$$

$$= M(x_1, y_1)\Delta x + \int_{x_1}^{x_1 + \Delta x} (M(x, y_1) - M(x_1, y_1))\, dx$$

$$= M(x_1, y_1)\Delta x + \Delta x(\Delta x),$$

where (Δx) tends to zero as $\Delta x \to 0$. This expression shows that the partial derivative f_x of the function $f(x, y)$ at the point (x_1, y_1) is equal to $M(x_1, y_1)$.

In the same way one can show that $f_y(x_1, y_1) = N(x_1, y_1)$. However, since (x_1, y_1) is an arbitrary point of the domain G and since the functions M and N are assumed to be continuous, it follows that the differential of $f(x, y)$ is

$$df(x, y) = M(x, y)\, dx + N(x, y)\, dy,$$

which was to be proved.

Hence, if, in addition to the assumptions (1) and (2), (11.7) also holds, the desired integral $f(x, y)$ exists and is uniquely determined up to an additive constant $(C = f(x_0, y_0))$.

If the domain G is not convex, we may define the integral $f(x, y)$ first for a convex subdomain of G. Starting from this subdomain, we may continue $f(x, y)$ to the whole of G by means of chains of disks. If G is simply connected, then the integral $f(x, y)$ is single-valued in the whole domain (cf. Chapter 8, §4).

11.7. Goursat's Proof

It remains for us to show that (11.7) is in fact a consequence of the assumptions (1) and (2), in other words, that

$$I = \int_{\partial \Delta} (M\, dx + N\, dy) = 0$$

for the boundary $\partial \Delta$ of an arbitrary triangle $\Delta \subset G$. The proof is completely analogous to that given in Section 8.12. We divide the triangle Δ into four congruent subtriangles, on at least one of which the line integral will have a largest value; we choose one of these triangles and call it Δ_1. By repeating this process we obtain an infinite sequence of nested similar triangles $\Delta \supset \Delta_1 \supset \ldots \supset \Delta_n \supset \ldots$. If we set

$$I_n = \int_{\partial \Delta_n} (M\, dx + N\, dy) \qquad (n = 1, 2, \cdots),$$

we may conclude, as in Section 8.12, that

$$\frac{|I|}{|\Delta|} \leq \frac{|I_1|}{|\Delta_1|} \leq \cdots \leq \frac{|I_n|}{|\Delta_n|} \leq \cdots. \qquad (11.8)$$

The length $|\partial \Delta_n| = |\partial \Delta|/2^n$ of the boundary $\partial \Delta_n$ tends to zero as $n \to \infty$. The closed triangles Δ_n $(n = 1, 2, \ldots)$ converge to a well-defined limit point (x_0, y_0) which belongs to the closed triangle.

Since M and N satisfy conditions (1) and (2) (Section 11.5), it follows from (11.3) that

$$I_n = \int_{\partial \Delta_n} (M\, dx + N\, dy)$$
$$= (N_x(x_0, y_0) - M_y(x_0, y_0))|\Delta_n| + \delta_n^2(\delta_n) = \delta_n^2(\delta_n),$$

where δ_n is the longest side of the triangle Δ_n and $(\delta_n) \to 0$ as $\delta_n \to 0$ (i.e., as $n \to \infty$). From this it follows that

$$\frac{|I_n|}{|\Delta_n|} = \frac{\delta_n^2}{|\Delta_n|}(\delta_n) = \frac{\delta^2}{|\Delta|}(\delta_n).$$

From the inequalities (11.8) we now have that

$$|I| \leq |\Delta|\frac{|I_n|}{|\Delta_n|} = \delta^2(\delta_n) \to 0 \qquad \text{as} \qquad n \to \infty,$$

which is only possible if $I = 0$. This proves (11.7).

We have thus proved the following theorem:

If the functions $M(x, y)$ and $N(x, y)$ satisfy conditions (1) and (2) (Section 11.5) in a simply connected domain G, then the differential $M\,dx + N\,dy$ has an integral (11.6) which is uniquely determined up to an additive constant.

11.8. Determination of the Conjugate Harmonic Function

We saw in Section 1.14 that the real and imaginary parts of an analytic function are harmonic functions which satisfy the Cauchy-Riemann differential equations. Such functions are said to be *conjugate* harmonic functions. We shall now consider the following problem: Given a harmonic function, determine its conjugate harmonic function. Let $u(x, y)$ be harmonic in a simply connected domain G. We seek a function $v(x, y)$ which satisfies the conditions

$$v_x = -u_y, \qquad v_y = u_x.$$

Since u_y and u_x are differentiable, and since $-u_y\,dx + u_x\,dy$ satisfies the integrability condition (Section 11.5), there exists a function

$$v = \int_{(x_0, y_0)}^{(x, y)} (-u_y\,dx + u_x\,dy),$$

which is uniquely determined up to an additive constant and whose total differential is $-u_y\,dx + u_x\,dy$. This function is the conjugate of u.

The function $w(z) = u + iv$ is analytic. The harmonic function $u(x, y)$ therefore determines an analytic function (unique up to an additive imaginary constant) whose real part is the given harmonic function u. If the imaginary part $v(x, y)$ is given, the analytic function $w(z)$ is determined up to an additive real constant.

Since an analytic function $w(z)$ has derivatives of all orders, *a harmonic function $u(x, y)$ has partial derivatives of all orders.* These partial derivatives (as real or imaginary parts of analytic functions) are also harmonic.

Conversely, the properties of analytic functions can be derived from the properties of harmonic functions. In particular, Cauchy's theorem is a consequence of the results proved above for real line integrals (Exercise 2, p. 208).

Proving that a given function is harmonic is often done most conveniently by showing that it is the real or imaginary part of an analytic function. For example, $r^n \cos n\phi$ and $r^n \sin n\phi$ are harmonic functions since they are the real and imaginary parts of the function $z^n = (r\,e^{i\phi})^n$.

11.9. Behavior under Conformal Mapping

If the function u is harmonic, then so is Cu, where C is a constant. If u and v are harmonic, then so is their sum $u + v$. From these observations it follows that the set of harmonic functions is *linear*: If $u_1, u_2, \ldots, u_n$ are harmonic functions, then $C_1u_1 + C_1u_2 + \cdots + C_nu_n$ is also a harmonic function, where $C_1, C_2, \ldots, C_n$ are constants.

On the other hand, the product and the quotient of two harmonic functions are not, in general, harmonic.

A change of variables,

$$x = x(\xi, \eta), \qquad y = y(\xi, \eta), \tag{11.9}$$

will transform a harmonic function $u(x, y)$ into a function of the new variables ξ and η,

$$u(x, y) = u(x(\xi, \eta), y(\xi, \eta)) = \bar{u}(\xi, \eta).$$

In general the function $\bar{u}(\xi, \eta)$ is not harmonic. However, if the equations (11.9) define a conformal mapping of a domain G of the (x, y)-plane onto a domain $\bar{G}$ of the (ξ, η)-plane, then $\bar{u}$ is harmonic. This can be proved by computing $\Delta\bar{u}$ and taking into account the conditions of conformality. Whenever the conformal mapping is orientation-preserving we can also give a proof based on the composition of analytic functions. For the functions (11.9) then satisfy the Cauchy-Riemann differential equations; thus if we write $x + iy = z$, $\xi + i\eta = \zeta$, then $z = x(\xi, \eta) + i\, y(\xi, \eta)$ is an analytic function $z(\zeta)$ of ζ.

We form the harmonic conjugate $v(x, y)$ of u and then the analytic function

$$w(z) = u(x, y) + i\, v(x, y). \tag{11.10}$$

The substitution $z = z(\zeta)$ transforms (11.10) into an analytic function of ζ:

$$w(z(\zeta)) = \bar{u}(\xi, \eta) + i\, \bar{v}(\xi, \eta).$$

Its real part $\bar{u}(\xi, \eta)$ is therefore harmonic, which is what we wanted to prove.

§2. GAUSS'S MEAN-VALUE THEOREM.
THE MAXIMUM AND MINIMUM PRINCIPLES

11.10. Gauss's Mean-Value Theorem

If we equate the real parts on both sides of formula (9.14), which was derived for analytic functions, we obtain *Gauss's mean-value theorem* for harmonic functions.

If $u(z) \equiv u(x, y)$ is harmonic in a domain which contains the disk $|z - a| \leqq r$, then

$$u(a) = \frac{1}{2\pi} \int_0^{2\pi} u(a + r\, e^{i\phi})\, d\phi.$$

Remark. The converse is also true: If $f(x, y)$ is a continuous real function in the domain G and satisfies the mean-value theorem for every disk contained

7*

in G, then $f(x, y)$ is harmonic. The proof is left as an exercise (Exercise 15, p. 210).

Thus the mean-value property can serve as the *definition* of a harmonic function.

11.11. The Maximum and Minimum Principles

In Section 9.12 we proved the maximum principle for the modulus of an analytic function. We also have a *maximum* and *minimum principle* for harmonic functions.

If the function $u(z)$, harmonic in the domain G, attains its upper or lower bound in G, then it is a constant.

Suppose that u attains its least upper bound M at a point $a \in G : u(a) = M$. By Gauss's mean-value theorem

$$u(a) = M = \frac{1}{2\pi} \int_0^{2\pi} u(a + r\, e^{i\phi})\, d\phi, \tag{11.11}$$

where the disk

$$|z - a| \leqq r \tag{11.12}$$

is contained in the domain G. It can be proved as in Section 9.12 that (11.11) is possible only if $u \equiv M$ everywhere in the disk (11.12). Applying the method of a chain of disks, we may then show that u is a constant throughout the domain G (cf. Section 9.9). It is recommended that the reader carry out in detail the proof outlined here.

The minimum principle can be proved in the same way, or can be deduced from the maximum principle by applying it to the function $-u$.

It follows from the maximum and minimum principles that a function harmonic on a closed domain attains its maximum and minimum on the boundary of the domain. Furthermore, if a function harmonic on a closed domain is constant on the boundary, then it is constant in the whole domain. It follows directly that if two functions u and v are harmonic on the closed domain and $u = v$ at every boundary point of G, then $u \equiv v$ throughout the domain G.

As an example, let us consider the harmonic function u defined as the real part of the analytic function $(1 + z)/(1 - z)$:

$$u = \operatorname{Re} \frac{1 + z}{1 - z} = \frac{1 - r^2}{1 + r^2 - 2r \cos \phi} = u(r\, e^{i\phi}),$$

where $z = r\, e^{i\phi}$. The function u is harmonic in the unit disk, and on its boundary $r = 1$ we have $u = 0$ except when $\phi = 0$. Nevertheless, u is not identically zero in the unit disk. The reason is that the assumptions of the maximum and minimum principles are not satisfied, since the function has a singularity on the boundary at the point $z = 1$. If we let z approach the point 1 along the real axis, then $u \to \infty$.

A function u is said to be harmonic at the point $z = \infty$ if the function $\bar{u}(\zeta) = u(1/\zeta)$ (the transform of $u(z)$ under the inversion $z = 1/\zeta$) is harmonic in the neighborhood of the point $\zeta = 0$.

It can easily be shown that the maximum and minimum principle is also valid in a domain of the extended z-plane.

As an example, we consider an analytic function $u + iv$ which is real on the real axis and regular in the upper half-plane. On the real axis we have $v = 0$, but it does not follow that $v \equiv 0$, since v need not be regular at $z = \infty$. For example, a polynomial with real coefficients is such a function.

11.12.

We can also formulate the maximum principle in the following way.

If the function $u(z)$ is harmonic in a domain G of the extended complex plane and if at every boundary point ζ of G

$$\limsup_{z \to \zeta} u(z) \leqq M, \tag{11.13}$$

then $u \leqq M$ throughout G.

Proof. Let α be the least upper bound of $u(z)$ in G. Then there is a point $z_0 \in G$ at which $u(z_0) = \alpha$, or there exists an infinite sequence

$$z_1, z_2, \ldots \tag{11.14}$$

such that

$$\lim_{n \to \infty} u(z_n) = \alpha.$$

The sequence (11.14) contains a subsequence

$$z_{\nu_1}, z_{\nu_2}, \ldots$$

such that

$$\lim_{i \to \infty} z_{\nu_i} = z', \qquad \lim_{i \to \infty} u(z_{\nu_i}) = \alpha.$$

In each case there is a point z_0, either in G or on its boundary, such that the least upper bound of $u(z)$ is equal to α in an arbitrarily small neighborhood of z_0.

If z_0 is on the boundary of G, then $\alpha \leqq M$ by (11.13). On the other hand, if $z_0 \in G$, then $u(z_0) = \alpha$ by continuity. Thus $u(z)$ assumes its maximum value in the interior of the domain, and, hence, is constant by the original maximum principle. In this case again $\alpha \leqq M$, and the theorem is proved.

11.13. Generalization of the Maximum Principle

The examples discussed in Section 11.11 show that the function $u(z)$ need not be less than or equal to M if condition (11.13) is not fulfilled at *every* boundary point. However, if we make an additional assumption, exceptional boundary points can be admitted.

In fact, one can state the following generalization of the maximum principle.

If

1) *The function $u(z)$ is harmonic and bounded in the domain G: $u(z) \leq K$;*
2) *There exists a positive number M such that $\limsup u(z) \leq M(< K)$ at every boundary point ζ of G, except at a finite number of points ζ_1, $\zeta_2, \ldots, \zeta_n$.*

        Then $u(z) \leq M$ at every point of G (provided that the boundary of G also contains points other than $\zeta_1, \ldots, \zeta_n$).

Proof. We assume first that G has exterior points. By means of a bilinear transformation we may reduce the problem to the case that G is contained in a disk of diameter d. The function

$$v(z) = u(z) - \lambda \sum_{\nu=1}^{n} \log \frac{d}{|z - \zeta_\nu|}, \tag{11.15}$$

where λ is an arbitrary positive constant, is harmonic in G and less than $u(z)$. Hence,

$$\limsup_{z \to \zeta} v(z) \leq M$$

if $\zeta \neq \zeta_\nu$ ($\nu = 1, 2, \ldots, n$). On the other hand, if $z \to \zeta_\nu$, then

$$\log (d/|z - \zeta_\nu|) \to \infty,$$

so that, for these points,

$$\limsup_{z \to \zeta_\nu} v(z) \leq M.$$

It follows from Section 11.12 that, for every interior point of G,

$$v(z) \leq M. \tag{11.16}$$

If z is a fixed point of the domain G, it follows from (11.15) and (11.16) that

$$u(z) \leq M + \lambda \sum_{\nu=1}^{n} \log \frac{d}{|z - \zeta_\nu|}. \tag{11.17}$$

The sum on the right-hand side has a finite value for any fixed z in G. Since λ is an arbitrary positive number, it follows from (11.17) that $u(z) \leq M$.

    Let us now consider the case when G has no exterior points. Let z_0 be an arbitrary interior point of G, and let $u(z_0) = u_0$. Because of the continuity of u, we know for every positive ϵ there exists a $\rho > 0$ such that $u(z) < u_0 + \epsilon$ for $|z - z_0| \leq \rho_0$. The theorem has already been proved for the domain obtained from G by removing the disk $|z - z_0| \leq \rho$. Since ϵ is arbitrary, it follows that $u(z)$ cannot exceed in G the larger of the numbers M and u_0. If $u_0 > M$, then $u_0 = \sup u$ and u attains its greatest value in the interior of the domain. By the maximum principle $u(z) \equiv u_0$, which contradicts assumption (2). Therefore $u_0 \leq M$, i.e., $u(z) \leq M$ throughout G. The theorem is thereby completely proved.

The minimum principle has a corresponding generalization.

The theorem remains true if the set of exceptional boundary points is countably infinite. The proof is analogous (cf. Exercise 11, p. 209).

§3. POISSON'S FORMULA

11.14.

If $w(z)$ is an analytic function regular on a closed domain, then the values of $w(z)$ in the interior of the domain are determined by its values on the boundary by means of Cauchy's integral formula. It was shown in Section 2 that harmonic functions have the same property. If the function $u(z)$ is harmonic in a disk $|z| \leq \rho$, then Gauss's mean-value theorem gives the value of $u(z)$ at the center $z = 0$ (Section 11.10):

$$u(0) = \frac{1}{2\pi} \int_0^{2\pi} u(\rho\, e^{i\psi})\, d\psi.$$

In order to express the value of u at an arbitrary interior point z of the disk by means of its values on the circumference, we map the disk $|z| \leq \rho$ conformally onto itself so that the point z goes into the origin.

We consider first a conformal mapping of the disk onto itself which takes the point a into the point b. It is of the form

$$\frac{z - a}{\rho^2 - \bar{a}z} = \lambda\, \frac{\zeta - b}{\rho^2 - \bar{b}\zeta}, \tag{11.18}$$

where λ is a constant (Section 3.9), which is to be determined in such a way that $|z| = \rho$ whenever $|\zeta| = \rho$. Multiplying the left-hand side of (11.18) by $\bar{z}/\bar{z}$ and the right-hand side by $\bar{\zeta}/\bar{\zeta}$, we obtain

$$\bar{z}\, \frac{z - a}{\rho^2 \bar{z} - \bar{a}|z|^2} = \lambda \bar{\zeta}\, \frac{\zeta - b}{\rho^2 \bar{\zeta} - \bar{b}|\zeta|^2}.$$

Now if this equation is to be satisfied for $|z| = |\zeta| = \rho$, we must have $|\lambda| = 1$ or $\lambda = e^{i\alpha}$, where α is real. The mapping is therefore defined by the equation

$$\frac{z - a}{\rho^2 - \bar{a}z} = e^{i\alpha}\, \frac{\zeta - b}{\rho^2 - \bar{b}\zeta}. \tag{11.19}$$

By logarithmic differentiation of (11.18) we obtain

$$\frac{\rho^2 - |a|^2}{(z - a)(\rho^2 - \bar{a}z)}\, dz = \frac{\rho^2 - |b|^2}{(\zeta - b)(\rho^2 - \bar{b}\zeta)}\, d\zeta. \tag{11.20}$$

This equation is also valid on the circles $|z| = \rho$, $|\zeta| = \rho$. We denote corresponding boundary points by

$$z = \rho\, e^{i\theta}, \qquad \zeta = \rho\, e^{i\psi}.$$

If we let the points z and ζ vary on these circles, we obtain

$$\frac{dz}{z} = i\, d\theta, \qquad \frac{d\zeta}{\zeta} = i\, d\psi. \tag{11.21}$$

On the circle $|z| = \rho$ we have $\rho^2/z = \bar{z}$ and similarly on $|\zeta| = \rho$ we have $\rho^2/\zeta = \bar{\zeta}$. From (11.20) and (11.21) we then have

$$\frac{\rho^2 - |a|^2}{|z - a|^2} \, d\theta = \frac{\rho^2 - |b|^2}{|\zeta - b|^2} \, d\psi. \tag{11.22}$$

11.15.

We assume now that the function $u(z)$ is harmonic in the disk $|z| \leq \rho$, and we wish to determine its value at the point $z_0 = r\,e^{i\phi}$ by means of the values taken by the function on $|z| = \rho$. We map the disk $|z| \leq \rho$ onto the disk $|\zeta| \leq \rho$ by means of a bilinear transformation in such a way that the point $z = z_0$ goes into $\zeta = 0$. Then $u(z)$ becomes a harmonic function of the new variable ζ; we denote the new function by $\bar{u}(\zeta)$. In particular,

$$u(z_0) = \bar{u}(0).$$

By Gauss's mean-value theorem,

$$u(z_0) = \bar{u}(0) = \frac{1}{2\pi} \int_0^{2\pi} \bar{u}(\rho\,e^{i\psi}) \, d\psi. \tag{11.23}$$

In order to make z once more the variable of integration, we apply formula (11.22) with $a = z_0, b = 0$. We obtain:

$$u(z_0) = u(r\,e^{i\phi}) = \frac{1}{2\pi} \int_0^{2\pi} u(\rho\,e^{i\theta}) \frac{\rho^2 - |z_0|^2}{|z - z_0|^2} \, d\theta. \tag{11.24}$$

If we replace z_0 by $z = r\,e^{i\phi}$ and the variable of integration z by $\zeta = \rho\,e^{i\theta}$, (11.24) takes the form

$$u(z) = u(r\,e^{i\phi}) = \frac{1}{2\pi} \int_0^{2\pi} u(\rho\,e^{i\theta}) \frac{\rho^2 - |z|^2}{|\zeta - z|^2} \, d\theta$$

$$= \frac{1}{2\pi} \int_0^{2\pi} u(\rho\,e^{i\theta}) \frac{\rho^2 - r^2}{\rho^2 + r^2 - 2\rho r \cos(\theta - \phi)} \, d\theta. \tag{11.25}$$

This is *Poisson's formula*.

If $u(z)$ is harmonic in the unit circle, we have ($\rho = 1$):

$$u(z) = u(r\,e^{i\phi}) = \frac{1}{2\pi} \int_0^{2\pi} u(e^{i\theta}) \frac{1 - r^2}{1 + r^2 - 2r \cos(\theta - \phi)} \, d\theta. \tag{11.26}$$

11.16. Schwarz's Formula

It can be proved directly from the integral (11.25) that $u(z) = u(r\,e^{i\phi})$ is a harmonic function. In fact, the *kernel* of the integral,

$$K(\rho\,e^{i\theta}, z) = \frac{\rho^2 - r^2}{\rho^2 + r^2 - 2\rho r \cos(\theta - \phi)},$$

is the real part of the analytic function $(\zeta + z)/(\zeta - z)$, and as such is a harmonic function of z. Hence, the integral (11.25) is also a harmonic function of z, since the required differentiations can be carried out under the integral sign.

Since we can represent the real part u of an analytic function $w(z) = u + iv$ as a Poisson integral (11.25), we can find a representation of $w(z)$ itself by means of the boundary values of its real part.

We form the integral

$$f(z) = \frac{1}{2\pi} \int_0^{2\pi} u(\rho\, e^{i\theta}) \frac{\zeta + z}{\zeta - z}\, d\theta, \tag{11.27}$$

which defines a regular function of z. The real part of $f(z)$ is $u(z)$, the same as the real part of $w(z)$. The difference of the functions $w(z)$ and $f(z)$ is therefore an imaginary constant. Hence,

$$w(z) = \frac{1}{2\pi} \int_0^{2\pi} u(\rho\, e^{i\theta}) \frac{\zeta + z}{\zeta - z}\, d\theta + iC,$$

where C is a real constant. If we set $z = 0$, we see that $C = v(0)$. We have thus established *Schwarz's formula*:

$$w(z) = \frac{1}{2\pi} \int_0^{2\pi} u(\rho\, e^{i\theta}) \frac{\zeta + z}{\zeta - z}\, d\theta + iv(0).$$

§4. HARMONIC MEASURE

11.17. The Geometric Meaning of the Poisson Kernel

The kernel

$$\frac{1 - r^2}{1 + r^2 - 2r \cos(\theta - \phi)} = \frac{1 - |z|^2}{|\zeta - z|^2} = \operatorname{Re} \frac{\zeta + z}{\zeta - z}$$

of the Poisson integral has a simple geometric interpretation. By the well-known theorem on secants (Fig. 33),

$$(1 + |z|)(1 - |z|) = |\zeta - z|\, |\zeta' - z|,$$

or

$$1 - |z|^2 = |\zeta - z|\, |\zeta' - z|. \tag{11.28}$$

On the other hand, if $d\theta'$ is the element of arc described by ζ' when ζ describes the element of arc $d\theta$, we have

$$\frac{d\theta}{|\zeta - z|} = \frac{d\theta'}{|\zeta' - z|}. \tag{11.29}$$

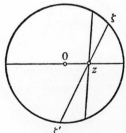

Figure 33

By (11.28) and (11.29) we have

$$\frac{d\theta'}{d\theta} = \frac{1 - |z|^2}{|\zeta - z|^2} = \frac{1 - r^2}{1 + r^2 - 2r\cos(\theta - \phi)}. \tag{11.30}$$

If ζ is fixed, then $d\theta'/d\theta$ is a function of z. It is clear from formula (11.29) and from the geometrical interpretation that the level curves of the Poisson kernel (11.30) are circles tangent to the unit circle at the point ζ. If z tends to any point ($\neq \zeta$) of the circle $|z| = 1$, then (11.30) tends to 0.

11.18. Definition of the Harmonic Measure

In view of formula (11.22), the differential

$$d\theta' = \frac{1 - |z|^2}{|\zeta - z|^2} d\theta = \frac{1 - r^2}{1 + r^2 - 2r\cos(\theta - \phi)} d\theta$$

is invariant under the group of bilinear transformations mapping the unit disk onto itself, where we replace $z = r e^{i\phi}$ and $\zeta = e^{i\theta}$ by their image points. This implies that the integral taken between two arbitrary limits θ_1 and θ_2 $(0 \leq \theta_1 < \theta_2 \leq \theta_1 + 2\pi)$

$$\omega(z; \theta_1, \theta_2) = \frac{1}{2\pi}\int_{=\theta'\theta_1}^{\theta_2} d\theta' = \frac{1}{2\pi}\int_{\theta_1}^{\theta_2} \frac{1 - r^2}{1 + r^2 - 2r\cos(\theta - \phi)} d\theta \tag{11.31}$$

is also invariant under this group. In other words, if we apply a linear transformation of the group which maps z onto z', and $e^{i\theta_1}$ and $e^{i\theta_2}$ onto $e^{i\theta'_1}$ and and $e^{i\theta'_2}$, then

$$\omega(z; \theta_1, \theta_2) = \omega(z'; \theta'_1, \theta'_2).$$

The quantity $2\pi\omega(z; \theta_1, \theta_2)$ is the arc length on the circle intercepted by the chords drawn from the points $e^{i\theta_1}$ and $e^{i\theta_2}$ through the point z. If Θ is the angle between these chords (Fig. 34), then

$$2\pi\omega = 2\Theta - (\theta_2 - \theta_1).$$

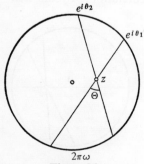

Figure 34

It is evident from the geometric interpretation that ω varies between 0 and 1. If Θ is fixed, then ω is also constant. Hence, the level curves of ω are the arcs of circles through the points $e^{i\theta_1}$ and $e^{i\theta_2}$. On the arc $\theta_1 < \theta < \theta_2$ of the unit circle the harmonic measure ω has the value 1; on the complementary arc $\theta_2 < \theta < \theta_1 + 2\pi$ its value is 0. At the point $z = 0$, ω is the arc length of $(e^{i\theta_1}, e^{i\theta_2})$ divided by 2π.

The function ω is a harmonic function of z, since its integrand (11.30) is harmonic. It can be considered as a generalized measure of the arc $(e^{i\theta_1}, e^{i\theta_2})$, calculated with respect to the point z, and $\omega(z; \theta_1, \theta_2)$ is called the *harmonic measure* of the arc $(e^{i\theta_1}, e^{i\theta_2})$ at the point z with respect to the unit disk.

The harmonic measure $\omega(z, \alpha)$ of an arc α of the circle $|z| = 1$ at the point z with respect to the unit disk G thus has the following properties:

1) $\omega(z, \alpha)$ *is harmonic and bounded in the domain G.*
2) $\omega = 1$ *at every interior point of the arc α; $\omega = 0$ at every interior point of the complementary arc β.*

It follows from the generalized maximum and minimum principles that the function $\omega(z, \alpha)$ is uniquely determined by these two conditions (Section 11.13). For, if two functions satisfy conditions (1) and (2), then their difference vanishes identically (cf. Section 11.11).

For an arbitrary domain G whose boundary is a Jordan curve (or is made up of a finite number of Jordan arcs), the harmonic measure $\omega(z, \alpha)$ of a boundary arc α is defined by conditions (1) and (2).

For the union $\cup\alpha$ of a finite or countably infinite number of boundary arcs, the harmonic measure is defined as the sum $\omega(z, \cup\alpha) = \sum \omega(z, \alpha)$ (see Exercise 20, p. 210).

If α is the whole boundary curve, then $\omega(z, \alpha) \equiv 1$. If α reduces to a point, then $\omega \equiv 0$. If z is fixed and α increases, then $\omega(z, \alpha)$ also increases.

11.19. Applications

We now introduce three results of Ernst Lindelöf (1870–1946) which can be easily proved by means of the harmonic measure.

Theorem 1. *Let $w = w(z)$, $z = x + iy$, be analytic in the open semi-circle $|z| < 1$, $y > 0$, and let $w(z)$ satisfy the following conditions:*

1) $w(z)$ *is bounded, $|w(z)| \leq 1$;*
2) $w(z)$ *is continuous on the diameter $y = 0$, $0 < |x| < 1$, and $\lim\limits_{x \to 0} w(x) = 0$.*

Then $\lim\limits_{z \to 0} w(z) = 0$ $(y \geq 0)$.

Proof. We form the harmonic measure $\omega(z)$ of the segment $y = 0$, $|x| \leq r$ with respect to the semi-circle C_r: $|z| < r$, $y > 0$. We find (Exercise 19, p. 210) that

$$\omega(z) = \frac{2\theta_r(z)}{\pi} - 1,$$

where $\theta_r(z)$ is the angle which the diameter $(y = 0, |x| \leq r)$ of C_r subtends at the point z.

If $w(z) \equiv 0$, the assertion of the theorem is obviously true. We therefore assume that $w(z)$ does not vanish identically. For every ϵ in the interval $0 < \epsilon < 1$ there exists an $r > 0$ so small that

$$|w(x)| < \epsilon^2 \qquad \text{if} \qquad 0 < |x| \leq r \, (< 1).$$

The function

$$u(z) = \log |w(z)| + 2\omega(z) \log \frac{1}{\epsilon} \qquad (11.32)$$

is harmonic in the domain C_r except at the zeros of $w(z)$. If we remove these zeros, we obtain a subdomain $\bar{C}_r$ whose boundary consists of the following parts: (1) the semicircle $|z| = r$, $y > 0$; (2) the segments $y = 0$, $0 < |x| \leqq r$; (3) the removed zeros; (4) the point $z = 0$.

At the boundary points (1) u is continuous; since $\omega = 0$ and $|w| < 1$, we have here

$$u(z) \leqq 0.$$

The same applies to the boundary points (2), at which $\log |w| < 2 \log \epsilon$ and $\omega = 1$, and to the boundary points (3), at which $u = -\infty$. Since u is bounded in the domain $\bar{C}_r$: $u \leqq 2 \log (1/\epsilon)$, it follows from the generalized maximum principle that $u(z) \leqq 0$ in the whole domain C_r, so that $\log |w| \leqq 2\omega \log \epsilon$, whence

$$|w(z)| \leqq \epsilon^{2\omega(z)}.$$

Now let γ be a circular arc ($y > 0$) which intersects the real axis at the points $x = \pm r$ at an angle of $\pi/4$. On this arc $\omega = \frac{1}{2}$. In the segment S_0 bounded by γ and the chord $y = 0$, $|x| < r$ we have $\omega \geqq \frac{1}{2}$. Hence, $|w(z)| \leqq \epsilon$ for $z \in S_0$, and the theorem is proved.

11.20.

A generalization of Theorem 1 is the following.

Theorem 2. *Let G be a simply connected domain bounded by a Jordan curve Γ, and let $f(z)$ be an analytic function in G which satisfies the following conditions:*

1) $|f(z)| \leqq 1$ *for $z \in G$;*
2) $f(z)$ *is continuous at all boundary points ζ of Γ with the exception of a single boundary point ζ_0;*
3) *as $\zeta \to \zeta_0$ on Γ, the boundary values of $f(z)$ tend to a well-defined limit $a = \lim f(\zeta)$.*

Then $f(z)$ is continuous at $z = \zeta_0$, that is,

$$\lim f(z) = a$$

as the point $z \in G$ tends to the point ζ_0.

In the proof we may assume that $\zeta_0 = 0$, $a = 0$ and $f(z) \not\equiv 0$. We go over to the variable

$$w = w(z) = u + iv = \int_{z_0}^{z} \frac{dz}{z} + \log z_0 = \log z,$$

where the path of integration $z_0 z \subset G$ and the branch of the function $\log z$ at the point z_0 are both fixed in some arbitrary way. Since G is simply connected, w is a single-valued regular function in the domain G. Its inverse $z = e^w$ is likewise single-valued. The function $w = w(z)$ therefore maps G one-to-one conformally onto a domain D of the w-plane, whose boundary γ contains the point $w = \infty$ $(u = -\infty)$.

Let $r > 0$, and let D_r denote the intersection of the domain D and the half-plane $u < \log r$. The boundary of the domain D_r will consist of certain arcs of γ $(u \leqq \log r)$ and a (countable) set of disjoint open segments (δ) of the line $u = \log r$, whose total length does not exceed 2π.

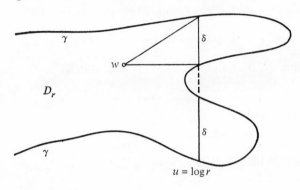

Figure 35

Theorem 2 will be proved if we can show that for every $0 < \epsilon < 1$ there exists a positive number $r = r_\epsilon$ such that

$$|f(z)| = |f(e^w)| < \epsilon$$

whenever $w \in D_{r_\epsilon}$.

First, by hypothesis, we can find an $r_0 > 0$ such that at every *finite* point† of the boundary arcs γ of the domain $D_0 = D_{r_0}$ we have

$$|f(e^w)| < \epsilon^2. \tag{11.33}$$

Let $\omega(w)$ denote the harmonic measure of the boundary segments (δ) of the domain D_0 with respect to the half-plane $u \leqq \log r_0$:

$$\omega(w) = \frac{1}{\pi} \sum_{(\delta)} \theta(w, \delta), \tag{11.34}$$

where $\theta(w, \delta)$ denotes the angle at which the segment δ is seen from the point w (Exercise 18, p. 210). We construct the function

$$U(w) = \log |f(e^w)| + 2(1 - \omega(w)) \log \frac{1}{\epsilon}, \tag{11.35}$$

---

† By hypothesis, one can first single out the sub-arc of γ starting at $w = \infty$, on which (11.33) holds. On the remaining part of γ the function u has a finite minimum u_0. Hence, by taking $\log r_0 < u_0$ we can make sure that (11.33) holds at every finite point of γ belonging to the boundary of D_0.

which is harmonic in the domain $\bar{D}_0$ obtained from D_0 by removing the zeros of f. The boundary of $\bar{D}_0$ consists of (1) the removed zeros; (2) the finite points of γ: $-\infty < u \leqq \log r_0$; (3) the segments δ; (4) the point $w = \infty$ $(u = -\infty)$. At the points (1) $U = -\infty$; at the points (2) $\log |f| \leqq 2 \log \epsilon$ (condition 11.33), so that $U \leqq 2\omega \log \epsilon \leqq 0$; at the points (3) $\omega = 1$, $U = \log |f| < 0$. At all finite boundary points of $\bar{D}_0$, therefore, $U \leqq 0$. Moreover, U is bounded in $\bar{D}_0$ $(U \leqq 2(1 - \omega(w)) \log (1/\epsilon) \leqq 2 \log (1/\epsilon)$. It then follows from the generalized maximum principle that $U(w) \leqq 0$ in the whole domain $\bar{D}_0$, and therefore also in the domain D_0. Thus

$$\log |f(e^w)| \leqq 2(1 - \omega) \log \epsilon = 2(\omega(w) - 1) \log \frac{1}{\epsilon} \qquad (11.36)$$

holds throughout the domain D_0. If we restrict u to the half-plane $u < \log r_0 - \pi$, then, by (11.34),

$$\omega(w) < \tfrac{1}{2}$$

and by (11.36) we have

$$|f(z)| = |f(e^w)| < \epsilon \qquad \text{whenever} \qquad u < \log r_0 - \pi.$$

Theorem 2 is thus proved.

11.21.

As a corollary of Theorem 2 we shall prove the following result.

> **Theorem 3.** *Let G be a simply connected domain whose boundary Γ is a Jordan curve. Let the function $f(z)$ be analytic in G and satisfy the following conditions:*
>
> 1) $|f(z)| \leqq 1$ *everywhere in G;*
> 2) $f(z)$ *is continuous at all boundary points with the exception of the single boundary point ζ_0;*
> 3) *if Γ_1 and Γ_2 denote the boundary arcs determined by ζ_0 and a second point $\zeta' \in \Gamma$, then the limits*
>
> $$a = \lim_{\Gamma_1 \ni \zeta \to \zeta_0} f(\zeta), \qquad b = \lim_{\Gamma_2 \ni \zeta \to \zeta_0} f(\zeta)$$
>
> *exist.*
> *Then $a = b$ and*
> $$\lim f(z) = a$$
> *as $z \in G$ tends to the point ζ_0.*

The theorem will be proved by contradiction. We assume that $a \neq b$, and we form the function

$$w(z) = (f(z) - a)(f(z) - b),$$

which is bounded in G $(|w(z)| \leqq (1 + |a|)(1 + |b|))$ and tends to the limit 0 as $\zeta \in \Gamma$ tends to ζ_0. By Theorem 2

$$\lim w(z) = 0$$

as $z \in G$ tends to ζ_0. Let ϵ be such that $0 < \epsilon < |a - b|/2$. Then there exists an $r > 0$ such that

$$|w(z)| < \epsilon^2 \tag{11.37}$$

if $z \in G_r$, where G_r denotes that component of the intersection of G and the disk $|z - \zeta_0| < r$ which has ζ_0 as a boundary point (cf. Fig. 36).

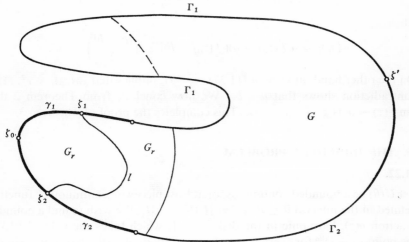

Figure 36

By hypothesis, we can find a sufficiently small subarc γ_1 of Γ_1, terminating at ζ_0, such that

$$|f(z) - a| < \frac{|a - b|}{2} \qquad \text{for} \qquad z \in \gamma_1.$$

Furthermore, we can choose γ_1 so small that it belongs to the boundary of G_r. Similarly, we choose a subarc γ_2 of Γ_2 which belongs to the boundary of G_r and which is such that

$$|f(z) - b| < \frac{|a - b|}{2} \qquad \text{for} \qquad z \in \gamma_2.$$

We join an arbitrary point ζ_1 of the arc γ_1 to a point ζ_2 of the arc γ_2 by means of a continuous curve l which lies entirely in the domain G_r.†

Since

$$|f(\zeta_1) - a| < \frac{|a - b|}{2} < |f(\zeta_1) - b|$$

---

† The domain G_r is a Jordan domain; any two points of a Jordan domain can be joined by means of a continuous curve which lies entirely in the domain (Exercises 5–6, p. 340) except for its end-points.

and

$$|f(\zeta_2) - b| < \frac{|a - b|}{2} < |f(\zeta_2) - a|,$$

and since $f(z) - a$ and $f(z) - b$ are continuous in G, there exists at least one point z_0 on the arc l at which

$$|f(z_0) - a| = |f(z_0) - b| \geqq \frac{|a - b|}{2}.$$

Then

$$|w(z_0)| = |(f(z_0) - a)(f(z_0) - b)| \geqq \left(\frac{|a - b|}{2}\right)^2 > \epsilon^2.$$

On the other hand, in view of (11.37), $z_0 \in G_r$ implies that $|w(z_0)| < \epsilon^2$. This contradiction shows that $a = b$. We now conclude from Theorem 2 that $\lim f(z) = a$ as $z \to \zeta_0, z \in G$. This completes the proof of Theorem 3.

§5. THE DIRICHLET PROBLEM

11.22.

Let $U(\theta)$ be a bounded continuous, or at least piecewise continuous,† function defined in the interval $0 \leqq \theta \leqq 2\pi$: $|U(\theta)| \leqq M$. We wish to find a bounded function $u(z)$, harmonic in the disk $|z| < 1$, which takes the value $U(\theta_0)$ at the point $\zeta_0 = e^{i\theta_0}$ for every point of continuity θ_0 of $U(\theta)$, that is, $u(z)$ should tend to the limit $U(\theta_0)$ as z tends to ζ_0 from within the disk $|z| < 1$. This problem is called the *Dirichlet problem*.

It follows from the generalized maximum and minimum principles (Section 11.13) that if such a function exists, it is uniquely determined.

We consider first the special case where $U(\theta) = 1$ for $\theta_1 < \theta < \theta_2$ and $U(\theta) = 0$ elsewhere. The unique bounded harmonic function which takes these boundary values is the harmonic measure of the arc $\theta_1 < \theta < \theta_2$. We have shown that it possesses the integral representation (11.31). On the other hand, we know that if $u(e^{i\theta})$ is replaced in the Poisson integral (11.26) by the given function $U(\theta)$ which takes the values 1 and 0, the Poisson integral reduces to the integral (11.31). Thus the solution of the Dirichlet problem for the boundary values 1, 0 can be obtained directly from Poisson's formula. We may therefore expect that in the general case the solution can also be found in a similar way.

---

† A function $f(x)$ of a real variable x is said to be piecewise continuous in the interval $a \leqq x \leqq b$ if the interval (a, b) can be decomposed into a finite number of subintervals $(x_{\nu-1}, x_\nu)$ $(\nu = 1, 2, \ldots, n; x_0 = a, x_n = b)$ in such a way that $f(x)$ is continuous in the intervals $x_{\nu-1} < x < x_\nu$, and the limits $\lim_{x \to x_{\nu-1}+0} f(x)$ and $\lim_{x \to x_\nu - 0} f(x)$ $(\nu = 1, 2, \ldots, n)$ exist.

To solve the Dirichlet problem in the general case we therefore consider the Poisson integral

$$u(z) = \frac{1}{2\pi} \int_0^{2\pi} U(\theta) \frac{1 - r^2}{1 + r^2 - 2r \cos(\theta - \phi)} \, d\theta \qquad (11.38)$$

and show that it represents a harmonic function in the unit circle which has the boundary values $U(\theta)$.

The fact that $u(z)$ is harmonic in the unit disk follows from the fact that the kernel

$$K(e^{i\theta}, z) = \frac{1 - r^2}{1 + r^2 - 2r \cos(\theta - \phi)}$$

is a harmonic function of z.

We shall show that if θ_0 is any point of continuity of $U(\theta)$ and if $\zeta_0 = e^{i\theta_0}$, then

$$\lim_{z \to \zeta_0} u(z) = U(\theta_0).$$

It follows from (11.31) that (11.38) may be written as

$$u(z) = \int_{\theta=0}^{2\pi} U(\theta) \, d\omega(z; 0, \theta).$$

If we set

$$U(\theta_0) = U(\theta_0) \int_{\theta=0}^{2\pi} d\omega(z; 0, \theta) = \int_{\theta=0}^{2\pi} U(\theta_0) \, d\omega(z; 0, \theta),$$

we obtain

$$u(z) - U(\theta_0) = \int_{\theta=0}^{2\pi} [U(\theta) - U(\theta_0)] \, d\omega(z; 0, \theta). \qquad (11.39)$$

Since U is continuous at the point θ_0, there exists for every $\epsilon > 0$ an interval $\theta_1 \leq \theta \leq \theta_2$ on which

$$|U(\theta) - U(\theta_0)| < \epsilon. \qquad (11.40)$$

We divide the interval of integration into the parts (θ_1, θ_2) and $(\theta_2, \theta_1 + 2\pi)$. Outside the interval $(0, 2\pi)$ we define $U(\theta)$ to be periodic with period 2π. On the interval (θ_1, θ_2) (11.40) holds, so that

$$\left| \int_{\theta=\theta_1}^{\theta_2} [U(\theta) - U(\theta_0)] \, d\omega \right| < \epsilon \int_{\theta_1}^{\theta_2} d\omega < \epsilon.$$

For the second integral we obtain the estimate

$$\left| \int_{\theta_2}^{\theta_1+2\pi} [U(\theta) - U(\theta_0)] \, d\omega \right| \leq 2M\omega(z; \theta_2, \theta_1 + 2\pi).$$

If z tends to a point ζ_0 which does not lie on the arc $(\theta_2, \theta_1 + 2\pi)$, then $\omega(z; \theta_2, \theta_1 + 2\pi)$ tends to zero. Thus there exists a $\rho_\epsilon > 0$ such that

$$\omega(z; \theta_2, \theta_1 + 2\pi) < \epsilon \quad \text{if} \quad |z - \zeta_0| < \rho_\epsilon \quad \text{and} \quad |z| < 1,$$

which implies that

$$|u(z) - U(\theta_0)| < \epsilon(2M + 1) \qquad \text{if} \qquad |z - \zeta_0| < \rho_\epsilon \qquad \text{and} \qquad |z| < 1.$$

Hence,

$$\lim_{z \to \zeta_0} u(z) = U(\theta_0).$$

We have thus proved the following theorem.

If $U(\theta)$ is a piecewise continuous bounded function in the interval $0 \leq \theta < 2\pi$, then the Poisson integral (11.38) defines a function $u(z)$ which is harmonic in $|z| < 1$ and which has the boundary value $u(\theta)$ at every point of continuity $e^{i\theta}$ of U on the unit circle. The function $u(z)$ is uniquely determined.

If, instead of the unit disk, we consider the disk $|z| < \rho$, then the solution of the Dirichlet problem is given by Poisson's formula (11.25), if we replace $u(\rho \, e^{i\theta})$ by the prescribed piecewise continuous function $U(\theta)$.

§6. HARNACK'S PRINCIPLE

11.23. Lemma

For the Poisson kernel $K(\rho \, e^{i\theta}, z)$ we have the following estimate:

$$\frac{\rho - r}{\rho + r} \leq K(\rho \, e^{i\theta}, z) \leq \frac{\rho + r}{\rho - r}.$$

This estimate and Poisson's formula (11.25) yield the following bound for *non-negative* harmonic functions:

$$u(z) \leq \frac{\rho + r}{\rho - r} \frac{1}{2\pi} \int_0^{2\pi} u(\rho \, e^{i\theta}) \, d\theta = \frac{\rho + r}{\rho - r} u(0).$$

We may also obtain a corresponding *lower* bound for $u(z)$. If we combine the upper and lower bounds we obtain

$$\frac{\rho - r}{\rho + r} u(0) \leq u(z) \leq \frac{\rho + r}{\rho - r} u(0). \tag{11.41}$$

11.24. Harnack's Principle

We assume now that the functions

$$u_1(z), u_2(z), \ldots, u_n(z), \ldots$$

are harmonic in the disk $|z| \leq \rho$ and that

$$u_1 \leq u_2 \leq \ldots \leq u_n \leq \ldots$$

holds for every z in $|z| \leq \rho$. Then the limit

$$\lim_{n \to \infty} u_n(z) = u(z) \tag{11.42}$$

exists for every z in $|z| \leq \rho$.

First we show that if this limit is infinite for some point z of the disk $|z| < \rho$ then it is infinite for every point of the disk, and that in fact $u_n(z) \to \infty$ *uniformly* in every disk $|z| \leq r_1 < \rho$. To show this, we apply the bound (11.41) to the function $u_n - u_1 \geq 0$:

$$\frac{\rho - r}{\rho + r}\left(u_n(0) - u_1(0)\right) \leq u_n(z) - u_1(z)$$

$$\leq \frac{\rho + r}{\rho - r}\left(u_n(0) - u_1(0)\right) \qquad (z = r\,e^{i\phi}). \tag{11.43}$$

Let us assume that $u_n(z_0) \to \infty$ as $n \to \infty$ for some z_0 in $|z| < \rho$. It follows from (11.43) that

$$u_n(0) - u_1(0) \geq \frac{\rho - |z_0|}{\rho + |z_0|}\left(u_n(z_0) - u_1(z_0)\right).$$

This implies that for any large positive M there exists an n_1 such that $u_n(0) > M$ whenever $n \geq n_1$. From (11.43) it follows that

$$u_n(z) \geq \min_{|z| \leq r_1} u_1(z) + \frac{\rho - r_1}{\rho + r_1}\left(u_n(0) - u_1(0)\right)$$

for every point z of the disk $|z| \leq r_1$. Thus our assertion is established.

On the other hand, if the limit (11.42) is finite at a single point, then the above argument shows that it is finite everywhere in the disk $|z| < \rho$. In this case (11.42) holds uniformly in every disk $|z| \leq r_1 < \rho$. To verify this assertion we apply the right-hand inequality of (11.41) to the function $u_{n+p}(z) - u_n(z)$ $(p = 1, 2, \ldots)$ and obtain the inequality

$$0 \leq u_{n+p}(z) - u_n(z) \leq \frac{\rho + |z|}{\rho - |z|}\left[u_{n+p}(0) - u_n(0)\right]$$

$$\leq \frac{\rho + r_1}{\rho - r_1}\left[u_{n+p}(0) - u_n(0)\right]$$

which is valid for $|z| \leq r_1$. Since the sequence u_n converges at $z = 0$, this expression is less than ϵ for $p = 1, 2, \ldots$ if n is sufficiently large. The uniform convergence now follows from the Cauchy criterion.

The limit function $u(z)$ is harmonic. To show this we apply Poisson's formula for the disk $|z| \leq r_1$ to the functions $u_n(z)$:

$$u_n(z) = \frac{1}{2\pi}\int_0^{2\pi} u_n(r_1\,e^{i\theta})K(r_1\,e^{i\theta}, z)\,d\theta.$$

Since the sequence $u_n(z)$ converges uniformly, Poisson's formula also holds for the function $u(z)$. Therefore $u(z)$ is harmonic.

The result we have just proved can be generalized to an arbitrary domain G. Every compact subset of G can be covered by a finite number of disks lying entirely in G. Since the above result holds for every disk, it is also valid for G. We have thus obtained *Harnack's theorem*:

> *If the functions* $u_1(z), u_2(z), \ldots, u_n(z), \ldots$ *are harmonic in a domain* G, *and if at every point of* G
>
> $$u_1 \leqq u_2 \leqq \ldots \leqq u_n \leqq \ldots,$$
>
> *then*
>
> $$\lim_{n \to \infty} u_n(z)$$
>
> *is either infinite at every point of the domain, or finite at every point of the domain. In either case* $\{u_n(z)\}$ *converges uniformly on every compact subset of* G. *In the second case* $u(z) = \lim_{n \to \infty} u_n(z)$ *is harmonic in* G.

We make a final remark. If the real parts $u_n(z)$ of the analytic functions $w_n(z) = u_n(z) + iv_n(z)$ $(n = 1, 2, \ldots)$ converge uniformly on every compact subset of a simply connected domain G, and if the functions $w_n(z)$ themselves converge at some point $z_0 \in G$, then the sequence $w_n(z)$ converges to a finite limit uniformly on every compact subset of G (cf. Exercise 24, p. 211).

EXERCISES ON CHAPTER 11

1. Let the functions $M(x, y)$ and $N(x, y)$ be continuously differentiable in a domain G. Prove Stokes's formula

$$\int_{\partial \Delta} (M \, dx + N \, dy) = \int \int_{\Delta} (N_x - M_y) \, dx \, dy,$$

where Δ is a triangle lying in G and $\partial \Delta$ is its positively oriented boundary.

Hint. Apply Goursat's method (Section 11.7) to the difference

$$J(\Delta) = \int_{\partial \Delta} (M \, dx + N \, dy) - \int \int_{\Delta} (N_x - M_y) \, dx \, dy.$$

2. Prove Cauchy's theorem starting from the theorem proved in Sections 11.5–11.7 on the integrability of real differentials.

Hint. Split $\int w \, dz$ into real and imaginary parts.

3. Find an analytic function in the disk $|z - 1| < 1$ whose real part is $\log \sqrt{x^2 + y^2}$.

4. Prove that the angle subtended at a point z of the half-plane $\operatorname{Im} z > 0$ by a given segment of the real axis is a harmonic function of z.

5. Suppose that the equations $x = x(\xi, \eta)$, $y = y(\xi, \eta)$ define a conformal mapping of a domain in the (x, y)-plane onto a domain of the (ξ, η)-plane

which transforms the harmonic function $u(x, y)$ of x and y into a function $u(x(\xi, \eta), y(\xi, \eta)) = \bar{u}(\xi, \eta)$ of ξ and η. By computing the Laplacian $\Delta\bar{u}$, show that $\bar{u}$ is a harmonic function of ξ and η.

6. If $u(z)$ and $v(z)$ are conjugate harmonic functions, prove that the product uv is harmonic.

7. Find a harmonic function $u(x, y)$ for which the product xu is harmonic.

Solution. $u = ay + b$, where a and b are constants.

8. Let $u(x, y) = u(z)$, $z = x + iy$, be harmonic in the domain G. Find a harmonic function $u_1(x, y)$ for which uu_1 is harmonic.

Hint. If u is a constant, then u_1 is an arbitrary harmonic function. If u is not a constant, then $u_x^2 + u_y^2 > 0$ in some subdomain of G, and the analytic function $w(z) = u(z) + i\,v(z)$, where v is the harmonic conjugate of u, is invertible. Let the inverse function be $z = z(w) = x(u, v) + i\,y(u, v)$, where x and y are harmonic functions of u and v. Consequently the function $u_1(u, v) = u_1(x(u, v), y(u, v))$ is also harmonic. By the previous exercise, uu_1 is harmonic only if $u_1(x, y) = av(x, y) + b$. This is the general solution of the problem.

9. Let the function $u(z)$ $(z = r\,e^{i\phi})$ be harmonic in the disk $|z| \leq \rho$. By means of Exercise 38, Chapter 1, prove that

$$\frac{d}{dr} \int_0^{2\pi} u(r\,e^{i\phi})\,d\phi = 0,$$

and derive Gauss's mean-value theorem from this.

10. Carry out in detail the proof of the maximum principle for harmonic functions.

11. Prove the generalized maximum principle (Section 11.13) in the case when the number of exceptional points ζ_ν is countably infinite.

Hint. Instead of the finite sum in (11.15), form the infinite series

$$\lambda \sum_{\nu=1}^{\infty} \lambda_\nu \log \frac{d}{|z - \zeta_\nu|}$$

where $\lambda > 0$, and the coefficients λ_ν are chosen so that the series converges.

12. If a Jordan curve γ is a level curve of a (non-constant) harmonic function, then the function cannot be harmonic everywhere in the domain bounded by γ.

13. Prove that the maximum principle for analytic functions is a consequence of the maximum principle for harmonic functions.

Hint. If $w(z)$ is regular in the domain G, then $\log |w(z)|$ is harmonic in the domain obtained from G by removing the zeros of $w(z)$; at these points $\limsup \log |w(z)| = -\infty$.

14. What forms do Poisson's formula and Schwarz's formula take when the center z_0 of the circle is not the origin?

15. Prove the following assertion: If the real function $u(x, y)$ is continuous in the domain G, and the mean-value identity

$$u(z) = \frac{1}{2\pi} \int_0^{2\pi} u(z + \rho\, e^{i\theta})\, d\theta \tag{a}$$

holds for each $z \in G$ whenever $\rho > 0$ is sufficiently small, then u is harmonic.

Hint. Choose $\rho > 0$ so small that (a) holds for $z = a$, and consider the function

$$U(z) = \frac{1}{2\pi} \int_0^{2\pi} u(a + \rho\, e^{i\theta})\, \frac{\rho^2 - r^2}{\rho^2 + r^2 - 2\rho r \cos(\theta - \phi)}\, d\theta \qquad (z = a + r\, e^{i\theta})$$

in the disk $|z - a| \leqq \rho$. This function is harmonic in the disk $|z - a| < \rho$, and, hence, it satisfies Gauss's mean-value theorem. The same applies to the difference $U - u$. This difference satisfies therefore the maximum and minimum principles. Since $U = u$ for $|z - a| = \rho$, we therefore have $U \equiv u$. Hence, u is harmonic at the point $z = a$.

16. Let the function $w(z) = u + iv$ be analytic in the half-plane $\operatorname{Im} z \geqq 0$ (including the point ∞). Prove that

$$w(z) = \frac{1}{\pi i} \int_{-\infty}^{+\infty} u(t)\, \frac{dt}{t - z} + iC,$$

where C is a real constant.

17. The harmonic measure of a circular arc α at the point z of the disk can be determined in the following way. At each end-point of the arc α draw the orthogonal circle which passes through the point z. Show that if λ is the angle formed at z by these two circles and lying opposite the arc α, then $(1/2\pi)\lambda$ is the harmonic measure of α.

18. Show that the harmonic measure of the segment $a < x < b$ of the real axis with respect to the half-plane $\operatorname{Im} z > 0$ at the point z is $\theta(z)/\pi$, where $\theta(z)$ is the angle at z subtended by the segment ab.

19. Find the harmonic measure of the diameter $y = 0$ with respect to the semicircle $|z| < r$, $y > 0$.

Hint. By the previous exercise, $2\theta(z)/\pi$ is a harmonic function in the half-plane $y > 0$ which takes the value 2 on the segment $-r < z < r$, and is zero on the remainder of the real axis. Thus $(2\theta(z)/\pi) - 1$ is harmonic in the half-plane $y > 0$, is 1 on the segment $-r < z < r$, and -1 on the rest of the real axis. This is the harmonic measure we are looking for.

20. The union $\cup\, \alpha$ of disjoint boundary segments α of a half-plane G has the harmonic measure

$$\omega(z,\, \cup\, \alpha) = \sum_{(\alpha)} \omega(z,\, \alpha)$$

(cf. Section 11.18). Prove that $\omega(z, \cup \alpha)$ is harmonic in G, satisfies the condition $0 \leq \omega(z, \cup \alpha) \leq 1$, and tends to 1 as z tends to an interior point of one of the segments α.

21. Let the function $w(z)$ be analytic in the annulus $r_1 \leq |z| \leq r_2$. Let $M(r) = \max |w(z)|$ on $|z| = r$. Then the following inequality (Hadamard's three-circle theorem) holds

$$\log M(r) \leq \frac{\log r_2 - \log r}{\log r_2 - \log r_1} \log M(r_1)$$

$$+ \frac{\log r - \log r_1}{\log r_2 - \log r_1} \log M(r_2) \qquad (r_1 < r < r_2). \qquad (a)$$

Hint. Suppose, for instance, that $M(r_1) < M(r_2)$. Omitting those points of the open annulus $r_1 < |z| < r_2$ at which $|w(z)| \leq M(r_1)$, we have in the domain that remains the inequality

$$\frac{\log \dfrac{M(r_2)}{|w(z)|}}{\log \dfrac{M(r_2)}{M(r_1)}} - \frac{\log \dfrac{r_2}{|z|}}{\log \dfrac{r_2}{r_1}} \geq 0.$$

This follows from the maximum principle for harmonic functions, and yields (a). Inequality (a) remains valid if r_1 and r_2 are replaced by arbitrary values r_1' and r_2' such that $r_1 \leq r_1' < r < r_2' \leq r_2$. This means that $\log M(r)$ is a convex function of $\log r$, i.e., the segment joining two arbitrary points of the graph (over the interval $r_1 \leq r \leq r_2$) lies above the graph.

22. Let θ_0 be a point of discontinuity of the (piecewise continuous) boundary value function $U(\theta)$ in the Poisson integral (cf. Section 11.22). Show that if z tends to the point $\zeta_0 = e^{i\theta_0}$ along a path making an angle $\lambda\pi$ with the positive tangent to the unit circle at ζ_0, then the function $u(z)$ defined by the Poisson integral tends to the limit $\lambda U(\theta_0 + 0) + (1 - \lambda)U(\theta_0 - 0)$.

23. What is the solution of the Dirichlet problem for the disk $|z - z_0| \leq \rho$?

24. Suppose that the analytic functions $w_n(z) = u_n(z) + i\, v_n(z)$ are regular in a simply connected domain G, and that the sequence $u_n(z)$ converges uniformly on every compact subset of G, while the sequence $w_n(z)$ converges at some point $z_0 \in G$. Show that the sequence $w_n(z)$ converges uniformly on every compact subset of G.

Hint. Apply Schwarz's formula (Section 11.16).

25. Assume that (1) the functions $w_n(z)$ $(n = 1, 2, \ldots)$ are single-valued and analytic in a domain G; (2) $|w_1(z)| \leq \ldots \leq |w_n(z)| \leq \ldots$ at every point $z \in G$; (3) For some point $z_0 \in G$ the limit $\lim_{n \to \infty} w_n(z_0)$ exists and is finite. Prove that $\lim_{n \to \infty} w_n(z)$ exists at every point of G.

Hint. Apply Harnack's principle and the preceding exercise to the functions

$\log |w_n(z)|$ in the domain obtained from G by the removal of the zeros of $w_1(z)$.

26. A real function $u(z)$ defined in the domain G is said to be *subharmonic* if for every $z = a \in G$ and every sufficiently small $r > 0$, the inequality

$$u(a) \leq \frac{1}{2\pi} \int_0^{2\pi} u(a + r\, e^{i\phi})\, d\phi$$

is satisfied. Show that a subharmonic function satisfies the maximum principle.

27. Let the boundary of the domain G be the union of two Jordan arcs α and β which have no common interior points. Let $u(z)$ be harmonic and bounded in G. Prove that if $\lim \sup u \leq m_1$ at the interior points of α and $\lim \sup u \leq m_2$ at the interior points of β, then

$$u(z) \leq m_1 \omega_1(z) + m_2 \omega_2(z),$$

everywhere in G, where $\omega_1(z)$ is the harmonic measure of α and $\omega_2(z)$ is the harmonic measure of β. When does equality hold?

28. Prove that if $w(z)$ is regular and bounded in the domain G of the preceding exercise, and that if $\lim \sup |w| \leq M_1$ at the interior points of α, and $\lim \sup |w| \leq M_2$ at the interior points of β, then for every $z \in G$,

$$|w(z)| \leq M_1^{\omega_1(z)} M_2^{\omega_2(z)}.$$

This is the so-called *two-constant theorem*.

29. Prove the *Phragmen-Lindelöf theorem*:

Let $w(z)$ be regular in the half-plane $\operatorname{Im} z > 0$. Further let (1) $\lim \sup |w| \leq 1$ at finite points of the real axis, (2) $\lim \inf (\log M(r))/r \leq 0$ as $r \to \infty$, where $M(r) = \sup |w(z)|$ on the upper semicircle $|z| = r$, $y > 0$. Show that $|w(z)| \leq 1$ in the whole half-plane.

Hint. Apply the two-constant theorem (Exercise 28) in the semicircle $|z| \leq r$, $y > 0$.

CHAPTER 12

ANALYTIC CONTINUATION

§1. THE PRINCIPLE OF ANALYTIC CONTINUATION

12.1. Analytic Continuation of a Function

Let the function $w_1(z)$ be regular in a domain G_1, and let the function $w_2(z)$ be regular in a domain G_2 such that the intersection $G_1 \cap G_2$ is non-empty and connected. Further, let us suppose that $w_1(z) = w_2(z)$ on an infinite set of points of $G_1 \cap G_2$ having a limit point in $G_1 \cap G_2$. Then $w_1(z) \equiv w_2(z)$ in the whole domain $G_1 \cap G_2$ (cf. Section 9.9). We now define a function $w(z)$ as follows:

$$w(z) \equiv \begin{cases} w_1(z) & \text{for} \quad z \in G_1, \\ w_2(z) & \text{for} \quad z \in G_2. \end{cases}$$

In the domain $G_1 \cap G_2$ we have $w \equiv w_1 \equiv w_2$. The function $w(z)$ so defined is regular in the domain $G_1 \cup G_2$. In view of Section 9.9, $w(z)$ is the only function regular in $G_1 \cup G_2$ which is equal to $w_1(z)$ in G_1. The function $w(z)$ is called the *analytic continuation* of the function $w_1(z)$ into the domain $G_1 \cup G_2$.

If the function $w_1(z)$ can be continued analytically into the domain $G_1 \cup G_2$, then it is possible in only one way: the analytic continuation therefore is unique.

12.2. Analytic Continuation along a Path

We have seen in Section 9.4 that an analytic function which is regular in a domain G can be expanded into a convergent power series in the neighborhood of any point of G. Conversely, any power series defines an analytic function in the interior of its circle of convergence.

For example, the series

$$\sum_{n=1}^{\infty} (-1)^{n-1} \frac{z^n}{n}$$

converges in the disk $|z| < 1$ and defines in this disk the analytic function $\log(1 + z)$. It can be analytically continued to the domain $z \neq -1, \infty$. The analytic continuation is defined by the function $\log(1 + z)$.

We shall now start with a given analytic function $w(z, K)$ defined in a disk K; we shall call $w(z, K)$ an *element of a general analytic function* or a *function-element*.

In the theory of analytic continuation we seek to construct a function which is analytic in a larger domain and which coincides with the given function in the original domain.

Suppose that K_1 and K_2 are intersecting disks. Let a function-element $w(z, K_1)$ be given in the disk K_1, and let $w(z, K_2)$ be its analytic continuation to the disk K_2. These function-elements are said to be *direct analytic continuations*. We consider a chain of n disks, K_1, K_2, ..., K_n, where any two consecutive disks have a non-empty intersection. We assume that in each disk K_ν ($\nu = 1, 2, \ldots, n$) there is a corresponding function-element $w(z, K_\nu)$ defined and that $w(z, K_{\nu-1})$ and $w(z, K_\nu)$ are direct analytic continuations. Then the function-element $w(z, K_n)$ is said to be the analytic continuation of $w(z, K_1)$ along this chain, and conversely.

If the disks K_n and K_1 have a non-empty intersection, the function-element $w(z, K_1)$ can be continued back to the initial disk K_1 along the chain K_1, K_2, ..., K_n, K_1. In general the function-element obtained in this way differs from the function-element $w(z, K_1)$.

If the disks K_1, K_2 and K_3 have a non-empty intersection $K_1 \cap K_2 \cap K_3$, and if the function-element $w(z, K_1)$ is continued along this chain to the disk K_3, then the function-element $w(z, K_3)$ so obtained will be a direct analytic continuation of $w(z, K_1)$ as well. In fact, this function-element will coincide with $w(z, K_1)$ in the domain $K_1 \cap K_2 \cap K_3$.

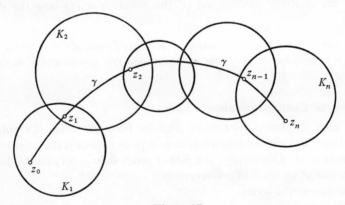

Figure 37

In the chain K_1, K_2, ..., K_n we choose the points z_0, z_1, ..., z_n in such a way that $z_0 \in K_1$, $z_\nu \in K_\nu \cap K_{\nu+1}$ ($\nu = 1, 2, \ldots, n - 1$) and $z_n \in K_n$ (Fig. 37). We join these points by a continuous arc γ such that the arc $z_{\nu-1}z_\nu$ lies entirely in the disk K_ν ($\nu = 1, \ldots, n$). Conversely, given an arbitrary continuous arc γ, we can always construct a chain of disks covering γ.

Let K_1', K_2', . . ., K_m' be another chain covering the arc γ. Further, let z_1', z_2', . . ., z_{m-1}', $z_m' = z_n$ be points of γ chosen in such a way that $z_\nu' \in K_\nu' \cap K_{\nu+1}'$ ($\nu = 1, 2, . . ., m - 1$). We assume that the function-element $w(z, K_1)$ can be continued along this chain too, and assert that we obtain the same value for the function at the point z_m' that we obtained at the point $z_n = z_m'$ by continuation along the first chain.

Let us suppose that z_1, z_1', z_2 (in this order) are the first points encountered when the arc γ is described, starting from z_0. The point z_1 then belongs to the disks K_1, K_1' and K_2; therefore, the function-elements $w(z, K_2)$ and $w(z, K_1')$ are direct analytic continuations. On the other hand, the point z_1' belongs to the disks K_1', K_2' and K_2, which implies that $w(z, K_1)$ and $w(z, K_2')$ are direct analytic continuations. Proceeding in this way, we see that $w(z, K_n)$ and $w(z, K_m')$ are also direct analytic continuations. Therefore they have the same value at the point z_n. This value is thus uniquely determined by the arc γ. We say that the function-element $w(z, K_1)$ has been continued analytically along the arc γ.

We now start with a given function-element $w(z, K_0)$ and continue it analytically in all possible ways. All elements obtained in this way constitute a well-defined function in the following sense.

If $w(z, K')$ and $w(z, K'')$ are any two such function-elements, then there exists a path γ along which the analytic continuation of $w(z, K')$ leads to the function-element $w(z, K'')$. The totality of these function-elements is called a *complete analytic function*. In general the analytic function defined in this way is not single-valued. In fact, if a function-element is continued along a closed path, the final function-element need not be the same as the initial one. Examples are provided by the functions $\log (1 + z)$ and $\sqrt{z}$.

Consequently the single-valued character of an analytic function "in the large," which we assumed in the definition in Section 1.14, is no longer required by this generalization of an analytic function (as an aggregate of function-elements).

It may happen that a function-element $w(z, K_0)$ cannot be continued analytically at all beyond its disk of definition. In this case we say that the circumference of K_0 is the *natural boundary* of the function. Such an example is given in Exercise 3, p. 223.

If a function $w(z)$ is regular in a domain G, and if K is a disk in G, then $w(z)$ restricted to the disk K defines a function-element $w(z, K)$. This function-element can be continued freely throughout the domain G without restriction and every function-element obtained by such continuation will coincide in its disk of definition with the function $w(z)$.

12.3. Singular Points

Suppose that the disk K_0 is contained in the disk K: $|z - a| < \rho$. If the function-element $w(z, K_0)$ can be continued analytically everywhere in the

8

disk K except to the point a, then a is said to be a *singular point* of the function. If γ is a closed curve in K which winds around the point a once, and if after analytic continuation along γ the function w returns to its initial value, then the function (or at least this branch of it) is single-valued in K. In this case a is a *pole* or an *essential singularity* of the function. On the other hand, if w does not return to its initial value after a single circuit around a, one of the following two situations must occur.

1) After encircling a a finite number of times, w returns to its initial value. In this case we say that a is an *algebraic* singularity.

2) w never returns to its initial value no matter how many times a is encircled. In this case we say that a is a *logarithmic* singularity.

§2. THE MONODROMY THEOREM

12.4.

We start with an arbitrary function-element $w(z, K_0)$ and assume that it can be continued analytically along every possible path lying in a *simply connected domain* G containing K_0. We assert that the resulting function is *single-valued*.

We first prove our assertion for the simple case in which the given domain G is *convex*. It is sufficient to show that there exists a single-valued regular function $w(z)$ in G which contains the function-element $w(z, K_0)$.

Let z_0 be the center of K_0. We define a single-valued function $w(z)$ in G by setting up a correspondence between every point z_1 of this circle and the well-defined *value* $w(z_1)$ which the analytic continuation of $w(z, K_0)$ along the straight-line segment $z_0 z_1$ assumes at the point z_1. We wish to show that the single-valued function $w(z)$ so defined is analytic.

The analytic continuation of $w(z, K_0)$ along the segment $z_0 z_1$ requires a chain of disks covering this segment. If the neighborhood T of z_1 is chosen in such a way that all segments leading from z_0 to a point of T belong entirely to the chain we started with, then we can use this chain to continue $w(z, K_0)$ to any point of T. At every point of T, therefore, $w(z)$ is defined by the same function-element. It follows that the function $w(z)$ is analytic in the domain T. Since z_1 is an arbitrary point of the domain G, $w(z)$ is analytic everywhere in G.

In view of the remarks at the end of Section 12.2, the analytic continuation of $w(z, K_0)$ coincides everywhere with the function $w(z)$. Thus a function obtained by arbitrary analytic continuation of an initial function-element $w(z, K_0)$ is *single-valued* in the convex domain G.

Let now G be an arbitrary simply connected domain. Suppose that the function-element $w(z, K_0)$ is continued from the point z_0 to the point z_1 along a path γ in G. If the path γ is subjected to an elementary deformation (cf. Section 8.16), then, as we have just seen, the analytic continuation of $w(z, K_0)$ to the point z_1 remains unaltered. Therefore, if we analytically continue the function-element $w(z, K_0)$ along two homotopic paths γ and γ' from z_0 to z_1, the analytic continuations will have the same value at the point z_1.

Since the domain G is simply connected, any two paths joining z_0 and z_1 are homotopic. The function obtained from the function-element $w(z, K_0)$ by analytic continuation is therefore single-valued. We have thus proved the *monodromy theorem.*

> *If a function-element can be continued analytically along every path in a simply connected domain, then the resulting function is single-valued.*

12.5. Meromorphic Function-Elements

In addition to regular function-elements we may also consider meromorphic function-elements in a disk K. By this we mean function-elements which are either regular in K or have a finite number of poles in K. Everything said up to now can be applied to meromorphic function-elements. The monodromy theorem also remains valid: if a function can be meromorphically continued along every path in a simply connected domain, then it is single-valued. The function is then meromorphic in the domain.

A neighborhood of the point at infinity can also be treated, for this may be reduced to the finite case by an inversion.

§3. THE INVERSE OF A RATIONAL FUNCTION

12.6   Construction of the Inverse Function

As an application of the monodromy theorem we shall investigate the inverse $z = z(w)$ of a rational function $w = w(z)$ as a complete analytic function.

Suppose the rational function $w = w(z)$ is of order n (cf. Chapter 2 and Chapter 9, Section 7). The mapping $z \to w$ maps the extended z-plane onto a covering surface R_w of the extended w-plane composed of n complete sheets. Its branch-points correspond to the finite points z where the derivative $w'(z) = 0$ and to the multiple poles of $w(z)$. Let $w = w_\nu$ ($\nu = 1, \ldots, q$) denote the distinct w-points over which the branch-points are situated. We join the points $w_1, \ldots, w_q, w_1$ by a simple closed polygon γ_w, which divides the extended w-plane into two simply connected polygonal regions P_w and P_w^*.

Let us choose $z = z^1$ in such a way that $w^1 = w(z^1) \neq \infty$ is in the interior of P_w. Then, by Section 9.24, there exists a well-defined regular function-element $z = z^1(w)$ of the inverse function of $w = w(z)$ with the property that $z^1 = z^1(w^1)$. The function-element $z^1(w)$ can be continued analytically or meromorphically along every path in P_w, and by the monodromy theorem the branch of the inverse function so obtained is single-valued. Since $w(z)$ is single-valued, this branch $z = z(w)$ maps the interior of P_w one-to-one conformally onto a simply connected domain P_z^1 of the z-plane. The mapping is also conformal on the boundary γ_w except at the points $w_1, \ldots, w_q$. These exceptional points are branch points of $z(w)$. In the neighborhood of a branch point w_ν, $z(w)$ has an *algebraic* function-element which can be expanded into powers of $(w - w_\nu)^{1/r_\nu}$ or (in case $w_\nu = \infty$) into powers of $(1/w)^{1/r_\nu}$, where $r_\nu - 1$ $(1 \leq r_\nu \leq n)$ denotes the order of the branch point w_ν (cf. Section 9.30).

The function $z_1(w)$ can be analytically continued into the domain P_w^* across each side $w_\nu w_{\nu+1}$ $(\nu = 1, \ldots, q; w_{q+1} = w_1)$ of the polygonal domain P_w. The branches of the inverse function so obtained (which may partially coincide) map P_w^* conformally onto mutually disjoint subdomains of the z-plane. If these branches are again continued analytically across γ_w into the domain P_w, and if the process is repeated again, then after a finite number of repetitions, we obtain the complete analytic function of the inverse function $z(w)$. This function is single-valued on a connected Riemann surface R_w composed of n "half-sheets" P_w and n half-sheets P_w^*. The image of R_w is the entire schlicht (i.e., one-sheeted) z-plane which is completely and simply covered by the polygonal regions $P_z^1, P_z^2, \ldots, P_z^n$ and $P_z^{*1}, \ldots, P_z^{*n}$ which are the images of P_w and P_w^*.

12.7. The Graph or Line-Complex of the Surface R_w

An overall view of the structure of the covering surface R_w can be obtained by the method described in Section 6.14. We take a point w in the region P_w, and a point w^* in P_w^*; let us denote their images in the regions P_z and P_z^* by $z^1, \ldots, z^n$ and $z^{*1}, \ldots, z^{*n}$, respectively. In our diagram the points $z^1, \ldots, z^n$ will be represented by small circles, the points $z^{1*}, \ldots, z^{n*}$ by crosses. If, as in Section 6.14, we now join these points by means of segments across the separating sides of the respective polygons P_z^ν, $P_z^{*\mu}$, we obtain a "graph" (or line-complex), which gives a good picture of the structure of the covering surface R_w. The graph divides the plane into a number of "elementary polygons" which correspond to the branch points of the surface in such a way that a branch point of order $r - 1$ corresponds to an elementary polygon with $2r$ sides.

As an example we consider the Riemann surface of a cubic polynomial. These surfaces fall into two classes which are represented by the graphs of Fig. 38. Here the elementary polygons containing no branch points $(r = 1)$ are represented by double segments (cf. Exercise 7, p. 224).

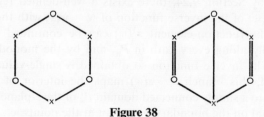

Figure 38

§4. HARMONIC CONTINUATION. THE REFLECTION PRINCIPLE

12.8. Harmonic Continuation

We now consider the continuation of harmonic functions which corresponds to analytic continuation. First we prove the following theorem.

If the function $u(z)$ is harmonic in the domain G and if $u(z) \equiv 0$ in a subdomain G^* of G, then $u(z) \equiv 0$ in the whole domain G.

Suppose first that G is a disk. If $v(z)$ is the harmonic conjugate of $u(z)$, then the function $f(z) \equiv u(z) + iv(z)$ is analytic in G. In view of the Cauchy-Riemann equations, it follows from the hypothesis that $v(z)$ is identically equal to a real constant C in the domain G^*, and therefore $f(z) \equiv iC$. It follows from the principle of analytic continuation that $f(z) \equiv iC$ in the whole domain G, and hence $u(z) \equiv 0$. For *arbitrary* domains the theorem may now be proved by using a chain of disks.

Now let G_1 and G_2 be two domains with a common subdomain $G_1 \cap G_2$. We assume that the function $u_1(z)$ is harmonic in G_1 and that the function $u_2(z)$ is harmonic in G_2, and also that $u_1(z) \equiv u_2(z)$ in the domain $G_1 \cap G_2$. These conditions determine the function $u_2(z)$ uniquely. Indeed, if $v_2(z)$ is another harmonic function satisfying the same conditions, then $v_2 - u_2 = 0$ in $G_1 \cap G_2$. In view of the theorem just proved, this implies that $v_2 \equiv u_2$ in the domain G_2.

The function u_2 is called the *harmonic continuation* of the function u_1 into the domain G_2.

12.9. The Reflection Principle for Harmonic Functions

For harmonic continuation we prove the *Schwarz reflection principle*.

Let G be a domain in the half-plane $\mathrm{Im}\, z > 0$ *whose boundary contains a segment l of the real axis as a free arc (that is, every interior point of l has a circular neighborhood whose upper half lies entirely in G).*

Suppose that the function $u(x, y) = u(z)$, $z = x + iy$ is harmonic in G and tends to zero as z tends to an arbitrary point of the segment l. Then $u(z)$ can be continued harmonically into the domain $\bar{G}$ which is symmetric to G with respect to the real axis. The harmonic continuation is defined by the function $U(z)$ which is $u(z)$ in the domain G, 0 on the segment l, and $u(\bar{z})$ in the domain $\bar{G}$.

We must prove that $U(z)$ is harmonic in all of the domain $G \cup \bar{G} \cup l$. By definition, U is harmonic in the domain G. In the domain $\bar{G}$ we have, by the definition of U, that

$$U(x, y) = -u(x, -y).$$

Using for a moment the notation

$$x = \xi, \qquad y = -\eta,$$

we have

$$U(x, y) = -u(\xi, \eta),$$

where (ξ, η) belongs to G if (x, y) is in $\bar{G}$. Differentiation yields

$$\frac{\partial^2 U}{\partial x^2} = -\frac{\partial^2 u}{\partial \xi^2}, \qquad \frac{\partial^2 U}{\partial y^2} = -\frac{\partial^2 u}{\partial \eta^2},$$

whence

$$\Delta U = -\left(\frac{\partial^2 u}{\partial \zeta^2} + \frac{\partial^2 u}{\partial \eta^2}\right) = 0.$$

Therefore U is harmonic in $\bar{G}$.

To show that U is also harmonic on the segment l, we consider a disk K: $|z - a| < \rho$ whose center lies on l, and whose radius ρ is so small that the disk belongs entirely to $G \cup \bar{G} \cup l$. We use the Poisson integral to define the function

$$V(z) = V(a + r\,e^{i\phi}) = \frac{1}{2\pi} \int_0^{2\pi} U(a + \rho\,e^{i\theta}) \frac{\rho^2 - r^2}{\rho^2 + r^2 - 2\rho r \cos(\theta - \phi)}\,d\theta,$$

which is harmonic in the whole disk K.

To prove that $U(z)$ is harmonic on the real axis, we will show that $U(z) \equiv V(z)$ in K. Suppose first that z is in the upper half of K. On the boundary arc $\operatorname{Im} z > 0$, $|z - a| = \rho$, the function $V(z)$ takes the boundary values $U(a + \rho\,e^{i\theta})$. If z lies on the real axis, the contributions to the integral from the upper and lower semi-circles cancel; hence, $V = 0 = U$ on that part of l which lies in K. By the maximum and minimum principles, $V(z) \equiv U(z)$ in the upper half of K. By the same argument $V(z) \equiv U(z)$ in the lower half of K. Thus $V \equiv U$ in the whole disk K. Since V is harmonic in K, so is U; consequently, U is harmonic on the segment l. The proof of the theorem is now complete.

12.10. The Reflection Principle for Analytic Functions

We shall now prove the analogous theorem for analytic functions.

Suppose that the function $w(z) = u(z) + i\,v(z)$ is regular in a domain G for which the conditions of Section 12.9 are fulfilled, and that $v(z)$ tends to the limit zero as z tends to any point of the segment l. Under these assumptions $w(z)$ may be continued analytically across l into the domain $\bar{G}$. The function so obtained assumes conjugate complex values at points that are symmetric with respect to the segment l.

Proof. In the domain $\bar{G}$ we define the function

$$f(z) = \overline{w(\bar{z})} = u(x, -y) - i\,v(x, -y),$$

which is an analytic function of z. Indeed, if we substitute $x = \xi$, $y = -\eta$, we have

$$\frac{\partial u}{\partial x} = \frac{\partial u}{\partial \xi}, \qquad \frac{\partial(-v)}{\partial x} = -\frac{\partial v}{\partial \xi},$$

$$\frac{\partial u}{\partial y} = -\frac{\partial u}{\partial \eta}, \qquad \frac{\partial(-v)}{\partial y} = \frac{\partial v}{\partial \eta}.$$

By hypothesis, the Cauchy-Riemann equations are valid in G; by the above identities they are also satisfied in $\bar{G}$, so that $f(z)$ is analytic in $\bar{G}$.

We now assert that $f(z)$ is the analytic continuation of $w(z)$ into the domain $\bar{G}$. Let K be a disk whose center lies on l and which belongs to the domain $G \cup l \cup \bar{G}$. In view of Section 12.9, the function $v(z) = \operatorname{Im} w(z)$ can be continued harmonically into the whole disk K. The harmonic continuation is given by the function $V(z)$, which is equal to $v(z)$ for $z \in G \cap K$, equal to 0 for $z \in l \cap K$, and equal to $-v(\bar{z})$ for $z \in \bar{G} \cap K$. The function $V(z)$ defines in K an analytic function

$$F(z) = U(z) + iV(z),$$

which is unique up to a real additive constant. We choose this constant so that $F(z_0) = w(z_0)$ at some arbitrarily fixed point $z_0 \in K \cap G$. Then $F(z) \equiv w(z)$ in the whole domain $G \cap K$. We show that $F(z) \equiv f(z)$ in $\bar{G} \cap K$. In fact, in this domain we have

$$\operatorname{Im} F(z) = V(z) = -v(\bar{z}) = \operatorname{Im} f(z),$$

which implies that the functions $F(z)$ and $f(z)$ coincide in $\bar{G} \cap K$ up to a real additive constant C. To show that this constant is zero, we let z tend to an arbitrary point $\zeta_0 \in l \cap K$ from within the domain $\bar{G} \cap K$. Then

$$\operatorname{Re} f(z) \equiv u(\bar{z}) = \operatorname{Re} F(\bar{z}) \to \operatorname{Re} F(\zeta_0),$$

because $F(z)$, as an analytic function, is continuous in K. Hence, $C = 0$ and $f(z) \equiv F(z)$ in $\bar{G} \cap K$. Therefore $f(z)$ is the analytic continuation of $w(z)$ into the domain $\bar{G}$.

12.11. Generalization of the Reflection Principle

If we apply the properties of bilinear transformations, together with the reflection principle of the preceding section, we obtain the following generalization.

Let G be a domain whose boundary contains an arc Γ of the circle C as a free arc and which lies in the interior of C. Let G^* be the domain obtained from G by reflection in the circle C. Further let $w(z)$ be a function which is analytic in G and which satisfies the following condition: If z tends to any point $\zeta_0 \in \Gamma$, then the image $w = w(z)$ of z tends to a circular arc K. Under these assumptions, $w(z)$ may be continued analytically across the arc Γ. The analytic continuation is effected by a function $f(z)$ which assumes at the point z^*—the reflection of z in Γ—the value w^* which is the reflection of $w(z)$ in K.

We consider finally the more general case in which the boundary of G contains a *regular analytic arc*. An arc γ is said to be *analytic* if it is defined by a parametric equation

$$z = z(\tau), \qquad \tau_1 \leqq \tau \leqq \tau_2, \tag{12.1}$$

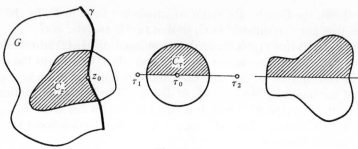

Figure 39

and if, in the neighborhood of any interior point τ_0 of the interval (τ_1, τ_2), the function $z(\tau)$ can be expanded into a power series

$$z(\tau) = c_0 + c_1(\tau - \tau_0) + \cdots \qquad (12.2)$$

which converges in some interval

$$|\tau - \tau_0| < \delta. \qquad (12.3)$$

If $c_1 = z'(\tau_0) \neq 0$, the curve is said to be *regular* at the point $z_0 = z(\tau_0)$. We shall now prove the following generalization of the reflection principle.

> *Let the function $f(z)$ be regular in a domain G whose boundary contains a regular analytic arc γ as a free arc: $z = z(\tau)$ $(\tau_1 \leq \tau \leq \tau_2)$. If $\operatorname{Im} f(z)$ tends to zero as z tends to an arbitrary interior point of the arc γ, then $f(z)$ can be analytically continued across the arc γ.*

Proof. If τ is allowed to assume complex values, the series (12.2) converges in the disk (12.3) and defines an analytic function in this disk. This function maps a disk C_τ with center τ_0 one-to-one conformally onto a certain neighborhood C_z of z_0 (Fig. 39). Let us assume that the point z describes the arc γ in the positive sense (with respect to G) as τ increases from τ_1 to τ_2. Then the intersection of C_τ with the upper half-plane corresponds to that part of C_z which lies in the domain G. The composite function

$$w = f(z(\tau)) \qquad (12.4)$$

is regular in the upper half of the disk C_τ. If $\operatorname{Im} \tau \to 0$, then z approaches the arc γ, so that $\operatorname{Im} w$ tends to zero. If we apply the Schwarz reflection principle, we see that (12.4) may be continued analytically into the whole disk C_τ. Since τ is a regular function of z in the domain C_z, the same is true of the function w in the domain C_z. Thus $f(z)$ can be continued analytically across the arc γ. The theorem is thereby proved.

EXERCISES ON CHAPTER 12

1. Show that on the circle of convergence of a power series there is always at least one point with the following property: the function defined by the

series cannot be continued analytically to the exterior of the disk along any curve passing through the point.

2. Suppose that the coefficients of the power series

$$w(z) = \sum_{n=0}^{\infty} a_n z^n$$

are non-negative. Show that the function $w(z)$ cannot be continued analytically along the positive real axis across the circle of convergence.

Hint. Let the radius of convergence be $R > 0$. If $|z_0| = r_0 < R$, it follows from the assumption $a_n \geq 0$ that $|w^{(\nu)}(z_0)| \leq w^{(\nu)}(r_0)$. By expanding $w(z)$ into powers of $z - z_0$ on the one hand, and into powers of $z - r_0$ on the other hand, one can show that if the function $w(z)$ could be continued analytically along the positive real axis across the circle of convergence, then it could be continued along any other radius as well. The radius of convergence would then be greater than R.

3. The function $w(z)$ defined by the power series

$$w(z) = \sum_{n=0}^{\infty} a_n z^{n!}, \qquad a_n > 0 \qquad (n = 0, 1, \ldots)$$

cannot be continued analytically beyond its circle of convergence.

Hint. Let $R > 0$ be the radius of convergence. If $z = e^{2\pi i p/q} \zeta$, where p and q are relatively prime integers, then $z^{n!} = \zeta^{n!}$ for $n \geq q$. Thus $w(z)$ and $w(\zeta)$ differ only by a rational function. If it were possible to continue $w(z)$ analytically across the circle of convergence along a radius $\arg z = 2\pi p/q$, then it could also be continued along the positive real axis. By Exercise 2 this is impossible. Since the points $R\, e^{2\pi i p/q}$ are everywhere dense on the circle $|z| = R$, $w(z)$ cannot be continued along any path across the circle of convergence.

4. Let the power series $\sum a_\nu z^\nu$ have radius of convergence $R > 0$. Substitute $z = z_0 + (z - z_0)$ and show that the radius of convergence of the resulting power series in $z - z_0$ is not less than $R - |z_0|$.

5. Show that the results obtained for analytic continuation are also valid for meromorphic continuation (i.e., using meromorphic function-elements), and are also valid if the path of continuation goes through the point ∞. Prove the monodromy theorem under these more general assumptions.

6. Let M be a polyhedral surface of spherical type in three-dimensional Euclidean space (that is, a surface which can be continuously deformed into a sphere). By Euler's formula we have $k - s + t = 2$, where k is the number of vertices, s the number of edges, and t the number of faces of the polyhedron. Show that Riemann's formula (9.58) is a consequence of Euler's formula.

Hint. Let $w = w(z)$ be a rational function of order n. Every branch-point of R_w of order $r_\nu - 1$ corresponds in the associated graph (Section 12.7) to

8*

an elementary polygon with $2r_\nu$ sides. Each side belongs to two polygons, so that the total number of sides is $\sum r_\nu$. Since $k = 2n$ and since t is the number of elementary polygons, the Euler formula gives

$$k - 2 = 2n - 2 = s - t = \sum r_\nu - t = \sum (r_\nu - 1).$$

7. For any cubic polynomial $P(z)$, the equation $w = P(z)$ can always be transformed either to the form $w = z^3$ or to the form $w = z^3 - 3z$ by suitable bilinear transformations of z and w. Construct the corresponding graph (cf. Fig. 38.)

8. Let the function $w(z)$ be analytic in the whole plane, real on the real axis, and purely imaginary on the imaginary axis. Show that $w(z)$ is an odd function.

9. Let the function $w(z)$ be analytic, apart from a finite number of poles, in the disk $|z| \leq 1$. Further, let $|w(z)| = 1$ for $|z| = 1$. Show that $w(z)$ is a rational function.

10. If it is assumed that the function $w(z)$ is continuous on the segment l, show that one can give a shorter proof of the reflection principle based upon Cauchy's integral formula.

CHAPTER 13

ENTIRE FUNCTIONS

§1. INFINITE PRODUCTS

13.1. Definition

Let $a_1, a_2, \ldots, a_n, \ldots$ be an infinite sequence of non-zero complex numbers, and set

$$P_n = \prod_{\nu=1}^{n} a_\nu.$$

The infinite product $\prod_{\nu=1}^{\infty} a_\nu$ is said to converge if the limit

$$\lim_{n \to \infty} P_n = P$$

exists and has a finite non-zero value.

We then define

$$P = \prod_{\nu=1}^{\infty} a_\nu.$$

If the product $\prod_{\nu=1}^{\infty} a_\nu$ converges, then

$$a_n = \frac{P_n}{P_{n-1}} \to 1 \qquad \text{as} \qquad n \to \infty. \tag{13.1}$$

This necessary condition is not sufficient for the convergence of the product. For example, if $a_n = 1 + 1/n = (n + 1)/n$, then

$$P_n = \frac{2}{1} \frac{3}{2} \cdots \frac{n+1}{n} = n + 1.$$

The corresponding product is therefore divergent (not convergent).

13.2. A Convergence Criterion

We shall derive an important criterion for the convergence of the product

$$\prod_{\nu=1}^{\infty} (1 + u_\nu) \qquad (u_\nu \neq -1, \nu = 1, 2, \ldots). \tag{13.2}$$

From the equation

$$P_n = \prod_{\nu=1}^{n} (1 + u_\nu)$$

it follows that

$$\log P_n = \log |P_n| + i \arg P_n = \sum_{1}^{n} \log (1 + u_\nu). \tag{13.3}$$

On the right-hand side we take the branch of the logarithm that satisfies

$$-\pi < \operatorname{Im} \log (1 + u_\nu) = \arg (1 + u_\nu) \leq \pi$$

for each ν. This determines the branch of $\log P_n$. We shall now show that if the product (13.2) converges, that is, if

$$\lim_{n \to \infty} P_n = P \neq 0, \infty, \tag{13.4}$$

then the series

$$S = \sum_{\nu=1}^{\infty} \log (1 + u_\nu) \tag{13.5}$$

also converges. By (13.4) for every $\epsilon > 0$ there exists an n_ϵ such that

$$\arg P_n = \arg P + \langle \epsilon \rangle + k_n \cdot 2\pi \qquad (k_n \text{ an integer}) \tag{13.6}$$

whenever $n \geq n_\epsilon$. For these values of n

$$\arg P_{n+1} - \arg P_n = \arg (1 + u_{n+1}) = \langle 2\epsilon \rangle + (k_{n+1} - k_n)2\pi.$$

Since the product (13.2) converges, we have, in view of (13.1),

$$\lim_{n \to \infty} u_{n+1} = 0,$$

so that $\arg (1 + u_n) \to 0$ as $n \to \infty$. It follows that $k_n = k_{n+1}$; the integer k_n is therefore independent of n whenever $n \geq n_\epsilon$ and $|u_{n+1}| < 1$. Accordingly, by (13.6), $\arg P_n$ and therefore also $\log P_n$ converge to a finite limit as $n \to \infty$. Because of (13.3), this implies the convergence of the series (13.5).

Conversely, if the series (13.5) converges, then the sequence P_n converges to a finite non-zero limit as $n \to \infty$. Hence, the product (13.2) converges and $\log P = S$, or $P \to e^S$.

A necessary and sufficient condition for the convergence of the product (13.2) is the convergence of the series (13.5).

13.3. Absolute Convergence

We prove the following proposition.

The series (13.5) *converges absolutely if and only if the series*

$$\sum_{1}^{\infty} u_\nu \tag{13.7}$$

converges absolutely.

If one of the two series (13.5) and (13.7) converges, then, from a certain n_0 onwards, $|u_n| \leq \frac{1}{2}$. Consequently,

$$\log (1 + u_n) = u_n - \frac{u_n^2}{2} + \frac{u_n^3}{3} - \cdots = u_n \left(1 - \frac{u_n}{2} + \frac{u_n^2}{3} - \cdots\right),$$

so that

$$|\log (1 + u_n)| = |u_n| \, |1 + v_n|,$$

where

$$|v_n| = \left| -\frac{u_n}{2} + \frac{u_n^2}{3} - \cdots \right| \leq \frac{|u_n|}{2} + \frac{|u_n|^2}{2} + \cdots = \frac{|u_n|}{2} \frac{1}{1 - |u_n|} \leq \frac{1}{2}.$$

Hence,

$$\tfrac{1}{2}|u_n| \leq |\log (1 + u_n)| \leq \tfrac{3}{2}|u_n| \qquad (n \geq n_0).$$

Therefore, the absolute convergence of either of the series (13.5) and (13.7) implies the absolute convergence of the other. If the series (13.5) converges absolutely, its sum is independent of the order of its terms. In this case the value of the product (13.2) is likewise *independent of the order of its factors*.

If (13.5) converges absolutely, then so does the series (13.7). Therefore the product $\prod (1 + |u_\nu|)$ also converges. *In this case the product* (13.2) *is said to be absolutely convergent.*

13.4. Functions Defined by Infinite Products

We now investigate the product

$$\prod_{\nu=1}^{\infty} (1 + u_\nu(z)), \tag{13.8}$$

where each $u_\nu(z)$ is regular and different from -1 in a simply connected domain G. If we denote

$$P_n(z) = \prod_{1}^{n} (1 + u_\nu(z)),$$

we have

$$\log P_n(z) = \sum_{1}^{n} \log (1 + u_\nu(z)) \tag{13.9}$$

for suitably chosen branches of the logarithms. If at some point of the domain G the branches on the right-hand side of (13.9) are fixed, the branch on the left-hand side is fixed at this point. If the functions $\log\left(1 + u_\nu(z)\right)$ are continued analytically from this point along an arbitrary path in the domain G, then, by the monodromy theorem, we obtain single-valued functions, and Eq. (13.9) is valid throughout G. If the series

$$S(z) = \sum_1^\infty \log\left(1 + u_\nu(z)\right) \tag{13.10}$$

converges uniformly on every compact subset of G, then it defines an analytic function regular in G. At the same time the product (13.8) also converges, and its value

$$P(z) = e^{S(z)}$$

is also regular in G.

If we apply the inequalities derived in Section 13.3, it follows that if the series

$$\sum_1^\infty |u_\nu(z)| \tag{13.11}$$

converges uniformly on every compact subset of G, then so does the series (13.10). The product (13.8) will then define a regular analytic function in G. We thus have the following theorem.

If the functions $u_\nu(z)\,(\neq -1)$ are regular in a simply connected domain G, and if the series (13.11) converges uniformly on every compact subset of G, then the infinite product (13.8) defines a regular analytic function in the domain G.

§2. PRODUCT REPRESENTATION OF THE FUNCTION $w = \sin \pi z$

13.5.

We return to the partial-fraction expansion of the function $\cot \pi z$ derived in Chapter 10, Section 3:

$$\pi \cot \pi z = \frac{1}{z} + \sum_{\nu=1}^\infty \frac{2z}{z^2 - \nu^2}. \tag{13.12}$$

If we restrict z to the disk $|z| \leq R$ and write

$$\pi \cot \pi z = \frac{1}{z} + \sum_{\nu=1}^n \frac{2z}{z^2 - \nu^2} + \sum_{\nu=n+1}^\infty \frac{2z}{z^2 - \nu^2} \quad (n \leq R < n + 1), \tag{13.13}$$

then the last series converges uniformly in the disk and its terms are regular functions of z. We can therefore integrate it term by term along any path in

$|z| \le R$ joining the origin to the point z. Integration of the individual terms yields

$$\int_0^z \frac{2z}{z^2 - v^2} \, dz = \log \left(1 - \frac{z^2}{v^2} \right),$$

where we choose that branch of the logarithm which vanishes at the origin. The sum of the series under consideration is therefore the derivative of the function

$$\sum_{v=n+1}^{\infty} \log \left(1 - \frac{z^2}{v^2} \right).$$

On the other hand, the sum of the first two terms on the right-hand side of (13.13) is the derivative of the function

$$\log \pi z + \sum_{v=1}^{n} \log \left(1 - \frac{z^2}{v^2} \right),$$

while the left-hand side is the derivative of $\log \sin \pi z$. Hence,

$$\log \sin \pi z = \log \pi z + \sum_{v=1}^{\infty} \log \left(1 - \frac{z^2}{v^2} \right) + C,$$

where C is a constant, or

$$\log \frac{\sin \pi z}{\pi z} = \sum_{v=1}^{\infty} \log \left(1 - \frac{z^2}{v^2} \right) + C.$$

Both sides are regular in the disk $|z| < 1$. If we set $z = 0$ and choose everywhere that branch of the logarithm which vanishes at the origin, it turns out that $C = 0$. By the principle of analytic continuation, the two sides are identically equal, so that

$$\log \frac{\sin \pi z}{\pi z} = \sum_{v=1}^{\infty} \log \left(1 - \frac{z^2}{v^2} \right).$$

For $z \ne \pm v$ this identity can be written in the form

$$\sin \pi z = \pi z \prod_{v=1}^{\infty} \left(1 - \frac{z^2}{v^2} \right). \tag{13.14}$$

This formula is also valid for $z = \pm v$, if we assign the value zero to an infinite product whenever one factor is zero.

13.6.

In formula (13.14) we may write

$$1 - \frac{z^2}{v^2} = \left(1 - \frac{z}{v} \right) \left(1 + \frac{z}{v} \right).$$

However, this factorization does not permit us to write the product in the form

$$\prod_{\substack{\nu=-\infty \\ \nu \neq 0}}^{\infty} \left(1 - \frac{z}{\nu}\right) \tag{13.15}$$

since by Section 1 this product diverges at least for all real values of z. Nevertheless, the convergence can be restored by the following modification.

We start from the divergent series

$$\sum_{\nu=1}^{\infty} \log\left(1 - \frac{z}{\nu}\right) \tag{13.16}$$

and construct a convergent series from it. We restrict z to the disk $|z| \leq R$ and choose $n_0 \geq 2R$. Then, for every $\nu \geq n_0$

$$\log\left(1 - \frac{z}{\nu}\right) = -\frac{z}{\nu} - \frac{1}{2}\left(\frac{z}{\nu}\right)^2 - \frac{1}{3}\left(\frac{z}{\nu}\right)^3 - \cdots, \tag{13.17}$$

and, hence,

$$\left|\log\left(1 - \frac{z}{\nu}\right) + \frac{z}{\nu}\right| \leq \frac{1}{2}\left(\frac{|z|}{\nu}\right)^2 + \frac{1}{3}\left(\frac{|z|}{\nu}\right)^3 + \cdots \leq \frac{1}{2}\frac{|z|^2}{\nu^2}\frac{1}{1 - \frac{|z|}{\nu}} \leq \frac{R^2}{\nu^2}.$$

Therefore, the series

$$\sum_{\nu=n0}^{\infty}\left[\log\left(1 - \frac{z}{\nu}\right) + \frac{z}{\nu}\right] \tag{13.18}$$

converges absolutely and uniformly in the disk $|z| \leq R$. Thus, by Section 13.3, the product

$$\prod_{\nu=n0}^{\infty}\left[\left(1 - \frac{z}{\nu}\right)e^{z/\nu}\right]$$

converges absolutely in the disk $|z| \leq R$.

In the same way we see that the product

$$\prod_{\nu=-n0}^{-\infty}\left[\left(1 - \frac{z}{\nu}\right)e^{z/\nu}\right]$$

also converges absolutely for $|z| \leq R$, and, hence, the same is true of the product

$$\prod_{\nu=-\infty}^{\infty}{}'\left[\left(1 - \frac{z}{\nu}\right)e^{z/\nu}\right], \tag{13.19}$$

if a finite number of factors is omitted. Here a prime has been added to the product sign to indicate that ν takes all values except $\nu = 0$. A corresponding notation will also be used for summations.

If we combine in pairs those factors of the product (13.19) for which the ν-values have opposite signs, we see that the product has the same value as the product

$$\prod_{\nu=1}^{\infty} \left(1 - \frac{z^2}{\nu^2}\right).$$

The product representation (13.14) of the function $\sin \pi z$ can therefore be written in the form

$$\sin \pi z = \pi z \prod_{\nu=-\infty}^{\infty}{}' \left[\left(1 - \frac{z}{\nu}\right) e^{z/\nu}\right]. \tag{13.20}$$

§3. THE WEIERSTRASS FACTORIZATION THEOREM

13.7. Entire Functions without Zeros

If $g(z)$ is an entire function, then

$$w(z) = e^{g(z)} \tag{13.21}$$

is an entire function without zeros. We shall prove that the converse is also true.

An entire function $w(z)$ without zeros can always be represented in the form (13.21), where $g(z)$ is an entire function.

By assumption, an arbitrary branch of the function $\log w(z)$ can be continued analytically along any path in the finite plane. By the monodromy theorem this function is single-valued. If we denote the entire function so defined by $g(z)$, we obtain for $w(z)$ the expression (13.21).

13.8. Generalization of the Factorization Theorem for a Polynomial

To any given finite set of points $\{a_1, a_2, \ldots, a_m\}$ there always exists an entire function with the zeros $a_1, a_2, \ldots, a_m$, for example, the polynomial

$$\left(1 - \frac{z}{a_1}\right)\left(1 - \frac{z}{a_2}\right) \cdots \left(1 - \frac{z}{a_m}\right).$$

We now consider an infinite sequence of points

$$a_1, a_2, \ldots, a_n, \ldots \tag{13.22}$$

such that

$$0 < |a_1| \leq |a_2| \leq \ldots \leq |a_n| \leq \ldots, \qquad \lim_{n \to \infty} |a_n| = \infty,$$

and pose the problem of constructing an entire function which vanishes at the points (13.22) and nowhere else. If the point a_ν appears as a multiple zero, we write it in the sequence (13.22) as many times as its order indicates. Let us consider now the infinite product

$$\prod_{\nu=1}^{\infty} \left(1 - \frac{z}{a_\nu}\right). \tag{13.23}$$

If the series

$$\sum_{\nu=1}^{\infty} \frac{1}{|a_\nu|}$$

converges, then the series

$$\sum_{\nu=1}^{\infty} \left|\frac{z}{a_\nu}\right|$$

converges uniformly on every bounded set. The product (13.23) then defines an entire function of z which vanishes at the points (13.22) and at no other points.

13.9. The General Case

If the product (13.23) does not converge, we construct the entire function corresponding to it by the same method which we used for the product representation of $\sin \pi z$.

We restrict z to the disk $|z| \leq R$ and choose n_0 so large that

$$|a_\nu| \geq 2R \qquad \text{for} \qquad \nu \geq n_0.$$

For these values of ν we have

$$\log \left(1 - \frac{z}{a_\nu}\right) = -\frac{z}{a_\nu} - \frac{1}{2}\left(\frac{z}{a_\nu}\right)^2 - \cdots - \frac{1}{n}\left(\frac{z}{a_\nu}\right)^n - \cdots.$$

We set

$$P_\nu(z) = \frac{z}{a_\nu} + \frac{1}{2}\left(\frac{z}{a_\nu}\right)^2 + \cdots + \frac{1}{n_\nu}\left(\frac{z}{a_\nu}\right)^{n_\nu}$$

and show that, by a suitable choice of the numbers n_ν, the series

$$\sum_{\nu=n0}^{\infty} \left[\log \left(1 - \frac{z}{a_\nu}\right) + P_\nu(z)\right] \tag{13.24}$$

converges in the disk $|z| \leq R$.

For the general term of the series (13.24) we have the estimate

$$\left|\log \left(1 - \frac{z}{a_\nu}\right) + P_\nu(z)\right| \leq \frac{1}{n_\nu + 1}\left|\frac{z}{a_\nu}\right|^{n_\nu+1} + \frac{1}{n_\nu + 2}\left|\frac{z}{a_\nu}\right|^{n_\nu+2} + \cdots$$

$$\leq \frac{1}{n_\nu + 1}\left|\frac{z}{a_\nu}\right|^{n_\nu+1} \left\{1 + \left|\frac{z}{a_\nu}\right| + \left|\frac{z}{a_\nu}\right|^2 + \cdots\right\}$$

$$= \frac{1}{n_\nu + 1}\left|\frac{z}{a_\nu}\right|^{n_\nu+1} \frac{1}{1 - \left|\frac{z}{a_\nu}\right|} \leq \frac{2}{n_\nu + 1}\left(\frac{R}{|a_\nu|}\right)^{n_\nu+1}.$$

The series (13.24) is therefore majorized by

$$2 \sum_{\nu=n_0}^{\infty} \frac{1}{n_\nu + 1} \left(\frac{R}{|a_\nu|} \right)^{n_\nu+1},$$

which certainly converges if the numbers n_ν are sufficiently large (for example, $n_\nu = \nu$ will ensure convergence). In this case the series (13.24) converges absolutely and uniformly in the disk $|z| \leqq R$. This implies that the infinite product

$$\prod_{\nu=n_0}^{\infty} \left\{ \left(1 - \frac{z}{a_\nu} \right) e^{P_\nu(z)} \right\} \tag{13.25}$$

converges absolutely in the disk $|z| \leqq R$, and defines an analytic function in this disk. If we multiply the expression (13.25) by the product

$$\prod_{\nu=1}^{n_0-1} \left\{ \left(1 - \frac{z}{a_\nu} \right) e^{P_\nu(z)} \right\},$$

the resulting function is regular in the disk $|z| \leqq R$, and, hence, in the whole plane, since R was arbitrary.

As an abbreviation, we shall use the notation

$$E \left(\frac{z}{a_\nu}, n_\nu \right) = \left(1 - \frac{z}{a_\nu} \right) e^{P_\nu(z)}. \tag{13.26}$$

The infinite product

$$\prod_{\nu=1}^{\infty} E \left(\frac{z}{a_\nu}, n_\nu \right) \tag{13.27}$$

is an entire function which vanishes at the points (13.22) and at no other points. If, in addition to the points (13.22), $z = 0$ is also a zero (of order m), we have to introduce the factor z^m into the product (13.27). We have therefore the following result.

If $a_1, a_2, \ldots, a_n, \ldots$ is an arbitrary sequence of complex numbers such that

$$0 < |a_1| \leqq |a_2| \leqq \ldots \leqq |a_n| \leqq \ldots, \qquad \lim_{n \to \infty} |a_n| = \infty,$$

then the infinite product

$$z^m \prod_{\nu=1}^{\infty} E \left(\frac{z}{a_\nu}, n_\nu \right)$$

defines an entire function whose only zeros are at the points $0, a_1, a_2, \ldots$.

For the convergence of the product (13.27) it is not necessary that the sequence n_ν should increase as rapidly as the sequence $n_\nu = \nu$. For example, the product will always converge if we choose

$$n_\nu = [\log \nu],$$

where $[\log \nu]$ denotes the greatest integer not exceeding $\log \nu$ (Exercise 8, p. 240).

13.10.

Now let $w(z)$ be an *arbitrary* entire function with the prescribed zeros. The quotient

$$\frac{w(z)}{z^m \prod_{\nu=1}^{\infty} E\left(\frac{z}{a_\nu}, n_\nu\right)}$$

is then an entire function without zeros. By Section 13.7, this function is of the form $e^{g(z)}$, where $g(z)$ is an entire function. We therefore obtain the following representation for the function $w(z)$:

$$w(z) = e^{g(z)} z^m \prod_{\nu=1}^{\infty} E\left(\frac{z}{a_\nu}, n_\nu\right). \tag{13.28}$$

Conversely, whenever $g(z)$ is an entire function, (13.28) defines a function satisfying the prescribed conditions.

All entire functions $w(z)$ with prescribed zeros at the points 0, a_1, a_2, ...
are given by the formula (13.28), *where $g(z)$ is an arbitrary entire function.*

Formula (13.28) constitutes the *Weierstrass product representation* of an entire function in terms of its zeros.

13.11. The Case $n_\nu =$ const.

Finally, we want to mention the important case where a *fixed* number of terms in the exponent of (13.26) suffices for the convergence of the product (13.27). If there exists an integer p such that

$$\sum_{\nu=1}^{\infty} \frac{1}{|a_\nu|^p} \tag{13.29}$$

converges, then we may choose $n_\nu = p - 1$ $(\nu = 1, 2, \ldots)$. Then, for sufficiently large values of ν (Section 13.9), we have

$$\left|\log E\left(\frac{z}{a_\nu}, n_\nu\right)\right| \leq \frac{2}{p}\left(\frac{R}{|a_\nu|}\right)^p = \frac{2R^p}{p}\frac{1}{|a_\nu|^p},$$

and therefore the convergence of the series (13.29) implies the convergence of the series (13.24), which, in turn, implies the convergence of the product (13.25).

If we wish to expand a *given* entire function into a Weierstrass product, then the function $g(z)$ appearing in (13.28) cannot, of course, be chosen arbitrarily. Its determination presents very often the principal difficulty of the problem. We refer to Exercises 7 and 10, p. 240.

The series (13.29) associated with the function $\sin \pi z$ converges for $p = 2$, and thus $n_\nu = 1$ $(\nu = 1, 2, \ldots)$ is an appropriate choice. This is also apparent from the representation derived in Section 2 (13.20).

The Weierstrass product formula can also be used to represent a *meromorphic* function with given zeros and poles as a quotient of two entire functions (Exercise 9, p. 240).

13.12. The Mittag-Leffler Theorem

If we differentiate the function (13.28) logarithmically, we obtain

$$\frac{w'(z)}{w(z)} = g'(z) + \frac{m}{z} + \sum_{\nu=1}^{\infty} \left(\frac{1}{z - a_\nu} + \frac{1}{a_\nu} + \frac{z}{a_\nu^2} + \cdots + \frac{z^{n_\nu - 1}}{a_\nu^{n_\nu}} \right). \qquad (13.30)$$

Since $w(z)$ is an entire function, the left-hand side of (13.30) is regular everywhere except at the zeros of $w(z)$. At each of these points (13.30) has a simple pole with residue 1 (cf. Section 10.8). (If some of the numbers a_ν coincide, the residue is not equal to 1, but in any case it is a positive integer.)

Formula (13.30) thus provides the partial-fraction representation for the function

$$f(z) = \frac{w'(z)}{w(z)}. \qquad (13.31)$$

This representation converges uniformly on every compact set which does not contain any poles of the function $f(z)$.

Conversely, if $f(z)$ is a meromorphic function with simple poles at the points a_ν $(\nu = 1, 2, \ldots)$, all of whose residues are positive integers, then the function

$$w(z) = \exp \left\{ \int_{z_0}^{z} f(z)\, dz \right\},$$

which is related to $f(z)$ by (13.31), is an entire function with zeros a_ν. Hence, the Weierstrass factorization theorem (13.28) is valid for $w(z)$, so that the partial-fraction expansion (13.30) holds for $f(z)$.

In the general case we have the following *theorem of Mittag-Leffler*:

Let z_ν $(\nu = 1, 2, \ldots)$ be an arbitrary sequence of points having no points of accumulation in the finite plane. If, to each point z_ν, a rational function

$$P_\nu \left(\frac{1}{z - z_\nu} \right) = \frac{\beta_{-1}}{z - z_\nu} + \frac{\beta_{-2}}{(z - z_\nu)^2} + \cdots + \frac{\beta_{-\lambda_\nu}}{(z - z_\nu)^{\lambda_\nu}} \qquad (13.32)$$

is assigned, then there always exists a meromorphic function $f(z)$, which is uniquely determined up to an additive entire function, such that $f(z)$ has poles at the points z_ν, and such that the principal part of the Laurent expansion of $f(z)$ about the point z_ν is the given function (13.32). The function $f(z)$ has the form

$$f(z) = \sum_{\nu=1}^{\infty} \left\{ P_\nu \left(\frac{1}{z - z_\nu} \right) - p_\nu(z) \right\} + g(z), \qquad (13.33)$$

where the functions $p_\nu(z)$ are polynomials

$$p_\nu(z) = \alpha_0^{(\nu)} + \alpha_1^{(\nu)} z + \cdots + \alpha_{n_\nu}^{(\nu)} z^{n_\nu}$$

obtained by expanding $P_\nu\big(1/(z - z_\nu)\big)$ into powers of z and taking a certain number of terms of this expansion.

The proof of this theorem is left as an Exercise (Exercise 11, p. 240).

An example is provided by the partial-fraction expansion of the function $\cot \pi z$ given in Section 10.7.

§4. JENSEN'S FORMULA. THE GROWTH OF ENTIRE FUNCTIONS

13.13. Jensen's Formula

If the function $w(z)$ is regular and non-zero in the disk $|z| \leqq \rho$, then $\log |w(z)|$ is harmonic in this disk. Thus, by Gauss's mean-value theorem

$$\log |w(0)| = \frac{1}{2\pi} \int_0^{2\pi} \log |w(\rho \, e^{i\theta})| \, d\theta.$$

Assume now that $w(z)$ has the zeros $a_1, a_2, \ldots, a_n$ in the disk $|z| < \rho$, but that $w(z) \neq 0$ on $|z| = \rho$ and that $w(0) \neq 0$. Multiple zeros are to be included in the sequence of zeros with distinct subscripts. The function

$$f(z) = w(z) \prod_{\nu=1}^{n} \frac{\rho^2 - \bar{a}_\nu z}{\rho(z - a_\nu)} \qquad (13.34)$$

is regular and non-zero in the disk $|z| \leqq \rho$, and $|f(z)| = |w(z)|$ on the circle $|z| = \rho$, since each factor of the product is of modulus 1 for $|z| = \rho$. If Gauss's mean-value theorem is applied to the function $\log |f(z)|$, it yields

$$\log |f(0)| = \frac{1}{2\pi} \int_0^{2\pi} \log |w(\rho \, e^{i\theta})| \, d\theta.$$

If we substitute the value of $f(0)$ obtained from formula (13.34), we obtain Jensen's formula

$$\log |w(0)| = -\sum_{\nu=1}^{n} \log \frac{\rho}{|a_\nu|} + \frac{1}{2\pi} \int_0^{2\pi} \log |w(\rho \, e^{i\theta})| \, d\theta. \qquad (13.35)$$

This formula establishes a connection between the moduli of the zeros of $w(z)$ in the disk $|z| < \rho$ and the values of $|w(z)|$ taken on the circle $|z| = \rho$ and at the point $z = 0$.

In the proof of formula (13.35) we assumed that $w(z) \neq 0$ for $|z| \neq \rho$. However, formula (13.35) is still valid if $w(z)$ has a finite number of zeros on the circle $|z| = \rho$. The left-hand side of the formula does not depend on ρ, and the right-hand side is a continuous function of ρ. That the sum appearing on the right-hand side is continuous is obvious. The continuity of the integral can be seen in the following way. If $w(z)$ has one zero of order μ at $z_0 = \rho_0 \, e^{i\theta_0}$ on the circle $|z| = \rho_0$, then

$$w(z) = (z - z_0)^\mu g(z),$$

where $g(z)$ is regular at the point z_0 and $g(z_0) \neq 0$. Hence,

$$\log |w(z)| = \mu \log |z - z_0| + \log |g(z)|.$$

It can be seen from this that the integral

$$\int_0^{2\pi} \log |w(\rho \, e^{i\theta})| \, d\theta \qquad (13.36)$$

also converges for $\rho = \rho_0$, and that one can enclose θ_0 in an interval $\theta_1 < \theta_0 < \theta_2$ such that

$$\left| \int_{\theta_1}^{\theta_2} \log |w(\rho \, e^{i\theta})| \, d\theta \right| < \epsilon$$

if ρ is sufficiently close to ρ_0. For the θ-values outside the interval (θ_1, θ_2) we have, uniformly in θ,

$$\lim_{\rho \to \rho_0} w(\rho \, e^{i\theta}) = w(\rho_0 \, e^{i\theta}).$$

We conclude that the integral (13.36) is continuous for $\rho = \rho_0$. The proof is similar if there are several zeros of $w(z)$ on the circle $|z| = \rho_0$.

The right-hand side of Eq. (13.35) is therefore a continuous function of ρ. Thus the equation is also valid for $\rho = \rho_0$.

13.14. The Order of an Entire Function

Let $w(z)$ be a non-constant entire function and let $M(r)$ denote the maximum of $|w(z)|$ on $|z| = r$. By the maximum principle $M(r)$ is a monotone increasing function of r. Moreover, $M(r)$ is continuous (cf. Exercise 15, p. 240).

We saw in Section 9.21 that if $M(r) < r^k$ for some constant k and for all large values of r, then $w(z)$ is a polynomial. Thus, if $w(z)$ is not a polynomial, $M(r)$ increases more rapidly than any power of r as $r \to \infty$.

For the simplest transcendental entire function, the exponential function e^z, we have $M(r) = e^r$. It is convenient to classify the entire functions by comparing their maximum modulus function $M(r)$ with the exponential functions e^{r^σ} ($\sigma > 0$). Let us assume that there exists a positive number σ for which the inequality

$$M(r) < e^{r^\sigma} \qquad (13.37)$$

is satisfied for large values of r. We denote by λ the greatest lower bound of all numbers σ for which (13.37) holds for sufficiently large values of r:

$$\lambda = \inf \sigma. \tag{13.38}$$

The number λ is called the *order* of the function $w(z)$. If (13.37) does not hold for any finite σ, we say that the order of $w(z)$ is infinite. For example, the order of e^z is 1, while that of a polynomial is 0. The condition (13.38) may be expressed more concisely by the formula

$$\lambda = \lim_{r \to \infty} \sup \frac{\log \log M(r)}{\log r} \tag{13.39}$$

(Exercise 17, p. 241).

13.15. The Connection between the Order and the Zeros of an Entire Function

We shall now prove that if $w(z)$ is an entire function of finite order λ, then it can be represented by a Weierstrass product (13.28) with a *fixed* number of terms in the expression for E (13.26) in the exponent. It suffices to establish the existence of an integer p for which the series (13.29) converges (cf. Section 13.11).

We assume that in the sequence $a_1, a_2, \ldots, a_n, \ldots$ of zeros of the function $w(z)$, each zero occurs as many times as its multiplicity and that the sequence is ordered in such a way that

$$0 < |a_1| \le |a_2| \le \ldots \le |a_n| \le \ldots .$$

Applying Jensen's formula (13.35) to the function $w(z)$ in the disk $|z| \le 2|a_n|$, we obtain, for large values of n,

$$\sum_{|a_\nu| < 2|a_n|} \log \frac{2|a_n|}{|a_\nu|} \le (2|a_n|)^\sigma - \log |w(0)|, \tag{13.40}$$

where σ is an arbitrary number greater than λ. If we omit on the left-hand side all the terms with $\nu > n$ and observe that each remaining term is greater than or equal to $\log 2$, we obtain from (13.40) the inequality

$$n \log 2 \le 2^\sigma |a_n|^\sigma - \log |w(0)|.$$

Hence,

$$n \le \frac{2^\sigma}{\log 2} |a_n|^\sigma - \frac{\log |w(0)|}{\log 2}. \tag{13.41}$$

On the right-hand side only the modulus $|a_n|$ depends on n, and it tends to infinity as $n \to \infty$. Thus, if τ is any number greater than σ, the right-hand side of (13.41) is less than $|a_n|^\tau$ for all sufficiently large values of n. Hence, for such values of n,

$$n < |a_n|^\tau, \qquad |a_n| > n^{1/\tau}. \tag{13.42}$$

Hence, for $p > \tau$ we have

$$\frac{1}{|a_n|^p} < \frac{1}{n^{p/\tau}},$$

which implies the convergence of the series

$$\sum_{n=1}^{\infty} \frac{1}{|a_n|^p}.$$

Clearly, any number greater than λ can be taken for p. Subsequently we can choose σ and τ so that $\lambda < \sigma < \tau < p$.

Thus, if $w(z)$ is of order λ, then we may take for p in the Weierstrass product the smallest integer greater than λ. Conversely, if the product representation of $w(z)$ holds for a constant number of terms in the exponent, then $w(z)$ is of finite order. We shall not go deeper into this question here.

EXERCISES ON CHAPTER 13

1. Derive Wallis's formula

$$\frac{\pi}{2} = \frac{2}{1} \frac{2}{3} \frac{4}{3} \frac{4}{5} \frac{6}{5} \cdots$$

by substituting $z = \frac{1}{2}$ into the product formula (13.14) for $\sin \pi z$.

2. Show that the following infinite products converge, and find their values:

$$\text{a)} \quad \prod_{n=1}^{\infty} \left(1 + \frac{1}{n(n+2)}\right), \qquad \text{b)} \quad \frac{2}{1} \frac{5}{4} \cdots \frac{n^2+1}{n^2} \cdots.$$

Hint for (b). Use the product formula for $\sin \pi z$.

3. Find the regions of absolute convergence for the following infinite products:

$$\text{a)} \quad \prod_{n=1}^{\infty} (1 - z^n), \qquad \text{b)} \quad \prod_{n=0}^{\infty} (1 + z^{2n}), \qquad \text{c)} \quad \prod_{n=0}^{\infty} (1 + c_n z),$$

assuming that $\sum |c_n|$ converges.

4. Prove that the so-called Blaschke product

$$\prod_{\nu=1}^{\infty} e^{-i\alpha\nu} \frac{z - a_\nu}{\bar{a}_\nu z - 1}, \qquad a_\nu = |a_\nu| e^{i\alpha\nu}, \qquad 0 < |a_\nu| < 1 \qquad (\nu = 1, 2, \ldots) \qquad \text{(a)}$$

converges if and only if the series

$$\sum_{\nu=1}^{\infty} (1 - |a_\nu|) \qquad \text{(b)}$$

converges. If the series (b) converges, show that the product (a) defines a function which is analytic in the disk $|z| < 1$ and has the zeros $z = a_\nu$

($\nu = 1, 2, \ldots$). However, if the series (b) diverges, show that the product is identically zero.

Hint. Consider first the convergence at the point $z = 0$, and then apply Harnack's principle.

5. Assume that the series (b) of the preceding exercise converges and that the numbers $\arg a_\nu$ ($\nu = 1, 2, \ldots$) are everywhere dense in the interval $0 \leq \arg a_\nu < 2\pi$. Show that the circle $|z| = 1$ is the natural boundary of the function (a), that is, the function cannot be continued analytically across the unit circle.

6. Construct an entire function with simple zeros at the points $a_\nu = \nu^2$ ($\nu = 1, 2, \ldots$).

7. Derive the product formula of $\sin \pi z$ from the Weierstrass formula.

Hint. The entire function $g(z)$ occurring in formula (13.28) can be determined (for example) by comparing the expansion obtained for the logarithmic derivative of $\sin \pi z$ by means of formula (13.28) with the expansion of $\cot \pi z$.

8. Prove that the Weierstrass product converges whenever $n_\nu = [\log \nu]$.

9. Construct a meromorphic function with given zeros and poles.

10. Find the infinite-product representation of the following entire functions:

$$\text{a)} \quad e^z - 1, \qquad \text{b)} \quad e^z - e^{z_0}, \qquad \text{c)} \quad \cos \pi z.$$

11. Prove the Mittag-Leffler theorem.

Hint. Show that the polynomials $p_\nu(z)$ may be always chosen in such a way that the series (13.33) converges uniformly on every finite region and that this expansion is uniquely determined up to an additive entire function.

12. What form does Jensen's formula take whenever $w(0) = 0$?

13. Let $w(z)$ be regular for $|z| \leq \rho$. Apply Poisson's formula to the logarithm of the modulus of the function (13.34) to derive the *Poisson-Jensen formula*

$$\log |w(z)| = -\sum_{\nu=1}^{n} \log \left| \frac{\rho^2 - \bar{a}_\nu z}{\rho(z - a_\nu)} \right|$$

$$+ \frac{1}{2\pi} \int_0^{2\pi} \log |w(\rho\, e^{i\theta})| \, \frac{\rho^2 - r^2}{\rho^2 + r^2 - 2\rho r \cos(\theta - \phi)} \, d\theta.$$

14. Generalize the Poisson-Jensen formula to functions meromorphic in the disk $|z| \leq \rho$.

15. Given an entire function $w(z)$, show that

$$M(r) = \max_{|z|=r} |w(z)|$$

is a continuous function of r.

16. Let $M(r)$ be the maximum modulus function (cf. previous exercise) of an entire function of order λ, let $\sigma > \lambda$, and let A and a be arbitrary positive constants. Show that the inequality

$$M(r) < A\ e^{ar^\sigma}$$

holds for all sufficiently large r.

17. Prove the following assertion: If $\lambda = \inf \sigma$, where σ assumes all values satisfying (13.37) for sufficiently large values of r, then

$$\lambda = \limsup_{r \to \infty} \frac{\log \log M(r)}{\log r}.$$

CHAPTER 14

PERIODIC FUNCTIONS

§1. DEFINITIONS OF SIMPLY AND DOUBLY PERIODIC FUNCTIONS

14.1. Simply Periodic Functions

A meromorphic function $w(z)$ (i.e. an analytic function which is regular in the finite plane except possibly for isolated poles) is said to be *periodic* (cf. Section 5.4) if for every complex z there exists a constant $\omega \neq 0$ such that

$$w(z + \omega) = w(z).$$

The number ω is called a *period* of the function w. If ω is a period, the numbers $n\omega$ $(n = \pm 1, \pm 2, \ldots)$ are also periods of w. The question arises whether the function w has any other periods. We exclude the special case where the function $w(z)$ is a constant. First we prove some auxiliary theorems.

Theorem 1. *The moduli of all periods have a positive lower bound.*

To prove the theorem we argue by contradiction. If the assertion were false, $w(z)$ would have arbitrarily small periods, from which we could choose a sequence $\omega_1, \omega_2, \ldots, \omega_n, \ldots$ such that $\lim \omega_n = 0$. At a regular point z_0 of the function we then have $w(z_0) = w(z_0 + \omega_n)$ $(n = 1, 2, \ldots)$. The function $w(z) - w(z_0)$ therefore has infinitely many zeros $z_0 + \omega_n$ $(n = 1, 2, \ldots)$ which converge to the point z_0. Hence, $w(z) - w(z_0)$ is identically 0 and $w(z)$ must be a constant. This contradicts the assumption that $w(z)$ is not constant. Thus the theorem is proved.

Theorem 2. *The periods have no point of accumulation in the finite plane.*

We first observe that if $\omega_1, \omega_2, \ldots, \omega_m$ are periods of $w(z)$, then the expression

$$n_1\omega_1 + n_2\omega_2 + \cdots + n_m\omega_m \qquad (n_1, n_2, \ldots, n_m \text{ integers})$$

is also a period of w.

Suppose that ω_0 is a finite point of accumulation of the periods. Then for every $\epsilon > 0$ we can find two distinct periods ω_1 and ω_2 in the neighborhood $|z - \omega_0| < \epsilon$ of ω_0. The difference $\omega_1 - \omega_2$ is also a period. Since $|\omega_1 - \omega_2| < 2\epsilon$, it follows that $w(z)$ has arbitrarily small periods, which contradicts Theorem 1, so that Theorem 2 is proved.

242

It follows from Theorems 1 and 2 that the moduli of the periods have a positive minimum m. Let ω_1 be a period with $|\omega_1| = m$. Each of the numbers $n\omega_1$ $(n = \pm 1, \pm 2, \ldots)$ is also a period, and points corresponding to these periods all lie on the same straight line l: $\arg z = \arg \omega_1$. No other points on this line can correspond to a period. For if ω were another period on l lying between $\nu\omega_1$ and $(\nu + 1)\omega_1$, then $\omega - \nu\omega_1$ would also be a period. But $|\omega - \nu\omega_1| < |\omega_1| = m$, which would contradict the definition of m.

If the function $w(z)$ has no other periods it is said to be *simply periodic*. The number ω_1 is called the *primitive period* of the function (Section 5.4).

14.2. Doubly Periodic Functions

Let us see whether $w(z)$ can have any other periods. We shall prove that if there are other periods, their distances from the straight line l has a *positive minimum*. If ω is some period which is not on l, then $\omega + n\omega_1$ $(n = 0, \pm 1, \pm 2, \ldots)$ is also a period of the function. It follows that there is a period on the line passing through ω and parallel to l which lies in the strip G bounded by two arbitrary parallel lines through the points 0 and ω_1. Now if the distances of the periods ω from the line l do not have a positive minimum, we can find an infinite sequence of periods in G whose distances from l have a non-negative lower bound and which have at least one finite point of accumulation. However, this contradicts Theorem 2. Hence, the distances of the periods ω from the line l must have a positive minimum d.

Let ω_2 be a period for which the minimal distance d is attained. Then $\omega = m_1\omega_1 + m_2\omega_2$ is also a period for arbitrary integers m_1 and m_2. All such points form the vertices of a parallelogram mesh (Fig. 40). Conversely,

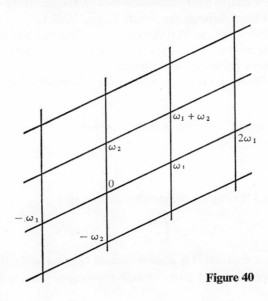

Figure 40

it follows that *all* periods of $w(z)$ are of the form $\omega = m_1\omega_1 + m_2\omega_2$, where m_1 and m_2 are integers. For if there were other period points, then one of them would have to lie in the fundamental parallelogram with vertices 0, ω_1, $\omega_1 + \omega_2$, ω_2. This would contradict the facts derived above, so that our assertion is proved. The numbers ω_1 and ω_2 are called the *primitive* periods or *fundamental* periods of the function. We have thus proved the following theorem.

Theorem 3. *A non-constant meromorphic function has at most two primitive periods whose ratio cannot be real.*

A function with two primitive periods is said to be a *doubly periodic* or *elliptic* function. It will be shown in Section 4 that such functions actually do exist.

§2. REDUCTION OF SIMPLY PERIODIC FUNCTIONS TO THE EXPONENTIAL FUNCTION

14.3.

Earlier we discussed the exponential function as the simplest example of a simply periodic function. The other periodic functions which have appeared so far, such as $\cos z$, $\sin z$, $\cot z$, and $\tan z$, are rational functions of the exponential function e^{iz} (Sections 6.1 and 6.4). Conversely, every rational function of $e^{\alpha z}$, where α is a constant, is periodic with period $2\pi i/\alpha$. This suggests the following question: Under what conditions can a given periodic function be expressed as a rational function of an exponential function $e^{\alpha z}$?

Let $w(z)$ be a simply periodic function with the primitive period ω. By drawing parallel lines through the points 0, $\pm\omega$, $\pm 2\omega$, . . ., we can divide the plane into parallel strips, so that each strip contains one and only one of the points congruent mod ω. Since $w(z)$ is meromorphic, its poles can only have $z = \infty$ as a possible point of accumulation.

Besides the function $w(z)$, we consider the exponential function

$$\zeta = e^{z \cdot 2\pi i/\omega}, \tag{14.1}$$

which is also periodic with the primitive period ω. Equation (14.1) defines z as a function of ζ:

$$z = \frac{\omega}{2\pi i} \log \zeta. \tag{14.2}$$

The function $w(z)$ becomes a composite function of ζ:

$$w(z) = w\left(\frac{\omega}{2\pi i} \log \zeta\right) = w^*(\zeta). \tag{14.3}$$

We show first that $w^*(\zeta)$ is *a single-valued function of* ζ. If ζ describes a closed path which does not pass through the origin, then in view of (14.2)

z increases by $k\omega$ $(k = 0, \pm1, \pm2, \ldots)$. At the same time, because of the periodicity of $w(z)$, w returns to its original value.

The function $w^*(\zeta)$ is therefore a single-valued function of ζ. In view of (14.3) this function is regular everywhere except at $\zeta = 0$, $\zeta = \infty$ and the points of the ζ-plane which correspond to the poles of $w(z)$. These points have no points of accumulation except possibly at $\zeta = 0$ and $\zeta = \infty$.

Let $z = b$ be a pole of $w(z)$ of order k. Then (Section 9.19)

$$\lim_{z \to b} w(z)(z - b)^k = B \neq 0, \infty. \tag{14.4}$$

By (14.1) the point $z = b$ corresponds to the point $\zeta = \beta = e^{2\pi i b/\omega}$. Therefore $\zeta(z)$ has the expansion

$$\zeta = \beta + C_1(z - b) + \cdots, \qquad C_1 \neq 0,$$

from which it follows (for the notation $[z - b]$, see footnote, p.153) that

$$(\zeta - \beta)^k = C_1^k(z - b)^k\{1 + [z - b]\},$$

and also

$$(\zeta - \beta)^k w^*(\zeta) = C_1^k(z - b)^k w(z)\{1 + [z - b]\}.$$

By (14.4) this expression tends to the limit $C_1^k B \neq 0$, ∞ as $z \to b$ and $\zeta \to \beta$. The function $w^*(\zeta)$ has therefore a pole of order k at the point $\zeta = \beta$. We have thus proved the following result.

The function $w^*(\zeta)$ is single-valued and analytic. Each pole of $w(z)$ corresponds to a pole of $w^*(\zeta)$ of the same order. The points $\zeta = 0$ and $\zeta = \infty$ can be limit points of poles, isolated essential singularities, poles, or points of regularity of the function $w^*(\zeta)$.

14.4.

We now investigate the question: Under what conditions are the points $\zeta = 0$ and $\zeta = \infty$ poles or points of regularity of the function $w^*(\zeta)$? We may assume without loss of generality that the primitive period is $2\pi i$, for the substitution $z_1 = 2\pi i z/\omega$ transforms a function with period ω into a function with period $2\pi i$. With this choice of ω_1 (14.1) takes the form

$$\zeta = e^z. \tag{14.5}$$

By Section 9.19, the point $\zeta = 0$ is a pole or a regular point of $w^*(\zeta)$ if and only if there exists a positive constant M and an integer $k \geq 0$ such that

$$|w^*(\zeta)| < \frac{M}{|\zeta|^k}$$

for sufficiently small values of $|\zeta|$. If we use (14.5) and (14.3), and write $z = x + iy$, the above inequality takes the form

$$|w(z)| < M e^{-kx} \qquad \text{for} \qquad x < -x_0, \tag{14.6}$$

where x_0 is positive.

In order that $\zeta = \infty$ be a pole or a point of regularity it is therefore necessary and sufficient that there should exist an $M > 0$ and a $k \geq 0$ such that

$$|w^*(\zeta)| < M|\zeta|^k$$

for all sufficiently large values of $|\zeta|$. In view of (14.5) and (14.3), this is equivalent to the condition

$$|w(z)| < M e^{kx} \qquad \text{for} \qquad x > x_0. \qquad (14.7)$$

We may combine (14.6) and (14.7) into the form

$$|w(z)| < M e^{k|x|} \qquad \text{for} \qquad |x| > x_0. \qquad (14.8)$$

Our result is then the following:

> If $w(z)$ is simply periodic with primitive period $2\pi i$, then $w(z)$ is a rational function of e^z if and only if (14.8) is satisfied.

This condition also implies that $w(z)$ may have at most a finite number of poles in a period strip.

§3. THE BASIC PROPERTIES OF DOUBLY PERIODIC FUNCTIONS

14.5. Poles

We now turn to the investigation of doubly periodic functions. Let $w(z)$ be doubly periodic, that is, let w be a non-constant meromorphic function such that

$$w(z + m_1\omega_1 + m_2\omega_2) = w(z) \qquad (m_1, m_2 = 0, \pm1, \pm2, \ldots)$$

for every z, where ω_1, ω_2 is a pair of primitive periods. The only possible finite singularities of w are a finite number of poles in each period parallelogram. We can therefore choose the mesh of period parallelograms in such a way that there are no poles on the sides of the period parallelograms. We shall label the periods in such a way that $\operatorname{Im} \omega_2/\omega_1 > 0$.

We prove first some theorems about the poles of doubly periodic functions.

Theorem 1. *There are no doubly periodic entire functions.*

If $w(z)$ is regular in the whole period parallelogram, then $|w(z)|$ is bounded in the period parallelogram and, hence, in the whole plane. But then, by Liouville's theorem, w must be a constant. However, this trivial special case was excluded from the start.

Theorem 2. *The sum of the residues of $w(z)$ at the poles in a period parallelogram is zero.*

Proof. If we apply the residue theorem to a period parallelogram $ABCD$ whose boundary is denoted by P, we obtain

$$\int_P w(z)\, dz = 2\pi i \sum R, \qquad (14.9)$$

where ΣR denotes the sum of residues of $w(z)$ at the poles enclosed by P.

Since the function is periodic, we have (Fig. 41)

$$\int_{AB} w(z)\, dz = \int_{DC} w(z)\, dz$$

or

$$\int_{AB} w(z)\, dz + \int_{CD} w(z)\, dz = 0.$$

Similarly,

$$\int_{BC} w(z)\, dz + \int_{DA} w(z)\, dz = 0,$$

so that

$$\int_{P} w(z)\, dz = 0.$$

Our assertion now follows from (14.9).

If $w(z)$ has only one simple pole at the point $z = b$ in the period parallelogram, and if at this point $w(z)$ has the expansion

$$w(z) = \frac{A}{z - b} + \mathfrak{P}(z - b) \qquad (A \neq 0),$$

where the notation $\mathfrak{P}(z - b)$ is that of Section 9.22, then we have a contradiction to Theorem 2. We have thus proved

Theorem 3. *The sum of the orders of the poles of a doubly periodic function in a periodic parallelogram is at least 2.*

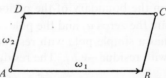

Figure 41

14.6. The Order of a Doubly Periodic Function

Let $w(z)$ have poles of orders $\nu_1, \nu_2, \ldots, \nu_k$ at the points $b_1, b_2, \ldots, b_k$ and zeros of orders $\mu_1, \mu_2, \ldots, \mu_h$ at the points $a_1, a_2, \ldots, a_h$ in the period parallelogram. Let $w(z) \neq 0$ on the boundary of the parallelogram.

We now show that *the sum of the orders of the zeros is equal to the sum of the orders of the poles.* By the argument principle

$$\Delta_P \arg w = \left(\sum_{i=1}^{h} \mu_i - \sum_{i=1}^{k} \nu_i \right) 2\pi. \qquad (14.10)$$

On the other hand (Fig. 41), we have

$$\Delta_P \arg w = \Delta_{AB} \arg w + \Delta_{BC} \arg w + \Delta_{CD} \arg w + \Delta_{DA} \arg w. \qquad (14.11)$$

Because of the periodicity we have

$$\Delta_{AB} \arg w = \Delta_{DC} \arg w = -\Delta_{CD} \arg w$$

and

$$\Delta_{BC} \arg w = -\Delta_{DA} \arg w.$$

9

Hence, (14.11) implies that $\Delta_P \arg w = 0$, whence, by (14.10), it follows that

$$\sum_{i=1}^{h} \mu_i = \sum_{i=1}^{k} \nu_i.$$

If we apply this result to the function $w(z) - \alpha$, where α is an arbitrary constant, we obtain

> **Theorem 4.** *A doubly periodic function assumes every value the same number of times in a period parallelogram.*

By this we mean that every point at which $w(z)$ assumes the value α must be counted according to the multiplicity as indicated by the order. Only a part of the boundary of the period parallelogram, for example, the vertex A and the open segments AB and AD, will be included.

If $w(z)$ assumes every value n times in a period parallelogram, we say that $w(z)$ is a function of *order n*.

14.7. A Relation between the Zeros and Poles

We shall prove a theorem concerning the position of the zeros and poles. The derivative of $w(z)$ is itself doubly periodic and has at least the same periods $\omega = m_1\omega_1 + m_2\omega_2$ as $w(z)$ (Exercise 6, p. 276).

We apply the residue theorem to the function $zw'(z)/w(z)$, which is regular on the boundary of the period parallelogram. Its only possible singularities are the zeros a_j and the poles b_j of $w(z)$. At a zero a_j the function $zw'(z)/w(z)$ has a simple pole with residue $\mu_j\alpha_j$. At a pole b_j it has again a simple pole with residue $-\nu_j b_j$. The residue theorem implies that

$$\int_P z \frac{w'(z)}{w(z)} \, dz = 2\pi i (\sum a_j - \sum b_j), \qquad (14.12)$$

where each term a_j and b_j must be counted according to multiplicity.

On the other hand, we have

$$\int_P z \frac{w'}{w} \, dz = \int_{AB} z \frac{w'}{w} \, dz + \int_{BC} z \frac{w'}{w} \, dz + \int_{CD} z \frac{w'}{w} \, dz + \int_{DA} z \frac{w'}{w} \, dz. \qquad (14.13)$$

By the periodicity of $w(z)$, we have (Fig. 41)

$$\int_{CD} z \frac{w'(z)}{w(z)} \, dz = \int_{BA} (z + \omega_2) \frac{w'(z + \omega_2)}{w(z + \omega_2)} \, dz$$

$$= \int_{BA} z \frac{w'(z)}{w(z)} \, dz + \omega_2 \int_{BA} \frac{w'(z)}{w(z)} \, dz,$$

and hence

$$\int_{AB} z \frac{w'(z)}{w(z)} \, dz + \int_{CD} z \frac{w'(z)}{w(z)} \, dz = \omega_2 \int_{BA} \frac{w'(z)}{w(z)} \, dz = \omega_2 \int_{BA} \log w(z). \qquad (14.14)$$

Since the function $w(z)$ is periodic, it has the same value at the points A and B. The increase of $\log w(z)$ from B to A is therefore $2\pi i m_2$, where m_2 is an integer. The value of (14.4) is then $2\pi i m_2 \omega_2$. Similarly,

$$\int_{BC} z \frac{w'}{w} \, dz + \int_{DA} z \frac{w'}{w} \, dz = 2\pi i m_1 \omega_1,$$

where m_1 is an integer.

It follows from (14.13) that

$$\int_P z \frac{w'}{w} \, dz = 2\pi i (m_1 \omega_1 + m_2 \omega_2) = 2\pi i \omega.$$

Combining this with (14.12), we have that

$$\sum a_j - \sum b_j = \omega.$$

We have thus established the following result.

Theorem 5. *If a_j and b_j are the zeros and poles of a doubly periodic function in a period parallelogram, then*

$$\sum a_j - \sum b_j = \omega,$$

where ω is a period, and where each a_j and b_j is counted according to multiplicity.

§4. THE WEIERSTRASS ℘-FUNCTION

14.8. Expansion of the ℘-Function about its Poles

By Theorem 3 of the preceding section, the sum of the orders of the poles in a period parallelogram is at least 2, and this suggests the question whether there exists a doubly periodic function which has one pole of order precisely two and is otherwise regular in the period parallelogram. In what follows we shall construct such a function.

If we place the pole at the origin, the remaining poles will be situated at the points $\omega = m_1 \omega_1 + m_2 \omega_2$, where m_1 and m_2 run over all integers.

Let us now assume that there exists a function $\wp(z)$ with the desired properties. In the neighborhood of a pole ω, the function $\wp(z)$ will have an expansion of the form

$$\wp(z) = \frac{A_2}{(z - \omega)^2} + \frac{A_1}{z - \omega} + a_0 + a_1(z - \omega) + \cdots.$$

Since A_1 is the sum of the residues at the poles in a period parallelogram, it follows that $A_1 = 0$. In the expansion corresponding to the pole $\omega = 0$ we may assume that $A_2 = 1$ and $a_0 = 0$; this can be achieved by multiplying $\wp$ by a constant and then adding a constant. Since $\wp$ is periodic, it follows that $A_2 = 1$ and $a_0 = 0$ in the expansion about an arbitrary pole ω, so that at each pole ω we have the expansion

$$\wp(z) = \frac{1}{(z - \omega)^2} + a_1(z - \omega) + \cdots. \qquad (14.15)$$

14.9. Expansion of the Derivative $\wp'(z)$

We now derive a series expansion for the derivative of the function $\wp(z)$ under the assumption that such a function exists.

To this end, we shift the period parallelogram so that its center lies at the origin. Let us denote its boundary by P_1. By adjoining to P_1 all the period parallelograms whose boundaries touch P_1 we obtain a new parallelogram whose boundary we denote by P_2. Continuing in this manner, we adjoin to P_2 all parallelograms whose boundaries touch P_2 and obtain a parallelogram whose boundary we denote by P_3, and so on.

Let $z_0 \neq \omega$ be an arbitrary point in the interior of the parallelogram bounded by P_n. By the residue theorem we have

$$\int_{P_n} \frac{\wp(z)}{z - z_0}\, dz = 2\pi i \sum R, \qquad (14.16)$$

where $\sum R$ is the sum of the residues at the poles of the function $f(z) = \wp(z)/(z - z_0)$ which lie in the interior of the parallelogram bounded by P_n. The function $f(z)$ is regular everywhere except at the points $z = z_0$ and $z = \omega = m_1\omega_1 + m_2\omega_2$.

At the point $z = z_0$ the residue of $f(z)$ is $R_{z_0} = \wp(z_0)$, and at the point $z = \omega$ the residue is $R_\omega = -1/(z_0 - \omega)^2$. Substituting these values into (14.16) we obtain

$$\int_{P_n} \frac{\wp(z)}{z - z_0}\, dz = 2\pi i \left\{ \wp(z_0) - \sum_{P_n} \frac{1}{(z_0 - \omega)^2} \right\}, \qquad (14.17)$$

where the sum is taken over all the poles ω of $\wp(z)$ inside the parallelogram bounded by P_n.

If we differentiate both sides of (14.17) with respect to z_0, we obtain

$$\int_{P_n} \frac{\wp(z)}{(z - z_0)^2}\, dz = 2\pi i \left\{ \wp'(z_0) + \sum_{P_n} \frac{2}{(z_0 - \omega)^3} \right\}. \qquad (14.18)$$

14.10.

We now let n tend to ∞ and show that the left-hand side of (14.18) then tends to zero. If we exclude the poles of $\wp(z)$ by means of disks $|z - \omega| < \rho$, then $|\wp(z)| \leq M$ everywhere else in the plane, where M is a finite constant. If ρ is sufficiently small, the contours P_n lie exterior to these disks. We then obtain for the left-hand side of (14.18) the estimate

$$\left| \int_{P_n} \frac{\wp(z)}{(z - z_0)^2}\, dz \right| \leq M \int_{P_n} \frac{|dz|}{(|z| - |z_0|)^2} \leq \frac{ML_n}{(d_n - |z_0|)^2},$$

where L_n is the length of P_n, d_n is the shortest distance of the origin from P_n, and n is so large that $d_n > |z_0|$. Since P_n and P_1 are similar, we have

$$\frac{L_n}{L_1} = \frac{d_n}{d_1} = 2n - 1, \tag{14.19}$$

so that

$$\left| \int_{P_n} \frac{\wp(z)}{(z - z_0)^2} \, dz \right| \leqq \frac{M(2n - 1)L_1}{[(2n - 1) \, d_1 - |z_0|]^2}.$$

This last expression tends to zero as $n \to \infty$. Hence, it follows from (14.18) that

$$\wp'(z) = \lim_{n \to \infty} \left(-\sum_{P_n} \frac{2}{(z - \omega)^3} \right). \tag{14.20}$$

Thus $\wp'(z)$ may be expressed as a sum extended over all the periods ω; in this sum the terms are grouped in such a way that the n-th group contains those terms for which the ω lie in the region bounded by P_{n-1} and P_n.

14.11. Absolute Convergence of the Expansion of $\wp'(z)$

We now show that the above arrangement of terms is irrelevant. It suffices to prove that the series

$$\sum \frac{1}{(z - \omega)^3} = \sum_{m1, \, m2 = -\infty}^{+\infty} \frac{1}{(z - m_1\omega_1 - m_2\omega_2)^3} \tag{14.21}$$

converges *absolutely*.

Let us restrict z to the disk $|z| \leqq \rho$ and omit the finite number of terms of the series (14.21) for which $|\omega| < 2\rho$. For the remaining terms we have

$$\frac{1}{|z - \omega|} \leqq \frac{1}{|\omega| - |z|} \leqq \frac{2}{|\omega|}$$

and

$$\frac{1}{|z - \omega|} \geqq \frac{1}{|z| + |\omega|} \geqq \frac{2}{3} \frac{1}{|\omega|},$$

so that

$$\left(\frac{2}{3} \right)^3 \frac{1}{|\omega|^3} \leqq \left| \frac{1}{(z - \omega)^3} \right| \leqq \frac{8}{|\omega|^3}.$$

Therefore the series (14.21) converges absolutely for every $z \neq \omega$ provided that the series

$$\sum{}' \frac{1}{|\omega|^3} \tag{14.22}$$

converges. The prime on the summation symbol means that the summation is taken over all the numbers $\omega = m_1\omega_1 + m_2\omega_2$ with the exception of $\omega = 0$. It will now be shown that the series (14.22) does in fact converge.

14.12. Investigation of the Series $\sum' 1/|\omega|^k$

We ask, generally, for what values of k does the series

$$\sum' \frac{1}{|\omega|^k} \qquad (14.23)$$

converge. For $k = 1$ the series clearly diverges, for if ω_1 is an arbitrary period, and if we consider only those terms in (14.23) for which $\omega = n\omega_1 \,(n = 1, 2, \ldots)$, we obtain the divergent series

$$\frac{1}{|\omega_1|} \sum \frac{1}{n}.$$

The condition $k > 1$ is therefore necessary for the convergence of (14.23). Let us now group the terms of (14.23) in such a way that the n-th group contains the terms corresponding to the periods which belong to the region Π_n bounded by P_n and P_{n-1}. The region Π_n consists of

$$(2n - 1)^2 - (2n - 3)^2 = 8(n - 1)$$

period parallelograms. The number of corresponding terms is therefore $8(n - 1)$.

Let d_1 be the least and D_1 the greatest distance of the origin from P_1. Then, for any point ω in the region Π_n, we have

$$n\left(2 - \frac{3}{n}\right) d_1 = (2n - 3)\, d_1 < |\omega| < (2n - 1)\, D_1 < n2D_1.$$

If we observe that $2 - 3/n \geqq \frac{1}{2}$ whenever $n \geqq 2$, we have

$$n\frac{d_1}{2} < |\omega| < n2D_1.$$

Hence,

$$\left(\frac{1}{2D_1}\right)^k \frac{1}{n^k} < \frac{1}{|\omega|^k} < \left(\frac{2}{d_1}\right)^k \frac{1}{n^k}. \qquad (14.24)$$

Since there are $8(n - 1)$ terms corresponding to the region Π_n, it follows from (14.24) that

$$8\left(\frac{1}{2D_1}\right)^k \frac{n - 1}{n^k} < \sum_{\Pi_n} \frac{1}{|\omega|^k} < 8\left(\frac{2}{d_1}\right)^k \frac{n - 1}{n^k}. \qquad (14.25)$$

For $n \geqq 2$ we have $(n - 1)/n^k = (1 - 1/n)/n^{k-1} \geqq 1/2n^{k-1}$.

By addition, it follows from (14.25) that

$$m \sum_{v=2}^{n} \frac{1}{v^{k-1}} < \sum_{P_n}' \frac{1}{|\omega|^k} < M \sum_{v=2}^{n} \frac{1}{v^{k-1}}, \qquad (14.26)$$

where m and M are positive constants. The sum in the middle is extended over all mesh points ω inside the parallelogram P_n with the exception of $\omega = 0$.

It then follows from (14.26) that the series $\sum'1/|\omega|^k$ converges if and only if the series

$$\sum_{\nu=1}^{\infty} \frac{1}{\nu^{k-1}}$$

converges, that is, if and only if $k > 2$.

The series

$$\sum' \frac{1}{|\omega|^k},$$

in which $\omega = m_1\omega_1 + m_2\omega_2$ and m_1 and m_2 assume independently all integer values (with the exception of $m_1 = m_2 = 0$), converges if and only if $k > 2$.

In particular the series (14.22) converges, and therefore *the series* (14.21) *converges absolutely and uniformly* on every compact set not containing any mesh points. The same is true of any bounded set if a finite number of terms is omitted.

In view of (14.20), the function $\wp'(z)$ has the expansion

$$\wp'(z) = \sum_{\omega} \frac{-2}{(z-\omega)^3}. \tag{14.27}$$

Here $\omega = m_1\omega_1 + m_2\omega_2$, where m_1 and m_2 range over the integers in any order.

14.13. Expansion of the $\wp$-Function

We now integrate (14.27) for $|z| \leqq \rho$. If we write the right-hand side of the equation in the form

$$\sum_{\omega} \frac{-2}{(z-\omega)^3} = \sum_{|\omega|\leqq\rho} \frac{-2}{(z-\omega)^3} + \sum_{|\omega|>\rho} \frac{-2}{(z-\omega)^3}, \tag{14.28}$$

then the last series converges uniformly in the domain $|z| \leqq \rho$. Therefore it can be integrated term by term between the limits 0 and z:

$$\int_0^z \sum_{|\omega|>\rho} \frac{-2}{(z-\omega)^3} \, dz = \sum_{|\omega|>\rho} \left\{ \frac{1}{(z-\omega)^2} - \frac{1}{\omega^2} \right\}.$$

This series converges uniformly, and even absolutely, in the disk $|z| \leqq \rho$, since it has a majorant of the form

$$\sum_{|\omega|>\rho} \frac{K}{|\omega|^3},$$

where K is a constant. The first sum on the right-hand side of (14.28), which has only a finite number of terms, is the derivative of the function

$$\frac{1}{z^2} + \sum_{0<|\omega|\le\rho} \left\{ \frac{1}{(z-\omega)^2} - \frac{1}{\omega^2} \right\}.$$

The entire right-hand side of (14.27) is therefore the derivative of the function

$$\frac{1}{z^2} + {\sum}' \left\{ \frac{1}{(z-\omega)^2} - \frac{1}{\omega^2} \right\}, \tag{14.29}$$

while the left-hand side is the derivative of $\wp(z)$. Thus the difference of $\wp(z)$ and (14.29) is a constant C. If we expand (14.29) into powers of z, it follows from (14.15) that $C = 0$. Thus we have shown that $\wp(z)$ has the expansion

$$\wp(z) = \frac{1}{z^2} + {\sum}' \left\{ \frac{1}{(z-\omega)^2} - \frac{1}{\omega^2} \right\}; \tag{14.30}$$

this is the *Weierstrass $\wp$-function*. To sum up, we have the following result.

If there exists a doubly periodic function $\wp(z)$ with primitive periods ω_1 and ω_2 which has a second-order pole at each of the points $\omega = m_1\omega_1 + m_2\omega_2$ and which has the expansion (14.15) at each such pole, then the function $\wp(z)$ is uniquely determined and has the expansion (14.30) at every point $z \ne \omega$.

14.14.

It now remains to show that the function $\wp(z)$ defined by (14.30) has in fact the required properties, that is, that $\wp(z)$ is a doubly periodic function with the primitive periods ω_1 and ω_2 which has double poles at the points $\omega = m_1\omega_1 + m_2\omega_2$ $(m_1, m_2 = 0, \pm1, \pm2, \ldots)$, where it possesses the expansion (14.15).

Since the series (14.30) converges uniformly on every compact set which does not contain any of the points ω, $\wp(z)$ is regular everywhere except at the points $z = \omega$. About each point $z = \omega$ the function (14.30) has the required expansion

$$\wp(z) = \frac{1}{(z-\omega)^2} + [z - \omega]. \tag{14.30}'$$

To prove that $\wp(z)$ is a doubly periodic function with primitive periods ω_1 and ω_2, we first show that ω_1 and ω_2 are periods of $\wp'(z)$, that is, that $\wp'(z + \omega_i) = \wp'(z)$ $(i = 1, 2)$. For the function $\wp'(z)$ we have the expansion (14.27). Hence,

$$\wp'(z + \omega_1) = \sum_\omega \frac{-2}{(z-(\omega - \omega_1)^3)},$$

which differs from (14.27) only in the ordering of its terms. Since we have established that (14.27) is absolutely convergent, it follows that

$$\wp'(z + \omega_1) \equiv \wp'(z).$$

The derivative of the function

$$f(z) = \wp(z + \omega_1) - \wp(z) \tag{14.31}$$

is therefore identically zero, and so $f(z)$ is a constant:

$$f(z) \equiv C. \tag{14.32}$$

To complete the proof we show that $C = 0$.

By Eq. (14.30), we have

$$\wp(-z) = \frac{1}{z^2} + \sum' \left\{ \frac{1}{(-z - \omega)^2} - \frac{1}{\omega^2} \right\}$$

$$= \frac{1}{z^2} + \sum' \left\{ \frac{1}{(z - (-\omega))^2} - \frac{1}{(-\omega)^2} \right\}.$$

This sum differs from (14.30) only in the arrangement of terms. Since (14.30) is absolutely convergent, it follows that $\wp(-z) = \wp(z)$ for all values of z, so that $\wp$ is an *even* function.

Hence, for $z = \omega_1/2$, we have

$$\wp\left(\frac{\omega_1}{2}\right) = \wp\left(-\frac{\omega_1}{2}\right).$$

On the other hand, it follows from (14.31) and (14.32) that

$$\wp\left(\frac{\omega_1}{2}\right) = \wp\left(-\frac{\omega_1}{2} + \omega_1\right) = \wp\left(-\frac{\omega_1}{2}\right) + C,$$

and, hence,

$$\wp\left(-\frac{\omega_1}{2}\right) = \wp\left(-\frac{\omega_1}{2}\right) + C,$$

which implies $C = 0$. Therefore $\wp(z + \omega_1) \equiv \wp(z)$. In the same way we can show that $\wp(z + \omega_2) = \wp(z)$.

Therefore $\wp(z)$ is a doubly periodic function having as periods all the numbers ω. On the other hand, ω_1 and ω_2 are necessarily primitive periods, because every parallelogram determined by ω_1 and ω_2 contains just one pole of the function. We have thus proved that $\wp(z)$ has all the required properties.

If we form the higher derivatives of the function $\wp(z)$, we obtain new functions which are also doubly periodic.

9*

§5. THE WEIERSTRASS ζ- AND σ-FUNCTIONS

14.15. The ζ-Function

We now investigate the function obtained from the $\wp$-function by integration. We denote by $\zeta(z)$ a function which satisfies the condition

$$\zeta'(z) = -\wp(z).$$

If we integrate term by term the uniformly convergent series (14.30) for $\wp(z)$, and if we choose the constant of integration suitably, we obtain

$$\zeta(z) = \frac{1}{z} + {\sum}' \left\{ \frac{1}{z - \omega} + \frac{1}{\omega} + \frac{z}{\omega^2} \right\}. \tag{14.33}$$

This series converges absolutely; in fact, for a fixed value of z, we have the estimate

$$\left| \frac{1}{z - \omega} + \frac{1}{\omega} + \frac{z}{\omega^2} \right| \leq \frac{|z|^2}{|\omega|^3 \left(1 - \dfrac{|z|}{|\omega|} \right)}$$

whenever $|\omega| > |z|$.

The function $\zeta(z)$ is regular everywhere except at the points $z = \omega$. These exceptional points are simple poles of $\zeta(z)$, with the expansions

$$\zeta(z) = \frac{1}{z - \omega} + \mathfrak{P}(z - \omega).$$

Since $\zeta(z)$ has only one simple pole in every period parallelogram of $\wp(z)$, $\zeta(z)$ cannot be a doubly periodic function with primitive periods ω_1 and ω_2. It follows, as in Section 14.14, that the expression $\zeta(z + \omega_i) - \zeta(z)$ $(i = 1, 2)$ has a value $2\eta_i$ which is independent of z, so that $\zeta(z)$ increases by $2\eta_i$ whenever z increases by ω_i. Hence, for all z we have

$$\zeta(z + \omega_1) = \zeta(z) + 2\eta_1, \qquad \zeta(z + \omega_2) = \zeta(z) + 2\eta_2. \tag{14.34}$$

Since $\zeta(z)$ is not doubly periodic, the case $\eta_1 = \eta_2 = 0$ cannot occur. The function $\zeta(z)$ is "doubly additively periodic" or *quasi-periodic*.

14.16. The Legendre Relation

The constants η_1 and η_2 are connected by an important relation. To find this relation, we place the period parallelogram so that the pole $z = 0$ lies at the center. Applying the residue theorem, we obtain

$$\int_{ABCDA} \zeta(z)\, dz = 2\pi i. \tag{14.35}$$

On the other hand, the relations (14.34) imply that (Fig. 41, p. 247)

$$\int_{CD} \zeta(z)\, dz = \int_{BA} \zeta(z + \omega_2)\, dz = \int_{BA} \zeta(z)\, dz + \int_{BA} 2\eta_2\, dz$$

$$= \int_{BA} \zeta(z)\, dz - 2\eta_2\omega_1,$$

so that

$$\int_{AB} \zeta(z)\, dz + \int_{CD} \zeta(z)\, dz = -2\eta_2\omega_1.$$

Similarly,

$$\int_{BC} \zeta(z)\, dz + \int_{DA} \zeta(z)\, dz = 2\eta_1\omega_2.$$

If we combine these identities with (14.35), we obtain the *Legendre relation*

$$\eta_1\omega_2 - \eta_2\omega_1 = \pi i.$$

The constants η_1 and η_2 can be expressed in terms of the values of the function $\zeta(z)$. It follows from (14.33) that

$$\zeta(-z) = -\frac{1}{z} + {\sum}' \left\{ \frac{1}{-z-\omega} + \frac{1}{\omega} + \frac{-z}{\omega^2} \right\}$$

$$= -\frac{1}{z} - {\sum}' \left\{ \frac{1}{z-(-\omega)} + \frac{1}{-\omega} + \frac{z}{(-\omega)^2} \right\}.$$

The last sum, however, is equal to the last sum in (14.33) except for the ordering of terms. We conclude from this that $\zeta(z)$ is an odd function:

$$-\zeta(z) \equiv \zeta(-z).$$

In particular, if we set $z = \omega_1/2$, we have

$$-\zeta\left(\frac{\omega_1}{2}\right) = \zeta\left(-\frac{\omega_1}{2}\right). \tag{14.36}$$

On the other hand, it follows from (14.34) that

$$\zeta\left(\frac{\omega_1}{2}\right) = \zeta\left(-\frac{\omega_1}{2} + \omega_1\right) = \zeta\left(-\frac{\omega_1}{2}\right) + 2\eta_1,$$

which, together with (14.36), implies that

$$\eta_1 = \zeta\left(\frac{\omega_1}{2}\right).$$

One can prove in the same way that

$$\eta_2 = \zeta\left(\frac{\omega_2}{2}\right).$$

14.17. The σ-Function

The function obtained by integrating the ζ-function is no longer single-valued, because the form of (14.33) shows that the integral will contain logarithmic terms. We first restrict z to the disk $|z| \leq \rho$, and split up the expansion (14.33) in the following way:

$$\zeta(z) = \frac{1}{z} + {\sum_{|\omega| \leq \rho}}' \left\{ \frac{1}{z-\omega} + \frac{1}{\omega} + \frac{z}{\omega^2} \right\} + {\sum_{|\omega| > \rho}}' \left\{ \frac{1}{z-\omega} + \frac{1}{\omega} + \frac{z}{\omega^2} \right\}. \tag{14.37}$$

The second series converges uniformly in the disk $|z| \leq \rho$, so that we may therefore integrate it term by term. The integral of the general term is

$$\int_0^z \left(\frac{1}{z - \omega} + \frac{1}{\omega} + \frac{z}{\omega^2} \right) dz = \log \left(1 - \frac{z}{\omega} \right) + \frac{z}{\omega} + \frac{z^2}{2\omega^2}.$$

Here we must choose that branch of the logarithm which vanishes at the origin. If we now integrate the rational function formed by the initial terms of the right-hand side of (14.37) and choose the constant of integration suitably, we obtain finally

$$f(z) = \int \zeta(z)\, dz = \log z + \sum_{|\omega| \leq \rho}' \left\{ \log \left(1 - \frac{z}{\omega} \right) + \frac{z}{\omega} + \frac{z^2}{2\omega^2} \right\}$$

$$+ \sum_{|\omega| > \rho} \left\{ \log \left(1 - \frac{z}{\omega} \right) + \frac{z}{\omega} + \frac{z^2}{2\omega^2} \right\}. \tag{14.38}$$

The last term is a series whose sum is single-valued and regular for $|z| \leq \rho$. The function (14.38) is therefore regular everywhere in this disk, except at the points $z = \omega$. It is multiple-valued, so that whenever z describes a closed path, $f(z)$ increases by $n2\pi i$, where n is an integer.

We may obtain a single-valued function by forming

$$\sigma(z) = e^{f(z)}, \tag{14.39}$$

which is regular everywhere and which does not vanish except at the singularities $z = \omega$ of $f(z)$. In a neighborhood of the origin we have

$$f(z) = \log z + \mathfrak{P}(z),$$

and therefore

$$\sigma(z) = e^{\log z + \mathfrak{P}(z)} = z\, e^{\mathfrak{P}(z)} = z\, e^{\mathfrak{P}(0)} + [z^2].$$

The function $\sigma(z)$ is therefore regular at $z = 0$ and has a simple zero at this point. The same argument shows that all the points $z = \omega$ are simple zeros of $\sigma(z)$. It is therefore an *entire function*. By means of (14.39) and (14.38) we find the product representation

$$\sigma(z) = z \prod_\omega' \left\{ \left(1 - \frac{z}{\omega} \right) e^{z/\omega + z^2/2\omega^2} \right\}. \tag{14.40}$$

14.18.

We now examine the behavior of $\sigma(z)$ as z increases by ω_1 or ω_2. If we write

$$F(z) = f(z + \omega_1) - f(z), \tag{14.41}$$

it follows from (14.38) and (14.34) that

$$F'(z) = \zeta(z + \omega_1) - \zeta(z) = 2\eta_1,$$

so that

$$F(z) = 2\eta_1 z + C_1,$$

where C_1 is a constant. It follows from (14.41) that

$$f(z + \omega_1) = f(z) + 2\eta_1 z + C_1,$$

and from (14.39) that

$$\sigma(z + \omega_1) = e^{f(z+\omega_1)} = e^{f(z)+2\eta_1 z + C_1} = \sigma(z)\, e^{2\eta_1 z + C_1}. \tag{14.42}$$

To determine C_1, we set $z = -\omega_1/2$:

$$\sigma\left(\frac{\omega_1}{2}\right) = \sigma\left(-\frac{\omega_1}{2}\right) e^{-\eta_1\omega}\, e^{C_1}. \tag{14.43}$$

It is a consequence of (14.40) that $\sigma(z)$ is an *odd function*. For if we replace z by $-z$ in (14.40), the only change in the product $\prod'$ is in the order of the factors of the product. Since the product converges absolutely, its value remains unchanged (Exercise 14, p. 276). Therefore (14.43) reduces to

$$e^{C_1} = -e^{\eta_1\omega_1}.$$

If we substitute this value into (14.42) we obtain the relation

$$\sigma(z + \omega_1) = -\sigma(z)\, e^{2\eta_1(z+\omega_1/2)},$$

and in the same way we obtain

$$\sigma(z + \omega_2) = -\sigma(z)\, e^{2\eta_2(z+\omega_2/2)}.$$

§6. REPRESENTATION OF DOUBLY PERIODIC FUNCTIONS BY MEANS OF THE σ-FUNCTION

14.19. Formulation of the Problem

In Section 14.6 we saw that the total number of zeros of a doubly periodic function inside its period parallelogram is equal to the total number of poles in the same region. If $a_1, a_2, \ldots, a_h$ are the zeros and $b_1, b_2, \ldots, b_k$ are the poles, then $h = k$, if the zeros and poles are counted according to multiplicity. Furthermore, we found in Section 14.7 that

$$\sum_{i=1}^{h} a_i - \sum_{i=1}^{h} b_i = \omega, \tag{14.44}$$

where $\omega = m_1\omega_1 + m_2\omega_2$ is a period.

Let us now assume, conversely, that a_i and b_i ($i = 1, 2, \ldots, h$) are given numbers belonging to the parallelogram determined by ω_1 and ω_2 and satisfying the condition (14.44). We ask whether there exists a doubly periodic function with the primitive periods ω_1 and ω_2, which has zeros at the points a_i and poles at the points b_i ($i = 1, 2, \ldots, h$).

Let us assume first that there exist *two* functions $f_1(z)$ and $f_2(z)$ with the required properties. Then $f_1(z)/f_2(z)$ is a doubly periodic function which has neither zeros nor poles. Therefore, by Theorem 1 (Section 14.5), it must be a constant, so that

$$f_1(z) = Cf_2(z).$$

Therefore, if there exists a function f (z) with the required properties, it is uniquely determined up to a constant factor.

14.20. Construction of the Solution

We now show that there actually exists a function $f(z)$ satisfying the required conditions. If the right-hand side ω of formula (14.44) is $\omega = \omega_0 \neq 0$, then we replace the zero a_1 by the number $a_1' = a_1 - \omega_0$, which causes the right-hand side to vanish:

$$a_1' + a_2 + \cdots + a_h = b_1 + b_2 + \cdots + b_h. \tag{14.44}'$$

The new zero a_1' does not lie in the same period parallelogram as the others.

We now make use of the σ-function which, according to (14.40), has simple zeros at the points $z = \omega = m_1\omega_1 + m_2\omega_2\,(m_1, m_2 = 0, \pm 1, \ldots)$. The function $\sigma(z - a)$ then has simple zeros at the points $z = a + \omega$. Therefore, the function

$$f(z) = C\,\frac{\sigma(z - a_1')\sigma(z - a_2)\ldots\sigma(z - a_h)}{\sigma(z - b_1)\sigma(z - b_2)\ldots\sigma(z - b_h)}, \tag{14.45}$$

where C is an arbitrary constant, has zeros at the points $a_1' + \omega$, $a_i + \omega$ ($i = 2, 3, \ldots, h$) and poles at the points $b_i + \omega$ ($i = 1, 2, \ldots, h$) for every period ω. Except for poles just mentioned, the function is regular. We assert that $f(z)$ is a doubly periodic function with the periods ω_1 and ω_2.

It follows from (14.42) that

$$\sigma(z + \omega_1 - a_i) = \sigma(z - a_i)\,e^{2\eta_1(z - a_i) + C_1} = \sigma(z - a_i)\,e^{2\eta_1 z + C_1}\,e^{-2\eta_1 a_i},$$

$$\sigma(z + \omega_1 - b_i) = \sigma(z - b_i)\,e^{2\eta_1 z + C_1}\,e^{-2\eta_1 b_i}.$$

Hence,

$$f(z + \omega_1) = C\,\frac{\sigma(z - a_1')\ldots\sigma(z - a_h)\,(e^{2\eta_1 z + C_1})^h\,e^{-2\eta_1(a_1' + a_2 + \cdots + a_h)}}{\sigma(z - b_1)\ldots\sigma(z - b_h)\,(e^{2\eta_1 z + C_1})^h\,e^{-2\eta_1(b_1 + b_2 + \cdots + b_h)}}.$$

By (14.44)' we have

$$f(z + \omega_1) = f(z).$$

By a similar argument we find that

$$f(z + \omega_2) = f(z).$$

The function $f(z)$ defined by (14.45) is therefore doubly periodic. It has all the required properties and we have the following result.

There exists a doubly periodic function with prescribed periods and with prescribed zeros and poles satisfying (14.44), which is unique up to a constant factor.

Every doubly periodic function can therefore be represented in the form (14.45) by means of the σ-function.

§7. THE DIFFERENTIAL EQUATION OF THE $\wp$-FUNCTION

14.21.

In Section 14.15 we derived for the function $\zeta(z)$ the expansion

$$\zeta(z) = \frac{1}{z} + \sideset{}{'}\sum \left(\frac{1}{z-\omega} + \frac{1}{\omega} + \frac{z}{\omega^2} \right). \tag{14.46}$$

The sum appearing in this formula is regular in a neighborhood of the point $z = 0$, so that it can be expanded into a power series whose radius of convergence is the smallest of the numbers $|\omega|$.

If we restrict z to the region $|z| < |\omega|$, we have

$$\frac{1}{z-\omega} = -\frac{1}{\omega} - \frac{z}{\omega^2} - \frac{z^2}{\omega^3} - \cdots.$$

The general term of the series (14.46) therefore has the expansion

$$\frac{1}{z-\omega} + \frac{1}{\omega} + \frac{z}{\omega^2} = -\frac{z^2}{\omega^3} - \frac{z^3}{\omega^4} - \cdots. \tag{14.47}$$

The series (14.46) still converges if each term in (14.47) is replaced by its modulus. One can therefore rearrange the terms without changing the value of the sum. Hence, we obtain the identity

$$\sideset{}{'}\sum \left(\frac{1}{z-\omega} + \frac{1}{\omega} + \frac{z}{\omega^2} \right) = -z^2 \sideset{}{'}\sum \frac{1}{\omega^3} - z^3 \sideset{}{'}\sum \frac{1}{\omega^4} - z^4 \sideset{}{'}\sum \frac{1}{\omega^5} - \cdots.$$

The coefficients of this power series will be denoted by

$$c_\nu = \sideset{}{'}\sum \frac{1}{\omega^\nu} \qquad (\nu = 3, 4, \ldots).$$

Since $-\omega$ is also a period whenever ω is, it follows that $c_{2n+1} = 0\,(n = 1, 2, \ldots)$. The function $\zeta(z)$ therefore has the following expansion in the neighborhood of the origin:

$$\zeta(z) = \frac{1}{z} - c_4 z^3 - c_6 z^5 - c_8 z^7 - \cdots.$$

Hence,

$$\wp(z) = -\zeta'(z) = \frac{1}{z^2} + 3c_4 z^2 + 5c_6 z^4 + \cdots, \tag{14.48}$$

and

$$\wp'(z) = -\frac{2}{z^3} + 6c_4 z + 20c_6 z^3 + \cdots. \tag{14.49}$$

By means of rational operations on $\wp$ and $\wp'$ we can construct a function without poles. Let us consider the expression

$$\wp'(z)^2 - \{4\wp(z)^3 - 60c_4\wp(z) - 140c_6\} = [z^2]. \qquad (14.50)$$

On the left-hand side we have a doubly periodic function with periods ω_1 and ω_2 whose only possible pole in the period parallelogram is the pole $z = 0$ of $\wp(z)$. But, in view of (14.50), it is regular at this point. Therefore it must be a constant, and since it vanishes at $z = 0$, it is identically zero. Hence,

$$\wp'(z)^2 = 4\wp(z)^3 - 60c_4\wp(z) - 140c_6. \qquad (14.51)$$

We adopt the notation

$$g_2 = 60c_4 = 60 \sum' \frac{1}{\omega^4}, \qquad g_3 = 140c_6 = 140 \sum' \frac{1}{\omega^6}.$$

The function $\wp(z)$ satisfies the differential equation

$$\left(\frac{d\wp}{dz}\right)^2 = 4\wp^3 - g_2\wp - g_3 \qquad (14.52)$$

or

$$\frac{d\wp}{dz} = \sqrt{4\wp^3 - g_2\wp - g_3}. \qquad (14.53)$$

In the neighborhood of every point where $\wp'(z) \neq 0$ the function $\wp(z)$ is invertible and z may be expressed as a well-defined function of $\wp$. From (14.53) we have

$$\frac{dz}{d\wp} = \frac{1}{\sqrt{4\wp^3 - g_2\wp - g_3}},$$

whence

$$z = z_0 + \int_{\wp_0}^{\wp} \frac{d\wp}{\sqrt{4\wp^3 - g_2\wp - g_3}}. \qquad (14.54)$$

The inverse function of the $\wp$-function is therefore the *elliptic integral* (14.54).

§8. REPRESENTATION OF DOUBLY PERIODIC FUNCTIONS AS RATIONAL FUNCTIONS OF $\wp$ AND $\wp'$

14.22. Representation of Even Functions

Let $f(z)$ be an even, doubly periodic function with primitive periods ω_1 and ω_2. Then the roots of the equation

$$f(z) = c \qquad (14.55)$$

may be grouped in opposite pairs. We choose the fundamental parallelogram in such a way that its center is at the origin, and we make the convention that the fundamental parallelogram contains the vertex $(\omega_1 + \omega_2)/2$ and the two open sides meeting at this vertex, but not the other two sides. If z_i is a root of (14.55), then so is $-z_i$, and if z_i lies in the fundamental parallelogram, so does $-z_i$.

On the other hand, if z_i is on the boundary of the period parallelogram, so is $-z_i$, but $-z_i$ does not belong to the fundamental period parallelogram. In this case one of the points $-z_i + \omega_1$, $-z_i + \omega_2$, $-z_i + \omega_1 + \omega_2$ will lie on the boundary of the fundamental parallelogram; this point will be denoted by z_i'.

The points z_i and z_i' coincide if and only if $z_i = -z_i + \omega_1$, $z_i = -z_i + \omega_2$, or $z_i = -z_i + \omega_1 + \omega_2$, so that z_i is one of the points $\omega_1/2$, $\omega_2/2$, $(\omega_1 + \omega_2)/2$. In this case z_i is a root of even order of Eq. (14.55).

Let z_i and z_i' $(i = 1, 2, \ldots, k)$ be the roots of Eq. (14.55) in the fundamental parallelogram.

Along with (14.55) we also consider a second equation

$$f(z) = d,$$

and denote its roots by u_i, u_i' $(i = 1, 2, \ldots, k)$.

The function

$$\frac{f(z) - c}{f(z) - d} \tag{14.56}$$

is then doubly periodic with primitive periods ω_1 and ω_2. Its zeros in the fundamental parallelogram are the points z_i, z_i', and its poles are the points u_i, $u_i'(i = 1, 2, \ldots, k)$.

A doubly periodic function with the same properties can also be constructed by means of the $\wp$-function, which is a function of order two. Now z_i and z_i' are both zeros of the function $\wp(z) - \wp(z_i)$, which can have no other zeros in the fundamental parallelogram. The function

$$Q(z) = \frac{[\wp(z) - \wp(z_1)][\wp(z) - \wp(z_2)] \ldots [\wp(z) - \wp(z_k)]}{[\wp(z) - \wp(u_1)][\wp(z) - \wp(u_2)] \ldots [\wp(z) - \wp(u_k)]},$$

like (14.56), has z_i, z_i' as zeros and u_i, u_i' as poles. The function

$$\frac{[f(z) - c]/[f(z) - d]}{Q(z)},$$

which is also doubly periodic, is regular everywhere. This function must therefore be a constant K, so that

$$\frac{f(z) - c}{f(z) - d} = KQ(z).$$

We see from this that $f(z)$ is a rational function of $\wp(z)$, $f = R(\wp)$. Therefore:

Every even doubly periodic function is a rational function of the $\wp$-function.

14.23. The General Case

Let now $f(z)$ be an *odd* doubly periodic function. Since $\wp'(z)$ is odd, the quotient $f(z)/\wp'(z)$ is even. We have just seen that such a function can be expressed as a rational function of $\wp(z)$. The function $f(z)$ is therefore a rational function of $\wp(z)$ and $\wp'(z)$ of the form $f(z) = \wp'R(\wp)$.

Every doubly periodic function $f(z)$ can be written as the sum of an even and an odd doubly periodic function:

$$f(z) = \frac{f(z) + f(-z)}{2} + \frac{f(z) - f(-z)}{2}.$$

It then follows that $f(z)$ can be expressed as a rational function of $\wp(z)$ and $\wp'(z)$, $f = R_1(\wp) + \wp'R_2(\wp)$. We have thus proved the following general theorem.

Every doubly periodic function can be expressed as a rational function of $\wp(z)$ and $\wp'(z)$.

§9. ADDITION THEOREM FOR DOUBLY PERIODIC FUNCTIONS

14.24. Algebraic Equation between Two Doubly Periodic Functions

Let $f_1(z)$ and $f_2(z)$ be two arbitrary doubly periodic functions with primitive periods ω_1 and ω_2. Both can be written as rational functions of $\wp$ and $\wp'$:

$$f_1(z) = R_1(\wp, \wp'), \qquad f_2(z) = R_2(\wp, \wp').$$

In addition, we have at our disposal the relation between $\wp$ and $\wp'$ (Section 14.21):

$$\wp'^2 = 4\wp^3 - g_2\wp - g_3.$$

If $\wp$ and $\wp'$ are eliminated from these three equations, we obtain an equation of the form

$$G(f_1, f_2) = 0,$$

where G is a polynomial in f_1 and f_2. Therefore:

Any two doubly periodic functions with the same periods are connected by an algebraic equation.

If we apply this theorem to a doubly periodic function and its derivative, which is also doubly periodic, we have the following theorem.

Every doubly periodic function $f(z)$ satisfies an algebraic differential equation of the first order:

$$G(f(z), f'(z)) = 0.$$

14.25. Addition Theorem for the $\wp$-Function

We shall prove that the $\wp$-function possesses an algebraic addition formula. The function

$$f(z) = \frac{d}{dz}\log\left(\wp(z) - \wp(u)\right) = \frac{\wp'(z)}{\wp(z) - \wp(u)} \qquad (u \neq \omega) \qquad (14.57)$$

is doubly periodic. It has simple poles at the points $z = u$, $z = -u$, and $z = 0$ with the residues 1, 1, and -2, provided that $\wp'(u) \neq 0$. Whenever $\wp'(u) = 0$ the denominator has a double zero at the point $z = u$ and the residue of $f(z)$ is 2. The function

$$\zeta(z - u) + \zeta(z + u) - 2\zeta(z) \tag{14.58}$$

has the same simple poles with the same residues as the function $f(z)$. The function (14.58) is also doubly periodic with primitive periods ω_1 and ω_2, which follows from the fact that $\zeta(z)$ is quasi-periodic. The difference of the functions (14.57) and (14.58) is therefore a doubly periodic function which is regular everywhere. Hence, it must be a constant C, and we have

$$\frac{\wp'(z)}{\wp(z) - \wp(u)} = C + \zeta(z - u) + \zeta(z + u) - 2\zeta(z). \tag{14.59}$$

If we replace z by $-z$ and observe that $\wp(z)$ is an even function, while $\wp'(z)$ and $\zeta(z)$ are odd functions, we have that $C = 0$. If we interchange z and u in (14.59) and add the resulting formula to (14.59), we obtain

$$\zeta(z + u) = \zeta(z) + \zeta(u) + \frac{1}{2} \frac{\wp'(z) - \wp'(u)}{\wp(z) - \wp(u)}.$$

If we differentiate this equation with respect to z, we have

$$\wp(z + u) = \wp(z) - \frac{1}{2} \frac{\partial}{\partial z} \frac{\wp'(z) - \wp'(u)}{\wp(z) - \wp(u)}. \tag{14.60}$$

In view of the differential equation (14.52) for the $\wp$-function, the right-hand side of (14.60) is a rational function of $\wp(z)$, $\wp'(z)$, $\wp(u)$ and $\wp'(u)$. Thus we have obtained for the $\wp$-function the following addition formula:

$$\wp(z + u) = R(\wp(z), \wp(u), \wp'(z), \wp'(u)),$$

where R is a rational function. Moreover since $\wp'(z)$ and $\wp'(u)$ can be expressed algebraically in terms of $\wp(z)$ and $\wp(u)$, we obtain an algebraic addition formula for the $\wp$-function. Carrying out the calculations, we finally arrive at the formula

$$(\wp_1 + \wp_2 + \wp_3)(4\wp_1\wp_2\wp_3 - g_3) = \left(\wp_1\wp_2 + \wp_1\wp_3 + \wp_2\wp_3 + \frac{g_2}{4}\right)^2, \tag{14.61}$$

where $\wp_1 = \wp(z)$, $\wp_2 = \wp(u)$, and $\wp_3 = \wp(z + u)$ (Exercise 18, p. 277).

14.26. Generalization

We shall prove the following general theorem.

Every doubly periodic function has an algebraic addition formula.

Let us write

$$\wp(z_1) = \wp_1, \qquad \wp(z_2) = \wp_2, \qquad \wp'(z_1) = \wp'_1, \qquad \wp'(z_2) = \wp'_2.$$

If $f(z)$ is an arbitrary doubly periodic function with primitive periods ω_1 and ω_2, then it follows from Section 14.23 that

$$f(z_1 + z_2) = R\big(\wp(z_1 + z_2),\ \wp'(z_1 + z_2)\big), \qquad (14.62)$$

where R is a rational function. The addition formula of the $\wp$-function yields

$$\wp(z_1 + z_2) = R_1(\wp_1, \wp_1', \wp_2, \wp_2'), \qquad (14.63)$$

where R_1 is a rational function. If we differentiate (14.63) with respect to z_1, we have

$$\wp'(z_1 + z_2) = \frac{\partial R_1}{\partial \wp_1}\, \wp_1' + \frac{\partial R_1}{\partial \wp_1'}\, \wp''(z_1) = R_2(\wp_1, \wp_1', \wp_2, \wp_2'), \qquad (14.64)$$

where the rational function R_2 is obtained by the substitution

$$\wp''(z_1) = 6\wp_1^2 - \tfrac{1}{2}g_2.$$

If we substitute (14.63) and (14.64) into (14.62), we obtain

$$f(z_1 + z_2) = R_3(\wp_1, \wp_1', \wp_2, \wp_2'), \qquad (14.65)$$

where R_3 again denotes a rational function. In addition, we also have

$$f(z_1) = R(\wp_1, \wp_1'), \qquad\qquad f(z_2) = R(\wp_2, \wp_2'),$$

$$\wp_1'^2 = 4\wp_1^3 - g_2\wp_1 - g_3, \qquad \wp_2'^2 = 4\wp_2^3 - g_2\wp_2 - g_3.$$

If we eliminate $\wp_1, \wp_2, \wp_1', \wp_2'$ from these equations and from (14.65), we obtain an equation of the form

$$G\big(f(z_1 + z_2), f(z_1), f(z_2)\big) = 0,$$

where G is a polynomial. This shows that the function $f(z)$ possesses an algebraic addition formula.

§10. DETERMINATION OF A DOUBLY PERIODIC FUNCTION WITH PRESCRIBED PRINCIPAL PARTS

14.27.

We now consider the problem of constructing a doubly periodic function, whose poles $b_1, b_2, \ldots, b_n$ and principal parts at these poles are prescribed in the period parallelogram. At the pole $z = b$ let

$$w(z) = \frac{\beta_{-\nu}}{(z - b)^\nu} + \cdots + \frac{\beta_{-1}}{z - b} + \mathfrak{P}(z - b).$$

According to Section 14.5, a necessary condition for the existence of such a function is that

$$\sum_{(b)} \beta_{-1} = 0. \qquad (14.66)$$

We are going to show that this condition is also sufficient.

As auxiliary functions we shall use the $\wp$-function and its derivatives. At $z = 0$ these functions have the expansions (cf. Section 14.21)

$$\wp(z) = \frac{1}{z^2} + \mathfrak{P}(z) = w_2(z),$$

$$(-1)^{k-1} \frac{\wp^{(k-1)}(z)}{k!} = \frac{1}{z^{k+1}} + \mathfrak{P}(z) = w_{k+1}(z) \qquad (k = 2, 3, \ldots). \tag{14.67}$$

All these functions are doubly periodic. At the origin they have a pole of order at least two.

We also need a function with a *simple* pole at the origin. We shall use here the ζ-function although it is not doubly periodic. By Section 14.21 its expansion at $z = 0$ is

$$\zeta = \frac{1}{z} + \mathfrak{P}(z) = w_1(z). \tag{14.68}$$

By means of the functions $w_1, w_2, \ldots$ we form the expression

$$\beta_{-\nu} w_\nu(z - b) + \cdots + \beta_{-2} w_2(z - b) + \beta_{-1} w_1(z - b),$$

whose only singularity in the fundamental parallelogram is at $z = b$. This point is a pole of order ν with the required principal part.

Constructing the corresponding expressions for each of the given poles $b_1, b_2, \ldots, b_n$, and adding them all together, we obtain the function

$$w(z) = \sum_{(b)} \{\beta_{-\nu} w_\nu(z - b) + \cdots + \beta_{-2} w_2(z - b) + \beta_{-1} w_1(z - b)\}. \tag{14.69}$$

This function has poles at the points $b_1, b_2, \ldots, b_n$ and at these poles it has the prescribed principal parts. It remains to show that $w(z)$ is doubly periodic. Since the functions $w_2, w_3, \ldots$ are doubly periodic, it suffices to show that the function

$$g(z) = \sum_{(b)} \beta_{-1} w_1(z - b) = \sum_{(b)} \beta_{-1} \zeta(z - b)$$

is doubly periodic.

From (14.34) we have

$$\zeta(z + \omega_1 - b) = \zeta(z - b) + 2\eta_1.$$

Using this relation, and taking into account the condition (14.66), we have that

$$g(z + \omega_1) = \sum_{(b)} \beta_{-1} \zeta(z + \omega_1 - b) = g(z) + 2\eta_1 \sum_{(b)} \beta_{-1} = g(z).$$

Hence, ω_1 is a period of the function (14.69). One can show in the same way that ω_2 is also a period. The function $w(z)$ is therefore doubly periodic; thus it has all the required properties.

If $f(z)$ is any other doubly periodic function with the same properties, then $f(z) - w(z)$ is a constant (Exercise 8, p. 276).

We have thus obtained the following result.

There exists a doubly periodic function, which is unique up to an additive constant, with prescribed poles in its period parallelogram and with prescribed principal parts such that the sum of the residues is zero. The general form of this function is given by (14.69), where the functions w_1, w_2, ... are defined by (14.68) and (14.67).

§11. MAPPING BY A DOUBLY PERIODIC FUNCTION OF ORDER 2

14.28. Branch Points

Since the function $\wp(z)$ assumes every complex value twice in a period parallelogram, it maps the period parallelogram onto a two-sheeted Riemann surface with a slit. The edges of the slit correspond to the boundary of the parallelogram. The slit Riemann surface is a simply connected region.

To investigate the mapping more closely, we determine first of all the points at which the mapping is not conformal. These include all the zeros of $\wp'(z)$, and, in addition, the poles of $\wp(z)$, which are all double poles.

To determine the zeros of the equation $\wp'(z) = 0$ we shall use the fact that $\wp'(z)$ is odd. If we note that any period ω of $\wp(z)$ is also a period of $\wp'(z)$, we obtain

$$-\wp'\left(\frac{\omega}{2}\right) = \wp'\left(-\frac{\omega}{2}\right) = \wp'\left(\frac{\omega}{2}\right),$$

and hence

$$\wp'\left(\frac{\omega}{2}\right) = 0,$$

provided that $\omega/2$ is not a pole of $\wp(z)$.

The only points of the form $\omega/2$ which belong to the fundamental parallelogram P_0 are the points $\omega_1/2$, $(\omega_1 + \omega_2)/2$, and $\omega_2/2$. Since the function $\wp'(z)$ is a doubly periodic function of order 3, it can have no other zeros in P_0. From this it follows that all the zeros of $\wp'(z)$ are simple. The only pole of $\wp(z)$ in P_0 is $z = 0$. We shall write

$$\wp\left(\frac{\omega_1}{2}\right) = e_1, \qquad \wp\left(\frac{\omega_1 + \omega_2}{2}\right) = e_2, \qquad \wp\left(\frac{\omega_2}{2}\right) = e_3. \qquad (14.70)$$

The numbers e_1, e_2 and e_3 are all distinct, for if, for example, $\omega_1/2$ is a double zero of $\wp(z) - e_1$, then the $\wp$-function, which is of order 2, cannot assume the value e_1 at any other point of P_0. Hence, $e_1 \neq e_2$ and $e_1 \neq e_3$.

Since $\wp'$ has a simple zero at $z = \omega_1/2$, $\wp(z)$ maps a neighborhood of the point $\omega_1/2$ onto a two-sheeted Riemann surface which has a first-order branch point at $\wp = e_1$ (Section 9.25). For the same reason, e_2 and e_3 are also first-order branch points. At the origin $\wp$ has a double pole, so that its image $e_4 = \wp(0) = \infty$ is again a first-order branch point of the Riemann surface (Section 9.26).

14.29. The Mapping by the $\wp$-Function

Again we choose the fundamental parallelogram in such a way that its center is at the origin. By means of straight lines through the origin parallel to the sides, we decompose the parallelogram into four congruent parts (Fig. 42).

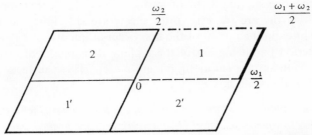

Figure 42

Since $\wp$ is an even function, it assumes the same values in the regions **1** and **1′**, so that these regions have the same image domain. The same applies to the parallelograms **2** and **2′**. The function $\wp(z)$ therefore maps the domain consisting of parallelograms **1** and **2** onto one sheet of the Riemann surface and the domain consisting of **1′** and **2′** onto the other sheet.

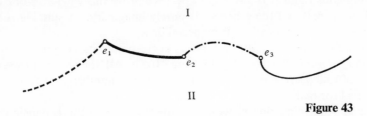

Figure 43

We now let the point z describe the boundary of parallelogram **1** once in the positive sense. If z moves from $z = 0$ to $z = \omega_1/2$, $\wp$ moves along a simple arc from ∞ to the point e_1. If z describes the segment joining $\omega_1/2$ to the point $(\omega_1 + \omega_2)/2$, $\wp$ moves from e_1 to e_2. Next, if z goes from $(\omega_1 + \omega_2)/2$ to $\omega_2/2$, $\wp$ moves from e_2 to e_3. Finally, if z returns from $z = \omega_2/2$ to the origin, $\wp$ moves from e_3 to infinity. Thus, as the point z describes the boundary of parallelogram **1** in the positive sense, $\wp$ describes a simple curve l, which extends to infinity in both directions (Fig. 43).

If z describes the boundary of parallelogram **2** in the positive sense, then $\wp$ describes the curve l in the opposite sense.

It follows from Section 10.13 that the function $\wp = \wp(z)$ maps parallelogram **1** one-to-one conformally onto that domain I bounded by the curve l which is on the left as l is described in the sense e_1, e_2, e_3. Parallelogram **2** is mapped one-to-one conformally onto the second domain II bounded by l which is connected with I along the arc of l from e_3 to ∞.

The region consisting of parallelograms **1′** and **2′** is mapped onto the second sheet of the Riemann surface. The two sheets are connected along the arc of l which joins e_1 to ∞. The entire fundamental parallelogram is thus mapped onto a two-sheeted Riemann surface whose sheets are joined together crosswise along the arc (∞, e_1). Both sheets are slit along the arc $e_1e_2e_3$. The surface has a branch point of the first order at infinity.

Every period parallelogram of the z-plane is mapped onto such a two-sheeted Riemann surface slit along the arc $e_1e_2e_3$. These surfaces are joined to one another along the slits e_1e_2 and e_2e_3.

The whole z-plane therefore is mapped onto a Riemann surface with infinitely many sheets which has infinitely many first-order branch points over the points ∞, e_1, e_2, e_3.

If the opposite sides of the parallelograms are identified, we obtain *a surface of torus-type*. This is mapped in a one-to-one way onto a two-sheeted Riemann surface with first-order branch points at the points ∞, e_1, e_2, e_3.

14.30. The Case Re $\omega_2/\omega_1 = 0$

If the fundamental parallelogram is a rectangle, then the boundary curve l of the domains I and II is a straight line. We prove this whenever one of the periods ω_1 is real and the other ω_2 is purely imaginary. A suitable rotation will reduce the general case to this special one.

To each period $\omega = m_1\omega_1 + m_2\omega_2$ corresponds its complex conjugate $\omega = m_1\omega_1 - m_2\omega_2$ which is also a period. If z is real, the terms of the expansion (14.30) of $\wp$ are pairwise complex conjugate numbers. It follows that $\wp(z)$ is real for real z.

If z is purely imaginary, we substitute $z = iy$ into the expansion of $\wp$, where y is real and greater than 0, and we obtain

$$\wp(iy) = -\frac{1}{y^2} + \sideset{}{'}\sum \left\{ \frac{1}{(iy - \omega)^2} - \frac{1}{\omega^2} \right\}$$

$$= -\frac{1}{y^2} - \sideset{}{'}\sum \left\{ \frac{1}{(y + i\omega)^2} + \frac{1}{\omega^2} \right\}.$$

We see that the terms are again pairwise complex conjugate and that $\wp(iy)$ is therefore real.

It can be shown by the same method that $\wp(z)$ is also real on the remaining sides of the rectangle (Exercise 23, p. 277).

Thus, in the case we have been considering, $\wp(z)$ maps the rectangle **1** onto the half-plane Im $\wp < 0$.

14.31. The Legendre Modular Function

By a bilinear transformation of the $\wp$-plane three branch points of the Riemann surface, for example, ∞, e_1, e_2, may be *transformed* into the points ∞, 0, 1. The mapping function is of the form

$$w = \frac{\wp - e_1}{e_2 - e_1}.$$

The fourth branch point e_3 is thus mapped into the point

$$\lambda = \frac{e_3 - e_1}{e_2 - e_1}.$$

In view of (14.70), λ depends only upon ω_1 and ω_2. One can prove that λ in fact depends only upon the ratio $t = \omega_1/\omega_2$: $\lambda = \lambda(\omega_1/\omega_2) = \lambda(t)$ and that this function (the so-called *Legendre modular function*) is an *automorphic function* of the variable t. By an automorphic function we mean a meromorphic function which is invariant under a group of bilinear substitutions. Later on we shall meet the function $\lambda(t)$ in another context (Section 17.35).

14.32. The Mapping by an Arbitrary
Doubly Periodic Function of Second Order

Any bilinear function of $\wp(z)$ is a doubly periodic function of order two. We now show the converse: Every doubly periodic function $w(z)$ of second order with primitive periods ω_1 and ω_2 is a bilinear function of $\wp$.

Since $w'(z)$ is also a doubly periodic function, there exists a point z_0 in the fundamental parallelogram where $w'(z_0) = 0$. In the neighborhood of this point $w(z)$ has an expansion

$$w(z) = w(z_0) + c(z - z_0)^2 + \cdots. \tag{14.71}$$

Here $c \neq 0$; otherwise $w(z) - w(z_0)$ would have a triple zero at z_0, and this is impossible, since $w(z)$ is of second order. By (14.71) we have

$$\frac{c}{w - w_0} = \frac{1}{(z - z_0)^2} \frac{1}{1 + [z - z_0]} = \frac{1}{(z - z_0)^2} + \frac{A_{-1}}{z - z_0} + \mathfrak{P}(z - z_0).$$

This function also is doubly periodic and of second order. Its only pole in the fundamental parallelogram is therefore z_0. It follows that $A_{-1} = 0$ and hence

$$\frac{c}{w - w_0} = \frac{1}{(z - z_0)^2} + \mathfrak{P}(z - z_0).$$

This function differs from $\wp(z - z_0)$ only by additive constant:

$$\wp(z - z_0) - \frac{c}{w(z) - w_0} = c'.$$

Hence it follows that $w(z)$ is a bilinear function of $\wp$, as asserted.

Therefore every second-order doubly periodic function maps the z-plane onto a Riemann surface with infinitely many sheets whose branch points are all of the first order and lie over four base points. The sheets of this surface are connected the same way as the sheets of the Riemann surface of the $\wp$-function.

§12. ELLIPTIC INTEGRALS

14.33. Change of the Variable of
Integration by Means of a Bilinear Transformation

We now consider the *elliptic integral of the first kind*

$$\int_{w_0}^{w} \frac{dw}{\sqrt{(w - e_1)(w - e_2)(w - e_3)(w - e_4)}}. \tag{14.72}$$

The integrand is a two-valued function, and e_1, e_2, e_3 and e_4 are the branch points of the associated surface. By means of a bilinear transformation we now introduce a new variable of integration

$$w' = \frac{\alpha w + \beta}{\gamma w + \delta} \qquad (\alpha\delta - \beta\gamma \neq 0) \tag{14.73}$$

and we write

$$e_\nu' = \frac{\alpha e_\nu + \beta}{\gamma e_\nu + \delta} \qquad (\nu = 1, 2, 3, 4).$$

Since the cross-ratio is invariant under a bilinear transformation, we have for corresponding values of w and w' the identity

$$(w, e_3, e_1, e_2) = (w', e_3', e_1', e_2')$$

or

$$\frac{(w - e_1)/(w - e_2)}{(e_3 - e_1)/(e_3 - e_2)} = \frac{(w' - e_1')/(w' - e_2')}{(e_3' - e_1')/(e_3' - e_2')}.$$

Differentiation yields

$$\frac{e_1 - e_2}{(w - e_2)^2} \frac{e_3 - e_2}{e_3 - e_1} dw = \frac{e_1' - e_2'}{(w' - e_2')^2} \frac{e_3' - e_2'}{e_3' - e_1'} dw'.$$

If we multiply this equation by the three equations obtained by cyclic permutation and integrate, we obtain, finally,

$$A \int_{w_0}^{w} \frac{dw}{\sqrt{(w - e_1)(w - e_2)(w - e_3)(w - e_4)}}$$

$$= A' \int_{w_0'}^{w'} \frac{dw'}{\sqrt{(w' - e_1')(w' - e_2')(w' - e_3')(w' - e_4')}}, \tag{14.74}$$

where

$$A = \sqrt{\frac{(e_1 - e_2)(e_2 - e_3)(e_3 - e_4)(e_4 - e_1)}{(e_1 - e_3)(e_2 - e_4)}}$$

and where A' is the analogous expression.

14.34. The Case $e_4' = \infty$

We consider the special case when the transformation (14.73) takes one of the points e_ν to infinity, for example, let $e_4' = \infty$. If we isolate all the factors on the right-hand side of (14.74) which contain e_4', we obtain a factor whose value for $e_4' = \infty$ is i. In the present case the transformation formula (14.74) therefore reduces to

$$A \int_{w_0}^{w} \frac{dw}{\sqrt{(w - e_1)(w - e_2)(w - e_3)(w - e_4)}}$$

$$= A' \int_{w_0'}^{w'} \frac{dw'}{\sqrt{(w' - e_1')(w' - e_2')(w' - e_3')}},$$

where now

$$A' = \sqrt{\frac{(e_1' - e_2')(e_2' - e_3')}{e_3' - e_1'}}.$$

Thus every elliptic integral of the first kind containing a polynomial of degree four in the radicand can be transformed into another one with a cubic polynomial in the radicand. One only has to apply a bilinear transformation which takes one of the branch points to infinity. Conversely, a cubic polynomial can be replaced by a polynomial of degree four by means of a bilinear transformation which maps the branch point at infinity into a finite point.

14.35. Normal Forms of the Integral of First Kind

For elliptic integrals of the first kind, one may employ any one of several normal forms.

If we choose the branch points e_1, e_2, e_3, and e_4 so that $e_4 = \infty$ and $e_1 + e_2 + e_3 = 0$, we obtain the *Weierstrass normal form*

$$\int_{w_0}^{w} \frac{dw}{\sqrt{4w^3 - g_2 w - g_3}}.$$

If we set $e_1 = \lambda$, $e_2 = 1$, $e_3 = 0$, and $e_4 = \infty$, we obtain the *Riemann form*

$$\int_{w_0}^{w} \frac{dw}{\sqrt{w(w - 1)(w - \lambda)}}.$$

The branch points may be mapped by a bilinear transformation into the points $e_1 = 1$, $e_2 = -1$, $e_3 = 1/k$ and $e_4 = -1/k$. The integral is then transformed into the *Legendre normal form*

$$\int_{w_0}^{w} \frac{dw}{\sqrt{(1 - w^2)(1 - k^2 w^2)}}.$$

14.36. Mapping by an Elliptic Integral

We proved in Section 14.32 that every elliptic function of second order maps the z-plane conformally onto a Riemann surface with infinitely many sheets, whose branch points lie over four points. If the period parallelogram is a rectangle, then the branch points lie on a circle. By a bilinear transformation the branch points can then be mapped into the points 1, -1, $1/k$, $-1/k$ with $0 < k < 1$. The inverse function of the resulting elliptic function is an elliptic integral in the Legendre form (cf. Exercise 19, p. 277).

Conversely, we now start from the elliptic integral

$$z = \int_{0}^{w} \frac{dw}{\sqrt{(1 - w^2)(1 - k^2 w^2)}}, \qquad (14.75)$$

where $0 < k < 1$, and investigate its mapping properties. First let us determine the image of the real axis.

Each branch of the root is single-valued in the half-plane $\operatorname{Im} w > 0$. We choose that branch which has the value $+1$ for $w = 0$. If we let w increase from 0 to 1 along the real axis, then the integrand remains positive so that $dz/dw > 0$. The point z therefore moves in the same direction as w, that is, along the positive real axis from $z = 0$ to the point

$$z = \int_{0}^{1} \frac{dw}{\sqrt{(1 - w^2)(1 - k^2 w^2)}},$$

which is clearly finite.

We now consider the interval $1 < w < 1/k$. To determine which branch of the square root we have to choose, we let w describe a small semicircle c in the upper half-plane about the point $w = 1$. Along this semicircle we have

$$\arg \frac{dz}{dw} = -\frac{1}{2} \arg (1 - w) - \frac{1}{2} \left\{ \arg (1 + w) + \arg \left(\frac{1}{k^2} - w^2 \right) \right\}.$$

The expression in brackets returns to its initial value 0 as w returns to the real axis to the right of $w = 1$. On the other hand, the increment of $\arg (1 - w)$ is $-\pi$ and hence

$$\Delta_c \arg \frac{dz}{dw} = \frac{\pi}{2}.$$

If w now moves along the segment $(1, 1/k)$, then $\arg dz/dw$ remains unchanged, so that it is equal to $\pi/2$. Hence, if w moves along the segment $(1, 1/k)$, the point z describes a segment in the direction of the positive imaginary axis Its length is given by the modulus of the following integral:

$$\int_1^{1/k} \frac{dw}{\sqrt{(1 - w^2)(1 - k^2 w^2)}} = i \int_1^{1/k} \frac{dw}{\sqrt{(w^2 - 1)(1 - k^2 w^2)}} .$$

We see in the same way that when w circumscribes the point $1/k$, the argument of dz/dw again increases by $\pi/2$. Thus in the interval $1/k < w$ we have $\arg dz/dw = \pi$. Hence, as w increases from $1/k$ to ∞ along the real axis, z describes a segment in the direction of the negative real axis whose length is

$$\int_{1/k}^{\infty} \frac{dw}{\sqrt{(w^2 - 1)(k^2 w^2 - 1)}} .$$

This segment has the same length as the segment which corresponds to the interval $(0, 1)$. In fact

$$\int_0^1 \frac{dw}{\sqrt{(1 - w^2)(1 - k^2 w^2)}} = \int_{1/k}^{\infty} \frac{dw}{\sqrt{(w^2 - 1)(k^2 w^2 - 1)}} , \qquad (14.76)$$

as can be seen easily if we make the substitution $w = 1/ku$ in the integral on the right-hand side. The image of the point $w = \infty$ therefore lies on the imaginary axis.

In the same way we find that if w moves along the negative real axis from 0 to ∞, z will describe a polygonal path which is symmetric with respect to the imaginary axis to the polygonal path obtained above. The entire real axis therefore is mapped onto the boundary of a rectangle with vertices $\pm\omega_1/4$ and $\pm\omega_1/4 + \omega_2/2$, where

$$\omega_1 = 4\int_0^1 \frac{dw}{\sqrt{(1 - w^2)(1 - k^2 w^2)}} , \qquad \omega_2 = 2i \int_1^{1/k} \frac{dw}{\sqrt{(w^2 - 1)(1 - k^2 w^2)}} .$$

The upper half-plane ($\operatorname{Im} w > 0$) is mapped onto the interior of the rectangle (Section 10.13).

If we pass from the upper to the lower half-plane ($\operatorname{Im} w < 0$) across the segment $(-1, 1)$, we obtain that branch of the function (14.75) which, by the reflection principle, maps the lower half-plane onto a rectangle that is symmetrical with respect to the segment $(-\omega_1/4, \omega_1/4)$ to the rectangle obtained above. Repeated application of the reflection principle leads us to the conclusion that the infinite-sheeted Riemann surface with its infinitely many first-order branch points over the points $-1/k, -1, 1, 1/k$ is mapped in a one-to-one way onto the whole z-plane. The half-planes of the Riemann surface are mapped onto a lattice of congruent rectangles in the z-plane.

From the foregoing discussion we conclude that the inverse function of the elliptic integral (14.75) is a doubly periodic function of second order.

EXERCISES ON CHAPTER 14

1. Show that a rational function cannot be periodic (unless it reduces to a constant).

2. Let $w(z)$ be a simply periodic function with the primitive period $2\pi i$, and let $w(z)$ remain bounded as z goes to infinity in one direction in the period strip. Show that $w(z)$ then tends to a finite limit.

3. Let $w(z)$ be a simply periodic function with the primitive period $2\pi i$, and let it satisfy condition (14.8). Show that if $w(z)$ is unbounded as z goes to infinity in one direction in the period strip, then $w(z) \to \infty$.

4. Let $w(z)$ be a simply periodic entire function with the primitive period $2\pi i$, and let $w(z)$ satisfy condition (14.8). Show that $w(z)$ can then be expressed as a polynomial in e^z and e^{-z}.

5. Prove that a simply periodic entire function with the primitive period $2\pi i$ can be expanded into an everywhere convergent series of the form $\sum_{n=-\infty}^{+\infty} a_n e^{nz}$.

6. Prove that if $w(z)$ is doubly periodic, then so is $w'(z)$.

7. Let $f(z)$ be an odd doubly periodic function and let ω be one of its periods. Show that $\omega/2$ is then either a zero or a pole of $f(z)$, and that the order of $f(z)$ is odd in both cases.

8. Let $f(z)$ and $w(z)$ be doubly periodic functions with the same periods and the same poles. Suppose further that at each pole the two functions have the same principal parts. Prove that $f(z) = w(z) + \text{const}$.

9. According to Section 2 every periodic function with the period ω can be expressed as a single-valued function $g(\zeta)$ of the variable $\zeta = e^{2\pi i z/\omega}$. What can be said about $g(\zeta)$ whenever $f(z)$ is a doubly periodic function with the primitive periods ω and ω'?

10. Prove that if $A_2 = 1$ in the expansion of $\wp(z)$ (Section 14.8) about one particular pole, then the same is true for the expansion about every other pole.

11. Derive the partial-fraction expansion of the function $1/\sin^2 \pi z$ by applying to $\cot \pi z/(z - a)$ the same method which was used in Sections 14.9 and 14.10 to derive the expansion of $\wp'(z)$.

12. Show that it follows from the expression (14.30) for $\wp(z)$ that $\wp(z)$ has the expansion (14.30)' in the neighborhood of every point ω.

13. Prove that the infinite series appearing as the last term on the right-hand side of (14.38) converges absolutely and uniformly in the disk $|z| \leq \rho$.

14. Prove that the product expansion (14.40) of the function $\sigma(z)$ converges absolutely at every point $z \neq \omega$.

15. Show that the series (14.46) remains convergent if each term in the series (14.47) is replaced by its absolute value.

16. Derive the series (14.48) for the $\wp$-function directly from the partial-fraction expansion of the $\wp$-function.

17. Let the coefficients c_k be defined as in Section 14.21. Prove that $c_8 = 3c_4^2/7$.

Hint. Derive two expressions for $\wp''(z)$, one from the power series of $\wp'(z)$ and the other from the differential equation of $\wp(z)$.

18. Prove the addition formula (14.61) for the $\wp$-function.

19. Show that the inverse function of a second-order doubly periodic function is an elliptic integral.

20. Prove that the inverse function of a doubly periodic function is an Abelian integral, i.e., a function of the form

$$z = z_0 + \int_{w_0}^{w} \frac{dw}{A(w)},$$

where $A(w)$ is an algebraic function of w.

21. Show that if the primitive periods of a doubly periodic function $f(z)$ of second order are integer multiples of the primitive periods of another doubly periodic function $w(z)$, then $w(z)$ can be expressed as a rational function of $f(z)$ and $f'(z)$.

22. Describe in detail how the sheets of the Riemann surface obtained by a mapping by the $\wp$-function are joined together.

23. Suppose that the fundamental parallelogram of the $\wp$-function is a rectangle whose sides are parallel to the real and imaginary axes. The perpendicular bisectors of the sides of the parallelogram divide the rectangle into four congruent rectangles. Show that $\wp(z)$ maps the boundary of any one of these rectangles onto the real axis (cf. Section 14.30).

24. Show that if the period parallelogram of the $\wp$-function is a rectangle, then $\wp(z)$ maps a quarter of the period parallelogram onto a half-plane, even though none of the periods is real.

25. Transform the elliptic integral in Riemann normal form into the Legendre normal form.

26. Construct the line complex or graph associated with the Riemann surface of the elliptic integral (14.75) (cf. Section 6.14).

CHAPTER 15

THE EULER Γ-FUNCTION

§1. DEFINITION OF THE Γ-FUNCTION

15.1. The Euler Integral

We shall consider the so-called *Euler integral of the second kind,*

$$\Gamma(z) = \int_0^\infty e^{-t} t^{z-1} \, dt. \tag{15.1}$$

The integral converges for all real positive values of z. For complex $z = x + iy$ we have

$$e^{-t} t^{z-1} = e^{-t} t^{x-1} \, e^{iy \log t},$$

where $\log t$ is to be taken real, so that

$$|e^{-t} t^{z-1}| = e^{-t} t^{x-1}.$$

The integral (15.1) therefore converges absolutely everywhere in the half-plane $x > 0$. Furthermore, if x_0 is any positive number, the convergence is uniform in the half-plane $x \geq x_0$. For

$$|e^{-t} t^{z-1}| \leq e^{-t} t^{x_0-1} \qquad \text{for} \qquad t < 1,$$

and the integral of the last expression converges.

15.2. Analyticity of the Function $\Gamma(z)$ in the Half-plane $x > 0$

To show that the function defined by (15.1) is analytic in the half-plane $x > 0$, we prove first the following general theorem.

If we assume:

1) *The function $f(t, z)$ is continuous in t and z for*

$$-\infty \leq a < t < b \leq \infty \qquad \text{and} \qquad z \in G; \tag{15.2}$$

2) *The partial derivative $f_z(t, z)$ is a continuous function of t and z for the values (15.2);*

3) *The integral*

$$\int_a^b f(t, z) \, dt$$

converges uniformly on every compact subset of G;

278

Then the function

$$w(z) = \int_a^b f(t, z) \, dt \qquad (15.3)$$

is regular in the domain G.

Proof. Let us consider two sequences $a_1, a_2, \ldots$ and $b_1, b_2, \ldots$ such that

$$a < \ldots < a_n < \ldots < a_2 < a_1 < b_1 < b_2 < \ldots < b_n < \ldots < b,$$

and

$$\lim_{n \to \infty} a_n = a, \qquad \lim_{n \to \infty} b_n = b.$$

According to Section 9.7, the integral

$$w_n(z) = \int_{a_n}^{b_n} f(t, z) \, dt \qquad (15.4)$$

is an analytic function with the derivative

$$w_n'(z) = \int_{a_n}^{b_n} f_z(t, z) \, dt$$

for every value of n. By assumption (3) the functions (15.4) converge uniformly to the function (15.3) on every compact subset of G. By Weierstrass's theorem (Section 9.8) the function $w(z)$ in (15.3) is therefore regular in G, and its derivative is

$$w'(z) = \lim_{n \to \infty} w_n'(z) = \int_a^b f_z(t, z) \, dt.$$

If we apply the theorem we have just proved, it follows that the function $\Gamma(z)$ defined by (15.1) is analytic in the half-plane $x > 0$ and that its derivative is given by

$$\Gamma'(z) = \int_0^\infty e^{-t} t^{z-1} \log t \, dt.$$

15.3. The Relation between the Γ-Function and the Factorial

If we integrate (15.1) by parts, we obtain for $x > 0$ the identity

$$\Gamma(z) = \int_0^\infty e^{-t} t^{z-1} \, dt = \frac{1}{z} \int_0^\infty e^{-t} t^z \, dt = \frac{1}{z} \Gamma(z + 1). \qquad (15.5)$$

If we apply this formula n times, we find that

$$\Gamma(z + n) = z(z + n) \ldots (z + n - 1)\Gamma(z). \qquad (15.6)$$

Substituting $z = 1$ and observing that

$$\Gamma(1) = \int_0^\infty e^{-t} \, dt = 1$$

we obtain the formula

$$\Gamma(n + 1) = n! \qquad (15.7)$$

Thus the function $\Gamma(z)$ generalizes the expression $n!$, which has been defined only for integer values of n.

15.4. Analytic Continuation of the Γ-Function

The identity (15.6) enables us to extend the definition of the function $\Gamma(z)$ to the left half-plane. At the moment, the left-hand side of the identity

$$\Gamma(z) = \frac{\Gamma(z + n)}{z(z + 1) \ldots (z + n - 1)} \qquad (x > 0) \qquad (15.8)$$

is defined only in the half-plane $x > 0$. On the other hand, $\Gamma(z + n)$ is defined for $x > -n$, so that the right-hand side of (15.8) is regular in the half-plane $x > -n$, with the exception of the points $0, -1, -2, \ldots, -(n - 1)$ which are simple poles of the function. Because equality holds in (15.8) for $x > 0$, the right-hand side of (15.8) is the analytic continuation of $\Gamma(z)$ into the half-plane $x > -n$. Here n can be chosen arbitrarily and $\Gamma(z)$ therefore admits a continuation into the whole plane.

The resulting function $\Gamma(z)$ is analytic in the whole finite z-plane, and is regular everywhere except at the points $0, -1, -2, \ldots$, which are simple poles of $\Gamma(z)$, so that $\Gamma(z)$ is a *meromorphic function*.

To determine the residue of the Γ-function at the point $z = -n$, we replace n by $n + 1$ in the identity (15.8); this yields the value $(-1)^n/n!$ for the residue at the point $z = -n$.

The formula (15.5) was derived above for $x > 0$. However, since both sides of the formula are analytic in the whole plane, it follows from the principle of analytic continuation that the formula is valid for all z.

§2. STIRLING'S FORMULA

15.5.

We now investigate the behavior of the Γ-function as z tends to infinity along the positive real axis. We set $z = x > 0$ and form the expression

$$\Gamma(x + 1) = \int_0^\infty e^{-t} t^x \, dt. \qquad (15.9)$$

The integrand assumes its maximum $e^{-x} x^x$ at the point $t = x$. As $x \to \infty$, the point at which the maximum is assumed tends to infinity; at the same time the corresponding maximum also tends to infinity.

We write the integral (15.9) in the form

$$\Gamma(x + 1) = e^{-x} x^x \int_0^\infty e^{-(t-x)} \left(\frac{t}{x}\right)^x \, dt,$$

and, after a change of variable $t - x = u$, we obtain

$$\Gamma(x + 1) = e^{-x}x^x \int_{-x}^{\infty} e^{-u}\left(1 + \frac{u}{x}\right)^x du. \tag{15.10}$$

We now estimate the integral

$$I(x) = \int_{-x}^{\infty} e^{-u}\left(1 + \frac{u}{x}\right)^x du \tag{15.11}$$

for large values of x.

The integrand assumes its maximum 1 at $u = 0$ and tends to 0 as $u \to -x$ or $u \to +\infty$.

We choose an arbitrary number y in the interval $0 < y < x$; its value will be fixed later. We then split the integral (15.11) into four parts

$$I = \int_{-x}^{-y} + \int_{-y}^{y} + \int_{y}^{x} + \int_{x}^{\infty} = I_1 + I_2 + I_3 + I_4, \tag{15.12}$$

which we shall estimate separately for large values of x.

15.6.

We show first that $I_4 \to 0$ as $x \to \infty$. To estimate the real branch of the logarithm of the integrand

$$\log\left[e^{-u}\left(1 + \frac{u}{x}\right)^x\right] = -u + x \log\left(1 + \frac{u}{x}\right)$$

$$= -u\left\{1 - \frac{x}{u} \log\left(1 + \frac{u}{x}\right)\right\}, \tag{15.13}$$

we substitute

$$\log\left(1 + \frac{u}{x}\right) = s$$

and obtain

$$\frac{x}{u} \log\left(1 + \frac{u}{x}\right) = \frac{s}{e^s - 1}. \tag{15.14}$$

As u increases from x to ∞, s increases from $\log 2$ to ∞. The derivative of the function (15.14) is negative in this interval. Hence, the function assumes its largest value $\log 2$ at the initial point $s = \log 2$ of the interval. Hence,

$$\log\left[e^{-u}\left(1 + \frac{u}{x}\right)^x\right] \leqq -u(1 - \log 2) = -u \log \frac{e}{2}.$$

Therefore the integrand in (15.11) satisfies the inequality

$$e^{-u}\left(1 + \frac{u}{x}\right)^x \leqq e^{-u \log (e/2)}.$$

From this we obtain the following bound for the integral I_4:

$$0 < I_4 < \int_x^\infty e^{-u \log (e/2)} \, du = \frac{e^{-x \log (e/2)}}{\log (e/2)}.$$

This upper bound tends to 0 as $x \to \infty$, so that

$$\lim_{x \to \infty} I_4 = 0.$$

15.7.

In the expression

$$I_1 = \int_{-x}^{-y} e^{-u} \left(1 + \frac{u}{x}\right)^x \, du$$

the integrand assumes its greatest value $e^y (1 - y/x)^x$ at the end-point $u = -y$ of the interval of integration. Thus we have the following estimate for I_1:

$$0 < I_1 < e^y \left(1 - \frac{y}{x}\right)^x (x - y). \tag{15.15}$$

Here

$$\log \left[e^y \left(1 - \frac{y}{x}\right)^x \right] = y + x \log \left(1 - \frac{y}{x}\right) = y + x \left(-\frac{y}{x} - \frac{y^2}{2x^2} - \cdots\right)$$

$$= -\frac{y^2}{2x} - \frac{y^3}{3x^2} - \cdots < -\frac{y^2}{2x}.$$

By (15.15) we therefore have the estimate

$$0 < I_1 < x \, e^{-y^2/2x}. \tag{15.15$'$}$$

The integrand in

$$I_3 = \int_y^x e^{-u} \left(1 + \frac{u}{x}\right)^x \, du$$

decreases as u increases from y to x. Therefore its greatest value is attained for $u = y$. Hence,

$$0 < I_3 < e^{-y} \left(1 + \frac{y}{x}\right)^x (x - y), \tag{15.16}$$

and

$$\log \left[e^{-y} \left(1 + \frac{y}{x}\right)^x \right] = -\frac{y^2}{2x} + \frac{y^3}{3x^2} - \cdots < -\frac{y^2}{2x} + \frac{y^3}{3x^2}$$

$$< -\frac{y^2}{2x} + \frac{y^2}{3x} = -\frac{y^2}{6x}.$$

It follows from (15.16) that

$$0 < I_3 < x \, e^{-y^2/6x}.$$

We now determine y in such a way that I_1 and I_3 tend to zero as $x \to \infty$. For this purpose, we set

$$\frac{y^2}{x} = x^\lambda \qquad \text{with} \qquad 0 < \lambda < 1, \qquad (15.17)$$

which gives

$$y = x^{(1+\lambda)/2}. \qquad (15.18)$$

From (15.15)′ we now obtain for I_1 the upper bound $x \, e^{-x\lambda/2}$, which tends to zero as $x \to \infty$. Similarly, we see that $I_3 \to 0$ as $x \to \infty$.

15.8.

Of the four integrals in (15.12), it only remains to estimate the integral

$$I_2 = \int_{-y}^{y} e^{-u} \left(1 + \frac{u}{x} \right)^x du. \qquad (15.19)$$

Since $|u/x| < 1$ throughout the interval of integration, we have

$$\log\left[e^{-u} \left(1 + \frac{u}{x} \right)^x \right] = -\frac{u^2}{2x} + \frac{u^3}{3x^2} - \cdots = -\frac{u^2}{2x} [1 + f(u)],$$

where

$$f(u) = -\frac{2}{3} \frac{u}{x} + \frac{2}{4} \left(\frac{u}{x} \right)^2 - \cdots.$$

The function $f(u)$ satisfies the inequality

$$|f(u)| \leq \frac{2}{3} \left\{ \frac{|u|}{x} + \left(\frac{|u|}{x} \right)^2 + \cdots \right\} < \frac{y}{x} \frac{1}{1 - \frac{y}{x}},$$

so that it follows from (15.18) that

$$|f(u)| < x^{-(1-\lambda)/2} \frac{1}{1 - x^{-(1-\lambda)/2}} \equiv \sigma(x). \qquad (15.20)$$

Hence, $\sigma(x) \to 0$ as $x \to \infty$. For the logarithm of the integrand we have

$$\log\left[e^{-u} \left(1 + \frac{u}{x} \right)^x \right] = -\frac{u^2}{2x} (1 + \langle \sigma \rangle), \qquad (15.21)$$

where $\langle \sigma \rangle$ denotes a number whose modulus is less than σ. Since $0 < \sigma < 1$ for large values of x, we have

$$-(1 + \sigma) \leq -(1 + \langle \sigma \rangle) \leq -(1 - \sigma). \qquad (15.22)$$

It follows from (15.21) and (15.22) that

$$\int_{-y}^{y} e^{-(1+\sigma)u^2/2x} du \leq I_2 \leq \int_{-y}^{y} e^{-(1-\sigma)u^2/2x} du. \qquad (15.23)$$

If we introduce a new variable t into the right-hand side by the substitution

$$u\sqrt{\frac{1-\sigma}{2x}} = t,$$

the integral then becomes

$$\int_{-y}^{y} e^{-(1-\sigma)u^2/2x}\, du = \sqrt{\frac{2x}{1-\sigma}} \int_{-t_1}^{t_1} e^{-t^2}\, dt,$$

where (cf. Eq. 15.17)

$$t_1 = y\sqrt{\frac{1-\sigma}{2x}} = x^{\lambda/2}\sqrt{\frac{1-\sigma}{2}}.$$

We transform the lower bound in (15.23) in a similar way:

$$\int_{-y}^{y} e^{-(1+\sigma)u^2/2x}\, du = \sqrt{\frac{2x}{1+\sigma}} \int_{-t_2}^{t_2} e^{-t^2}\, dt,$$

where

$$t_2 = y\sqrt{\frac{1+\sigma}{2x}} = x^{\lambda/2}\sqrt{\frac{1+\sigma}{2}}.$$

Thus we have for I_2 the bounds

$$\frac{1}{\sqrt{1+\sigma}}\int_{-t_2}^{t_2} e^{-t^2}\, dt \le \frac{I_2}{\sqrt{2x}} \le \frac{1}{\sqrt{1-\sigma}}\int_{-t_1}^{t_1} e^{-t^2}\, dt.$$

As $x \to \infty$ (whence $t_1 \to \infty$ and $t_2 \to \infty$), both sides tend to the limit

$$\int_{-\infty}^{+\infty} e^{-t^2}\, dt = \sqrt{\pi},$$

so that $I_2/\sqrt{2\pi x}$ tends to the limit 1. Therefore we have

$$I_2 = \sqrt{2\pi x}\left(1 + \left(\frac{1}{x}\right)\right),$$

where $(1/x)$ denotes a function of x which tends to zero as $1/x \to 0$.

Combining our results, we find that the integral (15.11) has the expansion

$$I = I_1 + I_2 + I_3 + I_4 = \sqrt{2\pi x}\left(1 + \left(\frac{1}{x}\right)\right) + \left(\frac{1}{x}\right) = \sqrt{2\pi x}\left(1 + \left(\frac{1}{x}\right)\right).$$

Equation (15.10) now yields *Stirling's formula*

$$\Gamma(x+1) = x^x\, e^{-x}\sqrt{2\pi x}\left(1 + \left(\frac{1}{x}\right)\right), \tag{15.24}$$

the asymptotic formula to be proved. For integer values $x = n$ we obtain

$$\Gamma(n+1) = n! = n^n\, e^{-n}\sqrt{2\pi n}\left(1 + \left(\frac{1}{n}\right)\right). \tag{15.25}$$

§3. THE PRODUCT REPRESENTATION OF THE Γ-FUNCTION

15.9.

We should like to derive another representation for the Γ-function as an infinite product. We assume that z is real and positive and begin with the formula (15.6):

$$\frac{1}{\Gamma(z)} = \frac{z(z+1)\ldots(z+n)}{\Gamma(z+n+1)} = \frac{n!}{\Gamma(z+n+1)} z \left(1 + \frac{z}{1}\right) \ldots \left(1 + \frac{z}{n}\right)$$

$$= \frac{\Gamma(n+1)}{\Gamma(z+n+1)} z \left(1 + \frac{z}{1}\right) \ldots \left(1 + \frac{z}{n}\right). \tag{15.26}$$

It follows from (15.25) and (15.24) that

$$\Gamma(n+1) = n^n e^{-n} \sqrt{2\pi n} \left(1 + \left(\frac{1}{n}\right)\right),$$

$$\Gamma(z+n+1) = (n+z)^{n+z} e^{-n-z} \sqrt{2\pi(n+z)} \left(1 + \left(\frac{1}{n}\right)\right)$$

$$= n^n n^z \left(1 + \frac{z}{n}\right)^n \left(1 + \frac{z}{n}\right)^z e^{-n} e^{-z} \sqrt{2\pi n} \sqrt{1 + \frac{z}{n}} \left(1 + \left(\frac{1}{n}\right)\right).$$

From the fact that

$$\left(1 + \frac{z}{n}\right)^n = e^z \left(1 + \left(\frac{1}{n}\right)\right), \quad \left(1 + \frac{z}{n}\right)^z = 1 + \left(\frac{1}{n}\right), \quad \sqrt{1 + \frac{z}{n}} = 1 + \left(\frac{1}{n}\right)$$

it follows that

$$\Gamma(z+n+1) = n^n n^z e^{-n} \sqrt{2\pi n} \left(1 + \left(\frac{1}{n}\right)\right),$$

whence

$$\frac{\Gamma(n+1)}{\Gamma(z+n+1)} = \frac{1 + \left(\frac{1}{n}\right)}{n^z}.$$

If we combine this with (15.26) we have

$$\frac{1}{\Gamma(z)} = \frac{1 + \left(\frac{1}{n}\right)}{n^z} z \left(1 + \frac{z}{1}\right) \ldots \left(1 + \frac{z}{n}\right),$$

which can also be written in the form

$$\frac{1}{\Gamma(z)} = z \exp\left\{\sum_1^n \log\left(1 + \frac{z}{\nu}\right) - z \log n + \left(\frac{1}{n}\right)\right\}, \tag{15.27}$$

where the real branch of the logarithm must be chosen.

15.10.

If we let n tend to infinity in (15.27), then both the sum and the term $z \log n$ tend to infinity in the exponent. We rearrange these expressions in such a way that, as $n \to \infty$, we obtain a convergent series. Thus we write

$$\sum_{\nu=1}^{n} \left\{ \log \left(1 + \frac{z}{\nu}\right) - z \log n = \sum_{\nu=1}^{n} \left\{ \log \left(1 + \frac{z}{\nu}\right) - \frac{z}{\nu} \right\} + z \left(\sum_{\nu=1}^{n} \frac{1}{\nu} - \log n \right). $$

$$(15.28)$$

If we omit a finite number of terms, the first series

$$\sum_{\nu=1}^{\infty} \left\{ \log \left(1 + \frac{z}{\nu}\right) - \frac{z}{\nu} \right\} \qquad (15.29)$$

converges absolutely and uniformly in every bounded region of the z-plane (Section 13.6). Since the left-hand side of (15.27) is finite for every positive z and does not depend on n, the whole expression (15.28) must tend to a finite limit as $n \to \infty$. It follows that the expression

$$\sum_{\nu=1}^{n} \frac{1}{\nu} - \log n,$$

which appears on the right-hand side of (15.28), tends to a finite limit as $n \to \infty$. This limit is called *Euler's constant* and is denoted by C:

$$C = \lim_{n \to \infty} \left(\sum_{1}^{n} \frac{1}{\nu} - \log n \right). \qquad (15.30)$$

A comparison of the sum in (15.30) with the integral

$$\int_{1}^{n} \frac{dx}{x}$$

shows that $0 < C < 1$ (Exercise 5, p. 228). An approximate value of the constant C is 0.5772.

If we now let $n \to \infty$ in formula (15.27), it follows from what has been shown that

$$\frac{1}{\Gamma(z)} = z \exp \left[\sum_{1}^{\infty} \left\{ \log \left(1 + \frac{z}{\nu}\right) - \frac{z}{\nu} \right\} + Cz \right]. \qquad (15.31)$$

If we write this expression as an infinite product (Section 13.2), we obtain the formula

$$\frac{1}{\Gamma(z)} = z\, e^{Cz} \prod_{\nu=1}^{\infty} \left\{ \left(1 + \frac{z}{\nu}\right) e^{-z/\nu} \right\}, \qquad (15.32)$$

whose validity has been proved until now for *positive values* of z.

To show the general validity of formula (15.32), we write it in the form

$$\frac{1}{\Gamma(z)} = z\, e^{Cz} \prod_{\nu=1}^{n_0} \left\{ \left(1 + \frac{z}{\nu}\right) e^{-z/\nu} \right\} \prod_{\nu=n_0+1}^{\infty} \left\{ \left(1 + \frac{z}{\nu}\right) e^{-z/\nu} \right\}. \qquad (15.33)$$

The second product defines an analytic function in the disk $|z| \leqq n_0$ (Section 13.4). The remaining part of the right-hand side is regular in the whole plane. Since n_0 may be chosen arbitrarily, the right-hand side of (15.33) is regular in the whole plane, and because Eq. (15.33) holds on the positive real axis, it holds everywhere.

The function $1/\Gamma(z)$ is therefore an *entire* function. *Hence, the Γ-function has no zeros anywhere.* We mention without proof that 0 is the only value not assumed by the Γ-function.

EXERCISES ON CHAPTER 15

1. Another method for the analytic continuation of $\Gamma(z)$ into the left half-plane is the following. Write

$$\Gamma(z) = f_1(z) + f_2(z),$$

where

$$f_1(z) = \int_0^1 e^{-t} t^{z-1}\, dt \qquad \text{and} \qquad f_2(z) = \int_1^\infty e^{-t} t^{z-1}\, dt.$$

Then $f_2(z)$ is an entire function. To continue $f_1(z)$ into the half-plane Re $z \leqq 0$, expand the integrand into powers of t, and integrate the resulting series term by term. Carry out the details of this argument.

2. There exists a third method for the analytic continuation of $\Gamma(z)$. Consider the function

$$H(z) = \int_\gamma e^{-t} t^{z-1}\, dt,$$

where the path of integration γ consists of the positive real axis from ∞ to the point $a > 0$, the circle $K: |t| = a$, described in the negative sense, and the positive real axis from the point a to ∞. If, to begin with, z is positive, we have

$$H(z) = (1 - e^{2\pi i z}) \int_a^\infty e^{-t} t^{z-1}\, dt + \int_K e^{-t} t^{z-1}\, dt.$$

If we let $a \to 0$ we obtain a relation between $H(z)$ and $\Gamma(z)$,

$$H(z) = (1 - e^{2\pi i z})\Gamma(z),$$

which is valid in the whole plane since $H(z)$ is an entire function. Carry out the details of this proof.

10*

3. Show that the function $H(z)$ introduced in Exercise 2 has zeros at the points 1, 2, ...

4. Show that $\Gamma(z)$ takes complex conjugate values at the points z and $\bar{z}$.

5. Give a geometric interpretation to the expression

$$\sum_{\nu=1}^{n} \frac{1}{\nu} - \log n = \sum_{1}^{n} \frac{1}{\nu} - \int_{1}^{n} \frac{dx}{x}$$

and show directly that this expression tends to the limit C as $n \to \infty$.

6. Prove the formula

$$\Gamma(z)\Gamma(1 - z) = \frac{\pi}{\sin \pi z}.$$

7. Prove Gauss's formula for the Γ-function:

$$\Gamma(z) = \lim_{n \to \infty} \frac{n!\, n^z}{z(z + 1) \ldots (z + n)}.$$

8. Using the product formula for $\Gamma(z)$, expand $\log \Gamma(1 + z)$ into powers of z.

CHAPTER 16

THE RIEMANN ζ-FUNCTION

§1. DEFINITION AND THE EULER PRODUCT FORMULA

16.1. Definition of the ζ-Function

The Riemann ζ-function is defined as the sum of the series

$$\zeta(s) = \sum_{n=1}^{\infty} \frac{1}{n^s}. \tag{16.1}$$

To find the region in which this definition is valid, we set $s = \sigma + it$ and consider the absolute value

$$\left| \frac{1}{n^s} \right| = \frac{1}{|e^{s \log n}|} = \frac{1}{e^{\sigma \log n}} = \frac{1}{n^\sigma}.$$

Since the series

$$\sum_{n=1}^{\infty} \frac{1}{n^\sigma}$$

converges for $\sigma > 1$, *the series* (16.1) *converges absolutely in the half-plane* $\sigma > 1$. The convergence is *uniform* in every half-plane $\sigma \geqq \sigma_0 > 1$, since the series (16.1) is majorized in this half-plane by the convergent series

$$\sum_{n=1}^{\infty} \frac{1}{n^{\sigma_0}}.$$

The terms of the series (16.1) are analytic functions in the whole plane. It follows from Weierstrass's theorem (Section 9.8) that the sum $\zeta(s)$ is *analytic in the half-plane* $\sigma > 1$.

16.2. The Euler Product Formula

We now derive a representation for the function $\zeta(s)$ which reveals an interesting connection between the ζ-function and the prime numbers. For any prime number p (2, 3, 5, . . .) and any real $s > 1$ we set

$$\frac{1}{1 - \dfrac{1}{p^s}} = 1 + \frac{1}{p^s} + \frac{1}{p^{2s}} + \cdots. \tag{16.2}$$

Let us denote the v-th prime number by $p = p_v$ ($p_1 = 2$, $p_2 = 3$, ...) and form the product

$$\prod_{v=1}^{m} \frac{1}{1 - \dfrac{1}{p_v^s}} .$$

For $m = 2$ it follows from Cauchy's product formula that

$$\frac{1}{1 - \dfrac{1}{p_1^s}} \frac{1}{1 - \dfrac{1}{p_2^s}} = \sum_{v_1, v_2 = 0}^{\infty} \frac{1}{(p_1^{v_1} p_2^{v_2})^s} ,$$

where v_1 and v_2 independently run through all non-negative integers. It then follows by induction that

$$\prod_{v=1}^{m} \frac{1}{1 - \dfrac{1}{p_v^s}} = \sum_{v_1, v_2, \ldots, v_m = 0}^{\infty} \frac{1}{(p_1^{v_1} p_2^{v_2} \ldots p_m^{v_m})^s} . \qquad (16.3)$$

In the summation v_1, v_2, ..., v_m independently assume all non-negative integer values from 0 to ∞.

Since every positive integer can be represented in one and only one way as a product of primes, (16.3) may be written as

$$\prod_{v=1}^{m} \frac{1}{1 - \dfrac{1}{p_v^s}} = {\sum_{}}' \frac{1}{n^s} . \qquad (16.4)$$

Here n assumes precisely those positive integral values which have no prime factor greater than p_m.

Since the sum (16.4) does not contain all the terms of the expansion for $\zeta(s)$, its value is less than $\zeta(s)$. On the other hand, the sum contains the terms 1, $1/2^s$, $1/3^s$, ..., $1/p_m^s$. Hence, for every m we have the following double inequality:

$$\sum_{n=1}^{p_m} \frac{1}{n^s} < \prod_{v=1}^{m} \frac{1}{1 - \dfrac{1}{p_v^s}} < \zeta(s).$$

If $m \to \infty$, p_m tends to infinity, and the left-hand side then approaches the limit $\zeta(s)$. It follows that the product

$$\prod_{v=1}^{\infty} \frac{1}{1 - \dfrac{1}{p_v^s}}$$

converges, and that its value is $\zeta(s)$:

$$\zeta(s) = \prod_{(p)} \frac{1}{1 - \dfrac{1}{p^s}} . \qquad (16.5)$$

Here p runs through the set of all prime numbers.

Formula (16.5) is the so-called *Euler product formula* for the ζ-function.

16.3.

To investigate the convergence of the Euler product for complex values of s, we write it in the form

$$\prod_{(p)} \left(1 + \frac{1}{p^s - 1}\right). \tag{16.6}$$

This product converges whenever the series

$$\sum_{(p)} \frac{1}{p^\sigma - 1}$$

converges.   Now this series converges uniformly in every half-plane $\sigma \geq \sigma_0 > 1$, from which it follows that the product (16.6) defines an analytic function in the half-plane $\sigma > 1$ (Section 13.4).   Both sides of (16.5) are therefore regular functions in the half-plane $\sigma > 1$, and since they coincide for real values of s, they must be equal throughout the entire half-plane.

The Euler product formula (16.5) is therefore valid in the entire half-plane $\sigma > 1$.

§2. INTEGRAL REPRESENTATION OF THE ζ-FUNCTION

16.4.

We now establish a connection between the functions $\zeta(s)$ and $\Gamma(s)$. We take the integral representation of $\Gamma(s)$ as our starting point:

$$\Gamma(s) = \int_0^\infty e^{-t}t^{s-1}\, dt; \tag{16.7}$$

this is valid for $\sigma > 0$. In what follows we shall assume that s is real and greater than 1.

If we substitute $t = \nu x$ into the integral (16.7), we obtain

$$\Gamma(s) = \nu^s \int_0^\infty e^{-\nu x}x^{s-1}\, dx.$$

Hence, it follows that

$$\sum_{\nu=1}^n \frac{1}{\nu^s} = \frac{1}{\Gamma(s)} \int_0^\infty \frac{e^{-x}(1 - e^{-nx})}{1 - e^{-x}} x^{s-1}\, dx$$

or

$$\sum_{\nu=1}^n \frac{1}{\nu^s} = \frac{1}{\Gamma(s)} \left\{ \int_0^\infty \frac{x^{s-1}}{e^x - 1}\, dx - \int_0^\infty \frac{e^{-nx}x^{s-1}}{e^x - 1}\, dx \right\}, \tag{16.8}$$

since both these integrals converge. We now let $n \to \infty$ and show that the last integral tends to 0. We choose an $\alpha > 0$ and write

$$\int_0^\infty \frac{e^{-nx}x^{s-1}}{e^x - 1} \, dx = \int_0^\alpha \frac{e^{-nx}x^{s-1}}{e^x - 1} \, dx + \int_\alpha^\infty \frac{e^{-nx}x^{s-1}}{e^x - 1} \, dx. \tag{16.9}$$

For $\epsilon > 0$ there exists an $\alpha_0 > 0$ such that

$$\int_0^\alpha \frac{e^{-nx}x^{s-1}}{e^x - 1} \, dx < \int_0^\alpha \frac{x^{s-1}}{e^x - 1} \, dx < \epsilon \qquad \text{whenever} \qquad \alpha \leq \alpha_0.$$

We now choose a fixed positive $\alpha \leq \alpha_0$ and bound the second integral in (16.9) by

$$\int_\alpha^\infty \frac{e^{-nx}x^{s-1}}{e^x - 1} \, dx < e^{-n\alpha} \int_\alpha^\infty \frac{x^{s-1}}{e^x - 1} \, dx.$$

Since the integral on the right-hand side is finite, we conclude that the integral (16.9) tends to zero as $n \to \infty$.

Since the left-hand side of Eq. (16.8) tends to the limit $\zeta(s)$ as $n \to \infty$, we obtain the representation

$$\zeta(s) = \frac{1}{\Gamma(s)} \int_0^\infty \frac{x^{s-1}}{e^x - 1} \, dx, \tag{16.10}$$

whose validity is now established for real values of s greater than 1.

Actually, the equation is valid in the entire half-plane $\sigma > 1$, for the function $1/\Gamma(s)$ is analytic everywhere in the finite plane. The integral on the right-hand side is regular in the half-plane $\sigma > 1$, since the assumptions of the theorem in Section 15.2 are fulfilled in the half-plane $\sigma \geq \sigma_0 > 1$ (Exercise 2, p. 304). The entire right-hand side of formula (16.10) is therefore regular in the half-plane $\sigma > 1$. The same applies to the left-hand side. Since the two sides coincide on the real axis, they are equal in the half-plane $\sigma > 1$. Therefore (16.10) is valid *throughout the half-plane $\sigma > 1$*.

§3. ANALYTIC CONTINUATION OF THE ζ-FUNCTION

16.5. Hermite's Method of Analytic Continuation

As was shown by Ch. Hermite (1822–1901), formula (16.10) enables us to continue $\zeta(s)$ analytically into the half-plane $\sigma \leq 1$.

We write the integral

$$f(s) = \int_0^\infty \frac{x^{s-1}}{e^x - 1} \, dx = f_1(s) + f_2(s), \tag{16.11}$$

where

$$f_1(s) = \int_0^1 \frac{x^{s-1}}{e^x - 1} \, dx, \qquad f_2(s) = \int_1^\infty \frac{x^{s-1}}{e^x - 1} \, dx. \tag{16.12}$$

It follows from the theorem in Section 15.2 that $f_2(s)$ is an entire function (Exercise 3, p. 304). On the other hand, the integral defining $f_1(s)$ is divergent for $\sigma \leqq 1$.

In order to continue $f_1(s)$ to the half-plane $\sigma \leqq 1$, we first assume that s is real and greater than 1. If we expand $1/(e^z - 1)$ into powers of z, we obtain

$$\frac{1}{e^z - 1} = \frac{1}{z} - \frac{1}{2} + [z],$$

and, further, since $1/(e^z - 1) + \frac{1}{2}$ is an odd function,

$$\frac{1}{e^z - 1} = \frac{1}{z} - \frac{1}{2} + A_1 z + A_3 z^3 + \cdots. \tag{16.13}$$

The coefficients are given by

$$A_{2\nu-1} = (-1)^{\nu-1} \frac{B_\nu}{(2\nu)!},$$

where the B_ν are the so-called Bernoulli numbers (Exercise 10, p. 182). These expressions for the coefficients $A_{2\nu-1}$ will not be needed in what follows.

The function (16.13) is regular everywhere except at the points $0, \pm 2\pi i$, $\pm 4\pi i, \ldots$. The series (16.13) therefore converges in the disk $|z| < 2\pi$.

It follows from (16.13) that the integrand of the first integral in (16.12) has the expansion

$$\frac{x^{s-1}}{e^x - 1} = x^{s-2} - \frac{x^{s-1}}{2} + A_1 x^s + A_3 x^{s+2} + \cdots,$$

which converges uniformly in the interval of integration $(0, 1)$. We may therefore integrate this series term by term, and in this way obtain for $s > 1$ the expansion

$$f_1(s) = \frac{1}{s-1} - \frac{1}{2s} + \sum_{\nu=1}^{\infty} \frac{A_{2\nu-1}}{s + 2\nu - 1}. \tag{16.14}$$

We shall show that the series on the right-hand side of (16.14) converges absolutely and uniformly in every disk $|s| \leqq R \ (< \infty)$. If n is the smallest integer for which $2n - 1 > R$, then for $|s| \leqq R$ and $\nu \geqq n$ we have

$$|s + 2\nu - 1| \geqq 2n - 1 - R = \Delta > 0.$$

The series

$$\sum_{\nu=n}^{\infty} \frac{A_{2\nu-1}}{s + 2\nu - 1} \tag{16.15}$$

therefore has as a majorant the series

$$\frac{1}{\Delta} \sum_{\nu=n}^{\infty} |A_{2\nu-1}|. \tag{16.16}$$

Since the radius of convergence of the series (16.13) is 2π, the series converges absolutely for $z = 1$. This implies the convergence of the series (16.16). The series (16.15) is therefore absolutely and uniformly convergent in the disk $|s| \leq R$, and, hence, it defines in this disk a regular function. Thus the sum of the series (16.14) represents the analytic continuation of the function $f_1(s)$ to the whole plane. The function $f_1(s)$ so obtained is regular everywhere with the exception of the points

$$1, 0, -1, -3, -5, \ldots, \tag{16.17}$$

where it has simple poles.

The function

$$f(s) = f_1(s) + f_2(s) \tag{16.18}$$

is now regular in the whole plane, except for the points (16.17), where it has simple poles. On the other hand, $1/\Gamma(s)$ is an entire function. If, in view of (16.10) and (16.11), we now set

$$\zeta(s) = \frac{1}{\Gamma(s)} f(s), \tag{16.19}$$

we obtain the analytic continuation of $\zeta(s)$ to the whole plane.

16.6. Singularities of the ζ-Function

It follows from the preceding investigation that $\zeta(s)$ is a meromorphic function whose only possible singularities are poles at the points (16.17). However, it can be shown that not all the points (16.17) are actual poles of $\zeta(s)$. It follows from (16.18) and (16.14) that in the neighborhood of $s = 1$, $f(s)$ has the expansion

$$f(s) = \frac{1}{s - 1} + \mathfrak{P}(s - 1).$$

On the other hand, $\Gamma(s)$ is regular at $s = 1$, and its value at this point is 1 (Section 15.3). Hence, in view of (16.19), $\zeta(s)$ has the following expansion:

$$\zeta(s) = \frac{1}{s - 1} + \mathfrak{P}(s - 1). \tag{16.20}$$

Therefore $\zeta(s)$ has a simple pole with residue 1 at $s = 1$.

At the remaining points (16.17), $s = 0, -1, -3, \ldots,$ $\Gamma(s)$ has simple poles. Hence, in view of (16.19), $\zeta(s)$ is regular at these points (cf. Exercise 4, p. 304).

Thus, we have the following result.

The function $\zeta(s)$ is regular everywhere in the finite plane except at the point $s = 1$. At this point it has a simple pole with residue 1.

The function $\Gamma(s)$ has poles not only at the points $s = 0$, $s = -(2\nu - 1)$ $(\nu = 1, 2, \ldots)$, but also at the points $s = -2\nu$ $(\nu = 1, 2, \ldots)$. Since $f(s)$ is regular at these points, it follows from (16.19) that $\zeta(s)$ has *zeros* at these points.

In the half-plane $\sigma > 1$, $\zeta(s)$ is represented by the convergent Euler product (Section 16.3). Hence, $\zeta(s)$ *does not vanish in this half-plane.*

§4. RIEMANN'S FUNCTIONAL EQUATION

16.7.

Let $s > 1$ be a fixed real number. We apply the residue theorem to the function

$$\frac{\pi \cot \pi z}{z^s} \tag{16.21}$$

in the domain G_n: $|z| \leqq n + \frac{1}{2}$, $x = \operatorname{Re} z \geqq a$ $(0 < a < 1)$. We denote the boundary of G_n by γ_n, and choose that branch of the function (16.21) which

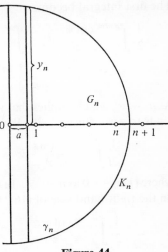

Figure 44

is single-valued in G_n. In the domain G_n the poles of the function (16.21) are at the points $1, 2, \ldots, n$. The residue at $z = \nu$ is $1/\nu^s$, so that if we apply the residue theorem, we have

$$\frac{1}{2i} \int_{\gamma_n} \frac{\cot \pi z}{z^s} \, dz = \sum_{\nu=1}^{n} \frac{1}{\nu^s}. \tag{16.22}$$

We break up the integral on the left-hand side of (16.22) in two parts

$$\frac{1}{2i} \int_{\gamma_n} \frac{\cot \pi z}{z^s} \, dz = \frac{1}{2i} \int_{K_n} \frac{\cot \pi z}{z^s} \, dz$$

$$+ \frac{1}{2i} \int_{a+iy_n}^{a-iy_n} \frac{\cot \pi z}{z^s} \, dz. \tag{16.23}$$

Here $a - iy_n$ and $a + iy_n$ are the points of intersection of the circle $|z| = n + \frac{1}{2}$ with the line $x = a$, K_n is the circular arc contained in γ_n, and the last integral in (16.23) is taken along the straight line $x = a$ (Fig. 44).

We shall show that the first integral on the right-hand side tends to zero as $n \to \infty$. Since $|\cot \pi z|$ is bounded on every circle $|z| = n + \frac{1}{2}$ by a fixed finite number M (Section 10.7), we obtain

$$\left| \frac{1}{2i} \int_{K_n} \frac{\cot \pi z}{z^s} \, dz \right| < \frac{\pi}{2} \frac{M}{(n + \frac{1}{2})^{s-1}}.$$

This expression tends to zero as $n \to \infty$.

We write the second integral on the right-hand side of formula (16.23) as

$$\frac{1}{2i} \int_{a+iy_n}^{a-iy_n} \frac{\cot \pi z}{z^s} \, dz = -\frac{1}{2i} \int_{a}^{a+iy_n} \frac{\cot \pi z}{z^s} \, dz + \frac{1}{2i} \int_{a}^{a-iy_n} \frac{\cot \pi z}{z^s} \, dz. \tag{16.24}$$

If we note that

$$\lim_{y \to +\infty} \frac{\cot \pi z}{2i} = -\frac{1}{2}, \qquad \lim_{y \to -\infty} \frac{\cot \pi z}{2i} = \frac{1}{2},$$

we substitute into the first integral on the right-hand side of (16.24) the expression

$$\frac{\cot \pi z}{2i} = -\frac{1}{2} - \frac{1}{e^{-2\pi i z} - 1}$$

and into the second the expression

$$\frac{\cot \pi z}{2i} = \frac{1}{2} + \frac{1}{e^{2\pi i z} - 1}.$$

The first integral becomes

$$-\frac{1}{2i} \int_a^{a+iy_n} \frac{\cot \pi z}{z^s} \, dz = \int_a^{a+iy_n} \left(\frac{z^{-s}}{2} + \frac{z^{-s}}{e^{-2\pi i z} - 1} \right) dz$$

$$= \frac{1}{2} \frac{a^{1-s}}{s-1} + \frac{1}{2} \frac{(a+iy_n)^{1-s}}{1-s} + \int_a^{a+iy_n} \frac{z^{-s}}{e^{-2\pi i z} - 1} \, dz.$$

As $n \to \infty$, which implies that $y_n \to \infty$, the middle term on the right-hand side tends to zero, since $s > 1$. We may therefore write this equation in the form

$$-\frac{1}{2i} \int_a^{a+iy_n} \frac{\cot \pi z}{z^s} \, dz = \frac{1}{2} \frac{a^{1-s}}{s-1} + \int_a^{a+iy_n} \frac{z^{-s}}{e^{-2\pi i z} - 1} \, dz + \left(\frac{1}{n} \right),$$

where $(1/n) \to 0$ as $n \to \infty$. In the same way, we obtain for the second integral on the right-hand side of (16.24) the expression

$$\frac{1}{2i} \int_a^{a-iy_n} \frac{\cot \pi z}{z^s} \, dz = \frac{1}{2} \frac{a^{1-s}}{s-1} + \int_a^{a-iy_n} \frac{z^{-s}}{e^{2\pi i z} - 1} \, dz + \left(\frac{1}{n} \right).$$

On the strength of these results we may write (16.22) as

$$\sum_{\nu=1}^{n} \frac{1}{\nu^s} = \frac{a^{1-s}}{s-1} + \int_a^{a+iy_n} \frac{z^{-s}}{e^{-2\pi i z} - 1} \, dz + \int_a^{a-iy_n} \frac{z^{-s}}{e^{2\pi i z} - 1} \, dz + \left(\frac{1}{n} \right).$$

$$(16.25)$$

Both of these integrals converge as $n \to \infty$, since

$$\left| \frac{z^{-s}}{e^{-2\pi i z} - 1} \right| \leqq \frac{|z|^{-s}}{e^{2\pi y} - 1} \qquad \text{for} \qquad y > 0,$$

$$\left| \frac{z^{-s}}{e^{2\pi i z} - 1} \right| \leqq \frac{|z|^{-s}}{e^{-2\pi y} - 1} \qquad \text{for} \qquad y < 0,$$

and since the integrals

$$\int_a^{a+i\infty} \frac{|z|^{-s}}{e^{2\pi y} - 1} \, |dz| \qquad \text{and} \qquad \int_a^{a-i\infty} \frac{|z|^{-s}}{e^{-2\pi y} - 1} \, |dz|$$

are convergent. As $n \to \infty$, Eq. (16.25) becomes

$$\zeta(s) = \frac{a^{1-s}}{s-1} + \int_a^{a+i\infty} \frac{z^{-s}}{e^{-2\pi i z} - 1} \, dz + \int_a^{a-i\infty} \frac{z^{-s}}{e^{2\pi i z} - 1} \, dz. \qquad (16.26)$$

We derived this formula under the assumption that $s > 1$. We now show that it is valid in the whole plane. The first term on the right-hand side is a mero-morphic function of s whose only pole is at $s = 1$. In view of the theorem proved in Section 15.2, both of the integrals are regular (cf. Exercise 6, p. 304), so that the formula is valid for *every* $s \neq \infty$.

16.8.

We now assume that s is a fixed negative number in the interval $-1 < s < 0$, and we investigate Eq. (16.26) as $a \to 0$.

The first term on the right-hand side tends to 0. We now show that the first integral on the right-hand side,

$$\int_a^{a+i\infty} \frac{z^{-s}}{e^{-2\pi i z} - 1} \, dz, \qquad (16.27)$$

converges uniformly in a certain interval $0 \leq a \leq \rho \, (\rho > 0)$.

First we estimate the integrand for small values of z. We have

$$\frac{z^{-s}}{e^{-2\pi i z} - 1} = \frac{i}{2\pi} z^{-s-1} \{1 + [z]\}.$$

There exists a disk $|z| \leq 2\rho$ in which $|1 + [z]| < 2\pi$, so that

$$\left| \frac{z^{-s}}{e^{-2\pi i z} - 1} \right| \leq |z|^{-s-1} \leq |y|^{-s-1}.$$

Since the integral

$$\int_0^1 y^{-s-1} \, dy$$

converges, the integral (16.27) converges uniformly for $0 \leq a \leq \rho$. It follows from the uniform convergence of the integral that

$$\lim_{a \to 0} \int_a^{a+i\infty} \frac{z^{-s}}{e^{-2\pi i z} - 1} \, dz = i \int_0^\infty \frac{y^{-s} e^{-i\pi s/2}}{e^{2\pi y} - 1} \, dy.$$

It can be shown in the same way that

$$\lim_{a \to 0} \int_a^{a-i\infty} \frac{z^{-s}}{e^{2\pi i z} - 1} \, dz = i \int_0^{-\infty} \frac{|y|^{-s} e^{i\pi s/2}}{e^{-2\pi y} - 1} \, dy.$$

Thus as $a \to 0$, formula (16.26) becomes

$$\zeta(s) = i \, e^{-i\pi s/2} \int_0^\infty \frac{y^{-s}}{e^{2\pi y} - 1} \, dy + i \, e^{i\pi s/2} \int_0^{-\infty} \frac{|y|^{-s}}{e^{-2\pi y} - 1} \, dy. \qquad (16.28)$$

In the second integral we introduce the new variable $y = -u$. We can then combine the two integrals and obtain, instead of (16.28), the formula

$$\zeta(s) = \frac{1}{i} (e^{i\pi s/2} - e^{-i\pi s/2}) \int_0^\infty \frac{y^{-s}}{e^{2\pi y} - 1} \, dy$$

$$= 2 \sin \frac{\pi s}{2} \int_0^\infty \frac{y^{-s}}{e^{2\pi y} - 1} \, dy.$$

If we then substitute $2\pi y = x$, we obtain the formula

$$\zeta(s) = 2(2\pi)^{s-1} \sin \frac{\pi s}{2} \int_0^\infty \frac{x^{-s}}{e^x - 1} \, dx. \qquad (16.29)$$

This formula has been derived for $-1 < s < 0$. Since, however, both sides are analytic functions in the half-plane $\sigma < 0$, the formula is valid in this whole half-plane.

16.9.

We now relate (16.29) to the formula (16.10) obtained earlier for $\sigma > 1$. Let s lie in the half-plane $\sigma < 0$. Then Re $(1 - s) > 1$, and (16.10) yields

$$\zeta(1 - s) = \frac{1}{\Gamma(1 - s)} \int_0^\infty \frac{x^{-s}}{e^x - 1} \, dx.$$

Since $\sigma < 0$, we can replace the integral here by the expression involving the integral in (16.29). We then obtain

$$\zeta(1 - s) = \frac{1}{\Gamma(1 - s)} \frac{\zeta(s)}{2(2\pi)^{s-1} \sin \dfrac{\pi s}{2}},$$

or

$$\zeta(s) = 2(2\pi)^{s-1} \sin \frac{\pi s}{2} \, \Gamma(1 - s)\zeta(1 - s). \qquad (16.30)$$

This is *Riemann's functional equation*. We have proved this formula for the half-plane $\sigma < 0$. However, since both sides of (16.30) are analytic functions for $s \neq \infty$, the functional equation holds for *all values of s.*

§5. THE ZEROS OF THE ζ-FUNCTION
AND THE DISTRIBUTION OF PRIME NUMBERS

16.10. The Riemann Conjecture

If s lies in the half-plane $\sigma < 0$, the functions $\zeta(1 - s)$ and $\Gamma(1 - s)$ on the right-hand side of (16.30) are both regular and non-zero, and the same is true of $(2\pi)^{s-1}$. Consequently $\zeta(s)$ has the same zeros in this half-plane as the function $\sin \pi s/2$, which vanishes at the points $s = -2, -4, -6, \ldots$ (cf. Section 16.6). All these zeros are simple. In the half-plane $\sigma > 1$ we have $\zeta(s) \neq 0$.

The only zeros of $\zeta(s)$ in the half-planes $\sigma > 1$ and $\sigma < 0$ are the simple zeros at $-2, -4, -6, \ldots$.

In the half-plane $\sigma > 1$ we have $\zeta(s) \neq 0$. Thus if $\zeta(s)$ has any zeros other than these so-called trivial zeros $-2, -4, \ldots$, then they must all lie in the strip $0 \leqq \sigma \leqq 1$.

Riemann asserted in 1859 that, aside from the trivial zeros, the ζ-function also has infinitely many zeros in the strip $0 \leqq \sigma \leqq 1$. This assertion was first proved by J. Hadamard in 1893. Riemann gave, also without proof, the following asymptotic formula for the number $N(T)$ of zeros in the rectangle $0 \leqq \sigma \leqq 1, 0 < t \leqq T$†:

$$N(T) = \frac{1}{2\pi} T \log T - \frac{1 + \log 2\pi}{2\pi} T + O(\log T). \tag{16.31}$$

A rigorous proof of this formula was first given in 1905 by H. v. Mangoldt. If the "Riemann conjecture" mentioned below is correct, then the $O(\log T)$ estimate for the remainder term of the formula can be replaced by the sharper estimate

$$O\left(\frac{\log T}{\log \log T}\right).$$

The famous *Riemann conjecture* asserts that *all non-trivial zeros of the ζ-function lie on the straight line $\sigma = \frac{1}{2}$.* To this date, no one has yet succeeded in proving this conjecture. G. H. Hardy proved (1914) that there are infinitely many zeros on the line $\sigma = \frac{1}{2}$, and E. C. Titchmarsh showed in 1935–1936 that there are 1041 zeros in the region $0 \leqq \sigma \leqq 1, 0 < t < 1468$, all of which lie on the "critical" line $\sigma = \frac{1}{2}$. With the help of electronic computers, it has been possible to extend these calculations much further in recent years. All the zeros found so far lie on the line $\sigma = \frac{1}{2}$.

16.11. Distribution of Prime Numbers

In his famous work published in 1859, Riemann showed that there exists an interesting connection between the Riemann conjecture and the distribution of primes.

The problem of determining $\pi(x)$, the number of primes not exceeding x, was posed rather early. Obviously $\pi(x) < x$. In 1808 A. M. Legendre conjectured that $\pi(x)$ is asymptotic to $x/\log x$ as $x \to \infty$:

$$\pi(x) = \frac{x}{\log x} + o\left(\frac{x}{\log x}\right). \tag{16.32}$$

This formula is called the *prime number theorem.*

---

† In the notation of E. Landau, $O(f(x))$ denotes a function whose ratio to $f(x)$ remains bounded as $x \to \infty$, and $o(f(x))$ stands for a function whose ratio to $f(x)$ tends to zero as $x \to \infty$. The same notation is also applied when describing the growth of a function as x tends to a finite singular point.

Before Legendre, Gauss had been led to the conjecture that

$$\pi(x) = l(x) + o(l(x)), \qquad (16.33)$$

where $l(x)$ is the so-called integral-logarithm:

$$l(x) = \int_2^x \frac{dt}{\log t}. \qquad (16.34)$$

For $l(x)$ we have the asymptotic formula

$$l(x) = \frac{x}{\log x} + O\left(\frac{x}{(\log x)^2}\right), \qquad (16.35)$$

whose proof is left to the reader as an exercise (Exercise 8, p. 304). Thus formula (16.33) contains the prime number theorem (16.32).

The prime number theorem was first proved in 1896 almost simultaneously by C. de La Vallée Poussin and Hadamard. For the difference

$$r(x) = \pi(x) - l(x),$$

de La Vallée Poussin derived the estimate

$$|r(x)| < x\, e^{-c\sqrt{\log x}}, \qquad (16.36)$$

where c denotes a positive constant. This estimate implies (16.33), since the ratio of the right-hand side of (16.36) to $l(x)$ tends to 0 as $x \to \infty$.

The proofs of de La Vallée Poussin and Hadamard are based on the methods of complex analysis. The first elementary proof of the prime number theorem, that is, not using the methods of function theory, was found in 1948 by A. Selberg and P. Erdös.

As x increases, the right-hand side of the inequality (16.36) increases more rapidly than any power $x^{1-\epsilon}$ of x, where $\epsilon > 0$. There are good reasons to believe that $r(x)$ increases much more slowly than it would appear from the estimate (16.36). It is probably true that

$$|r(x)| < c\sqrt{x}\, \log x \qquad (c > 0). \qquad (16.37)$$

This estimate is equivalent to the Riemann conjecture concerning the zeros of the ζ-function. J. E. Littlewood proved in 1914 that there exist arbitrarily large values of x for which the absolute value of the remainder term $r(x)$ is greater than $c\sqrt{x}/\log x$, with both positive and negative values of $r(x)$. If we draw the curves

$$y = c\sqrt{x}\, \log x \qquad \text{and} \qquad y = c\,\frac{\sqrt{x}}{\log x}, \qquad (16.38)$$

which lie above and below the parabola $y = c\sqrt{x}$, then if the Riemann conjecture is true, all the points $y = |r(x)|$ lie under the first curve of (16.38).

On the other hand, there exist arbitrarily large values of x for which $y = |r(x)|$ lies above the second curve of (16.38).

16.12. The Connection between the Riemann Conjecture and the Distribution of Primes

To make clear the connection between the Riemann conjecture and the distribution of prime numbers, we show that if

$$|r(x)| < x^{1/2+\alpha}, \tag{16.39}$$

where $0 < \alpha < \frac{1}{2}$, then the ζ-function has no zeros in the half-plane $\sigma > \frac{1}{2} + \alpha$. We assume first that $\sigma = \operatorname{Re} s > 1$. From the Euler product (16.5) we have

$$\log \zeta(s) = -\sum_{(p)} \log \left(1 - \frac{1}{p^s}\right),$$

where we choose that branch of the logarithm which is real whenever $s > 1$. If we expand each term in powers of $1/p^s$, we obtain

$$\log \zeta(s) = \sum_{(p)} \left(\sum_{n=1}^{\infty} \frac{1}{n} \frac{1}{p^{ns}}\right).$$

Since this double series converges absolutely, we can interchange the order of summation to obtain

$$\log \zeta(s) = \sum_{(p)} \frac{1}{p^s} + \frac{1}{2} \sum_{(p)} \frac{1}{p^{2s}} + \frac{1}{3} \sum_{(p)} \frac{1}{p^{3s}} + \cdots. \tag{16.40}$$

We now let s tend to 1. At the point $s = 1$, $\zeta(s)$ has the expansion (cf. Eq. 16.20)

$$\zeta(s) = \frac{1}{s-1} + \mathfrak{P}(s-1),$$

which implies that

$$\log \zeta(s) = \log \frac{1}{s-1} + \log \{1 + [s-1]\}.$$

As $s \to 1$ in formula (16.40), the left-hand side tends to ∞. The second series on the right-hand side of (16.40) converges for $\sigma > \frac{1}{2}$, the next series converges for $\sigma > \frac{1}{3}$, and so on. All the series on the right-hand side, except for the first series, converge for $\sigma > \frac{1}{2}$, and their sum is finite, because

$$\sum_{(p)} \left|\frac{1}{p^{ks}}\right| = \sum_{(p)} \frac{1}{p^{k\sigma}} < \int_1^{\infty} \frac{dx}{x^{k\sigma}} = \frac{1}{k\sigma - 1}$$

and because the series

$$\sum_{k=2}^{\infty} \frac{1}{k(k\sigma - 1)}$$

converges. If we write

$$f(s) = \frac{1}{2} \sum_{(p)} \frac{1}{p^{2s}} + \frac{1}{3} \sum_{(p)} \frac{1}{p^{3s}} + \cdots, \tag{16.41}$$

then, by (16.40),

$$\log \zeta(s) = \sum_{(p)} \frac{1}{p^s} + f(s). \tag{16.42}$$

The function $f(s)$ is regular in the half-plane $\sigma > \frac{1}{2}$. The sum in (16.42),

$$\phi(s) = \sum_{(p)} \frac{1}{p^s}, \tag{16.43}$$

will now be continued analytically to the left of the line $\sigma = 1$.

First, let s be real and greater than 1. Then $\phi(s)$ may be represented by a Stieltjes integral:

$$\phi(s) = -\int_2^\infty \pi(x) \, dx^{-s}. \tag{16.44}$$

In fact,

$$-\int_2^\infty \pi(x) \, dx^{-s} = -\sum_{n=1}^\infty \int_{p_n}^{p_{n+1}} \pi(x) \, dx^{-s}$$

$$= -\sum_{n=1}^\infty n \int_{p_n}^{p_{n+1}} dx^{-s} = \sum_{n=1}^\infty n(p_n^{-s} - p_{n+1}^{-s}) = \sum_{n=1}^\infty p_n^{-s}.$$

If we replace $\pi(x)$ in (16.44) by the expression

$$\pi(x) = l(x) + r(x)$$

we obtain

$$\phi(s) = -\int_2^\infty l(x) \, dx^{-s} - \int_2^\infty r(x) \, dx^{-s}.$$

If we integrate by parts the first integral, we have

$$\phi(s) = \int_2^\infty x^{-s} \, dl(x) - \int_2^\infty r(x) \, dx^{-s}.$$

By (16.34) we have

$$\phi(s) = \int_2^\infty \frac{dx}{x^s \log x} + s \int_2^\infty \frac{r(x)}{x^{s+1}} \, dx. \tag{16.45}$$

The function

$$u(s) = \int_2^\infty \frac{dx}{x^s \log x} \tag{16.46}$$

is regular in the half-plane $\sigma > 1$. Its derivative is

$$u'(s) = -\int_2^\infty \frac{dx}{x^s} = \frac{2^{1-s}}{1-s} = \frac{1}{1-s} e^{(1-s)\log 2}$$

$$= \frac{1}{1-s} \{1 + (1-s)\log 2 + \cdots\} = -\frac{1}{s-1} + \mathfrak{P}(s-1).$$

Hence, we have the following representation for $u(s)$ in the half-plane $\sigma > 1$:

$$u(s) = \log \frac{1}{s-1} + H(s), \tag{16.47}$$

where $H(s)$ is an entire function.

If we combine Eqs. (16.42)–(16.47), we obtain for $\log \zeta(s)$ the expression

$$\log \zeta(s) = \log \frac{1}{s-1} + H(s) + f(s) + s \int_2^\infty \frac{r(x)}{x^{s+1}} \, dx,$$

which can be also written as

$$\log [\zeta(s)(s-1)] = s \int_2^\infty \frac{r(x)}{x^{s+1}} \, dx + H(s) + f(s). \tag{16.48}$$

This formula is valid whenever s is real and greater than 1. Let us investigate (16.48) for complex values of s. The function $H(s) + f(s)$ is regular in the half-plane $\sigma > \frac{1}{2}$. Now $\zeta(s)\,(s-1)$ is an entire function (Section 16.6), so that $\log [\zeta(s)(1-s)]$ is regular everywhere except for the points at which $\zeta(s) = 0$. We show now that the first term on the right-hand side of (16.48),

$$R(s) = s \int_2^\infty \frac{r(x)}{x^{s+1}} \, dx, \tag{16.49}$$

is regular for

$$\sigma > \tfrac{1}{2} + \alpha. \tag{16.50}$$

By the assumption (16.39), the inequality

$$\left| \frac{r(x)}{x^{s+1}} \right| < \frac{x^{1/2+\alpha}}{x^{\sigma+1}} = x^{-\sigma-1/2+\alpha}$$

holds for the integrand of (16.49). The integral

$$\int_2^\infty x^{-\sigma-1/2+\alpha} \, dx$$

converges uniformly in the half-plane

$$\sigma \geq \sigma_0 > \tfrac{1}{2} + \alpha.$$

Hence, $R(s)$ is regular in the half-plane (16.50). It now follows that (16.48) is valid in whole half-plane (16.50), so that $\zeta(s)$ cannot have any zeros in this half-plane.

If the estimate (16.39) holds for every $\alpha > 0$, then $\zeta(s)$ has no zeros in the half-plane $\sigma > \frac{1}{2}$.

For recent work on the ζ-function, see the book of Karl Prachar, *Primzahlverteilung*, Springer, Berlin-Göttingen-Heidelberg, 1957.

EXERCISES ON CHAPTER 16

1. Prove that the integrals in formula (16.8) converge for $s > 1$.

2. Prove that the integral

$$\int_0^\infty \frac{x^{s-1}}{e^x - 1}\, dx$$

defines an analytic function in the half-plane $\sigma > 1$.

3. Show that

$$f_2(s) = \int_1^\infty \frac{x^{s-1}}{e^x - 1}\, dx$$

is an entire function of s.

4. Evaluate $\zeta(0)$ and $\zeta(-(2n-1))$ $(n = 1, 2, \ldots)$.

Hint. Expand both factors on the right-hand side of (16.19) into powers of s and $s + 2n - 1$, respectively.

5. Show that the constant term in the expansion (16.20) is Euler's constant C (cf. Section 15.10).

Hint. Compare the series expansion of $\zeta(s)$ with the integral $\int_1^\infty \dfrac{dx}{x^s}$ and let $s \to 1$.

6. Prove that the integrals

$$\int_a^{a+i\infty} \frac{z^{-s}}{e^{-2\pi iz} - 1}\, dz \quad \text{and} \quad \int_a^{a-i\infty} \frac{z^{-s}}{e^{2\pi iz} - 1}\, dz \quad (0 < a < 1)$$

are entire functions of s.

7. Derive the following formula:

$$\zeta(1 - s) = \frac{2}{(2\pi)^s} \cos\left(\frac{\pi}{2} s\right) \Gamma(s)\zeta(s).$$

8. Prove formula (16.35).

Hint. Integrate (16.34) term by term and split the interval of integration into the intervals $(2, \sqrt{x})$ and $(\sqrt{x}, x)$.

CHAPTER 17

THE THEORY OF CONFORMAL MAPPING

§1. THE RIEMANN MAPPING THEOREM

17.1. The Main Problem

In investigating the behavior of the elementary functions, we encountered a variety of special conformal mappings. It is now our object to consider conformal mapping from a more general point of view.

Let G_1 and G_2 be two open, *simply connected* domains. Our goal is to solve the following general problem, which was posed by Riemann.

Find a one-to-one and (directly) conformal mapping of G_1 onto G_2.

17.2. Special Cases

In two special cases, the problem can be solved immediately.

1) Suppose that one of the domains, G_1 for example, coincides with the extended plane $|z| \leq \infty$.

Then the requirement that the mapping $G_1 \leftrightarrow G_2$ be *topological* (that is, one-to-one and continuous) implies that the domain G_2 also consists of the extended plane.

The proof of this fact is based upon the compactness of the domain G_1: Every infinite sequence of points in G_1 has a point of accumulation in G_1. As the topological image of a compact set, G_2 is also compact, for an arbitrary infinite sequence of points (b) in G_2 has as its image an infinite sequence of points (a) in G_1, which in turn has a point of accumulation $a_0 \in G_1$; the image $b_0 \in G_2$ of a_0 is then a point of accumulation of the sequence (b).

Since G_2 is an open, compact subset of the closed plane, it must contain the entire plane, for if there were a point B not in G_2, there would be at least one boundary point ζ of the domain G_2 on the line segment joining the point B with an arbitrary interior point of G_2. A sequence $b_\nu \in G_2$ having ζ as limit would than have no interior accumulation point in this domain.

If the Riemann problem has a solution in this special case, then G_2 must consist of the entire closed plane. The one-to-one (directly) conformal mappings of the plane onto itself are just the linear transformations (cf. Sections 9.16 and 9.21):

$$w = \frac{az + b}{cz + d} \qquad (ad - bc \neq 0). \qquad (17.1)$$

2) For the second case, we suppose that one of the domains, say G_1, consists of the entire closed plane with the exception of a *single* point $z = \zeta_1$, which is therefore a boundary point (indeed, the only boundary point) of the domain. The inversion $1/(z - \zeta_1)$ maps this domain topologically and conformally onto the plane $z \neq \infty$. Thus we may assume from the start that G_1 is the plane $z \neq \infty$.

If the function $w = w(z)$ effects the conformal mapping $G_1 \leftrightarrow G_2$, then it is regular in the plane $z \neq \infty$ unless G_2 contains the point $w = \infty$. If G_2 contains this point, then there exists a well-defined point $z_0 \neq \infty$ at which $w(z_0) = \infty$, and $w(z) \to \infty$ as $z \to z_0$, since the mapping is continuous. The point z_0 is therefore a pole of the function $w(z)$.

In order to analyze the behavior of the function $w = w(z)$ in the neighborhood of the point $z = \infty$, we fix a point $z = z_1 \neq \infty$. The image domain K in G_2 of the disk $|z - z_1| < r$ contains the point $w_1 = w(z_1)$; otherwise the points $w = w(z)$ for $r \leq |z - z_1| < \infty$ lie in the exterior of K. In the latter domain the difference $|w(z) - w_1|$ has a positive lower bound. Weierstrass's theorem (Section 9.20) then implies that $z = \infty$ cannot be an essential singularity of the function $w = w(z)$. Since this function has no essential singularities in the plane $|z| \leq \infty$, it must be a rational function of z (cf. Section 9.23). Since it assumes no value more than once, it is of order 1. The function $w(z)$ must therefore be of the form (17.1). This linear transformation maps the domain G_1 ($z \neq \infty$) onto the domain $w \neq \zeta_2 = a/c$ and the point $w = \zeta_2$ is the only boundary point of the domain G_2. The boundary points $z = \zeta_1 = \infty$ and $w = \zeta_2$ must therefore correspond, and the mapping is conformal even at these points. Thus we have proved:

If one of the two domains has only a single boundary point, then the Riemann problem has a solution only if the other domain has the same property. The general solution of the mapping problem is given by formula (17.1), where the coefficients must be chosen in such a way that the boundary points ζ_1 and ζ_2 correspond.

Remark. If the domain G_1 coincides with the closed plane $|z| \leq \infty$, then a domain of the type treated in (2) can be obtained from G_1 by removing a point z_0. Hence, the solution found for the second case also leads us to the solution of the first case.

17.3. The General Case

Having dealt with the special cases in which one of the two domains G_1 and G_2 has at most one boundary point, we proceed to the general case and assume that both domains have *at least two*† boundary points.

---

† If a *simply* connected domain has two boundary points, then it has an infinite number of boundary points which form a continuum. We shall not need this property, however, when we solve the Riemann problem later on.

To solve this problem, we prove the *Riemann Mapping Theorem*.

A simply connected domain with at least two boundary points can be mapped one-to-one conformally onto the unit disk E.

Once this particular problem is solved, we can obtain the required mapping $G_1 \leftrightarrow G_2$ by carrying out first the individual mappings $G_1 \leftrightarrow E$ and $G_2 \leftrightarrow E$. The composite mapping $G_1 \leftrightarrow E \leftrightarrow G_2$ then provides a particular solution of the mapping problem $G_1 \leftrightarrow G_2$.

The general solution then follows easily. First we determine the general solution for the mapping $G_1 \leftrightarrow E$. If $w = w(z)$ effects the mapping $G_1 \leftrightarrow E$, then we map E conformally onto itself. By Sections 9.16 and 3.10, the latter mappings are given by linear transformations

$$S(w) = \frac{aw + b}{cw + d}, \qquad c = \bar{b}, d = \bar{a}, |b| < |a|. \tag{17.2}$$

Every transformation in this group maps the disk $|w| \leq 1$ onto itself, and, conversely, every self-mapping of the disk belongs to the group (17.2). Hence, we can obtain *all* the conformal mappings $G_1 \leftrightarrow E$ from formula (17.2) by replacing w by any particular mapping $w = w(z)$.

The general solution of the mapping problem $G_1 \leftrightarrow G_2$ can now be constructed once any two mappings $G_1 \leftrightarrow E$ and $G_2 \leftrightarrow E$ have been found: we first carry out the mapping $G_1 \leftrightarrow E$, then apply an arbitrary mapping $E \leftrightarrow E$ (with the aid of Eq. 17.2) and finally go over from E to G_2 by means of the mapping $E \leftrightarrow G_2$.

17.4. Normalization of the Mapping

If $w = w(z)$ maps the domain G onto the unit disk, there exists (Sections 3.9–3.10) a mapping of the form

$$S(w) = e^{i\alpha} \frac{w - w_0}{1 - \bar{w}_0 w}$$

which takes the image $w_0 = w(z_0)$ of any arbitrary point $z = z_0 \in G$ into the origin. This mapping is unique up to a rotation factor $e^{i\alpha}$. If the real number α is chosen appropriately, then a given direction through the point z_0 can be made to correspond to a given direction through the point $w = 0$ (for example, the direction of the positive real axis). This means that if we have an arc whose tangent is defined at the point z_0 then we can find a mapping such that the tangent to the image curve at the point $w = 0$ has a prescribed direction. This requirement determines the value of α, and we have the following conclusion.

If there exists a conformal mapping $G_1 \leftrightarrow G_2$, then two prescribed points $z_\nu \in G_\nu$ ($\nu = 1, 2$) and two prescribed directions at these points may be made to correspond, and the mapping is uniquely determined.

§2. CONSTRUCTION OF THE SOLUTION

17.5. Preliminary Mapping

We now proceed to the construction of the conformal mapping of a domain G onto the unit disk $|w| < 1$ under the hypothesis already mentioned earlier.

G is a simply connected domain of the z-plane whose boundary contains more than one point.

We show first that G can be mapped one-to-one conformally onto a domain inside the unit disk $|z| < 1$.

1) If there is a point $z = a$ exterior to G, then the disk $|z - a| \leq \rho$ lies exterior to G for $\rho > 0$ sufficiently small. The transformation $\rho/(z - a) = \zeta$ maps this disk conformally onto the domain $|\zeta| \geq 1$, and maps G conformally onto a schlicht subdomain of the disk $|\zeta| < 1$.

2) If G has no exterior points, we first use an inversion to bring the domain into such a position that one of its boundary points lies at $z = \infty$. By hypothesis, the domain G has another boundary point; let us denote it by $z = a \neq \infty$. We now choose an arbitrary point $z = z_0 \in G$ and form the integral

$$w = \int_{z_0}^{z} \frac{dt}{t - a} = \log \frac{z - a}{z_0 - a},$$

where the path of integration $z_0 z$ lies in the domain G. Since the integrand $1/(t - a)$ is regular in G, which is *simply connected*, the integral represents a single-valued, analytic function of z which is independent of the path $z_0 z$. Its inverse function

$$z = a + (z_0 - a) e^w \tag{17.3}$$

is also single-valued, so that the function $w(z)$ maps the domain G one-to-one conformally onto some domain G_w in the w-plane. The point $z = z_0$ corresponds to the origin $w = 0$.

We now claim that the points $w = n \cdot 2\pi i$ ($n = \pm 1, \pm 2, \ldots$) are *exterior* to the image domain G_w. To show this, we choose a number $\rho(0 < \rho < \pi)$ so small that the disk $|w| \leq \rho$ belongs to the domain G_w. The disks $|w - n \cdot 2\pi i| \leq \rho$ ($n \neq 0$) then lie outside of G_w. For, if a point $w = w_1$ of the disk $|w - n \cdot 2\pi i| \leq \rho$ ($n \neq 0$) should belong to the domain G_w, we could find a point z_1 in G corresponding to it. The function (17.3) would then assume the same value at two distinct points $w = w_1$ and $w = w_1 - n \cdot 2\pi i \neq w_1$ in G_w, namely, the value $z_1 \in G$. This contradicts the univalence (or topological character) of the mapping $G \leftrightarrow G_w$.

Hence, there are points exterior to G_w. As we showed in (1), we may map G_w conformally onto a schlicht subdomain of the unit disk $|\zeta| < 1$ by an inversion; by an appropriate linear transformation, we may assume that this subdomain contains the point $\zeta = 0$.

17.6. An Auxiliary Mapping

Our problem now is to map a simply connected domain G lying inside the unit disk $|z| < 1$ and containing the point $z = 0$ conformally onto the whole disk $|w| < 1$ in such a way that the origin remains fixed and such that a prescribed direction through the point $z = 0$ corresponds to a prescribed direction through the point $w = 0$. If we choose these two directions to be the direction of the positive real axis, then we may simply assume that the derivative dw/dz is to be real and positive at the origin. As we have seen (cf. Section 17.4), the mapping $z \leftrightarrow w$, whenever it exists, is uniquely determined.

In order to construct the solution, we apply an iteration method due to Constantin Carathéodory (1873–1950) and Paul Koebe (1882–1945). We may describe it as follows. The given domain is mapped successively onto subdomains $G_1, G_2, \ldots$ of the unit disk in such a way that the origin remains fixed and the other points of the domain move towards the boundary of the unit disk; as $n \to \infty$, the subdomains G_n converge to the full unit disk.

A sequence of mappings of this sort, $G \leftrightarrow G_1$, $G_1 \leftrightarrow G_2$, $\ldots$ may be constructed in many ways. The method of Carathéodory and Koebe is particularly elementary, for it is based upon the use of the inverse of a simple rational function of second order.

17.7.

It was shown in Chapter 4 that a rational function of second order $z = z(w)$ in the variable w may be written in the form

$$\frac{z - z_1}{z - z_2} = k \left(\frac{w - w_1}{w - w_2} \right)^2.$$

This transformation maps the schlicht w-plane onto a two-sheeted Riemann surface which covers the z-plane. The values $w = w_1, w_2$ correspond to the branch points $z = z_1, z_2$; at all other points the mapping is conformal. The transformation sets up a correspondence between the pencils or bundles of Steiner circles associated with these pairs of points.

We now choose these four base points and the constant k in such a way that the unit circles $|z| = 1$ and $|w| = 1$ correspond. To this end we choose each pair of base points to be reflections in the unit circle, $z_1 = r$ $(0 < r < 1)$, $z_2 = 1/r$ and $w_1 = \rho$ $(0 < \rho < 1)$, $w_2 = 1/\rho$. Now if the origin is invariant under the mapping, then $k = 1$ and $\rho = \sqrt{r}$, and the mapping assumes the form

$$\frac{z - r}{z - \dfrac{1}{r}} = \left(\frac{w - \sqrt{r}}{w - \dfrac{1}{\sqrt{r}}} \right)^2. \tag{17.4}$$

Moreover, the direction of the positive real axis remains fixed at the origin.

The disk $|w| \leqq 1$ is thereby mapped onto a two-sheeted covering of the unit disk $|z| \leqq 1$. If we cut both sheets along the segment $(r, 1)$, then the edges of the cut go over into a circular arc through $w = \sqrt{r}$ which is orthogonal to the unit circle and to the real axis. This arc divides the disk $|w| \leqq 1$ into two circular lunes which correspond to the two sheets of the slit disk $|z| \leqq 1$ (Fig. 45). The origin in one of the sheets corresponds to the point $w = 0$ while the origin in the other sheet corresponds to the point

$$w = \lambda = \frac{2\sqrt{r}}{1 + r} < 1.$$

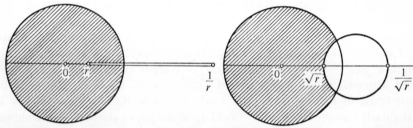

Figure 45

If we solve (17.4) for z, we have

$$z = w\,\frac{\lambda - w}{1 - \lambda w}. \tag{17.4}'$$

The factor $(\lambda - w)/(1 - \lambda w)$ maps the disk $|w| < 1$ onto itself in such a way that $w = \lambda$ goes into the origin. Hence,

$$|z| = |w|\left|\frac{\lambda - w}{1 - \lambda w}\right| < |w|, \tag{17.5}$$

whenever $0 < |w| < 1$. The mapping $w \to z$ therefore takes the points w closer to the origin.

We remark that the derivative at the point $w = 0$, which corresponds to $z = 0$, is real and positive:

$$\frac{dz}{dw} = \lim_{w \to 0} \frac{z}{w} = \lim_{w \to 0} \frac{\lambda - w}{1 - \lambda w} = \lambda = \frac{2\sqrt{r}}{1 + r}. \tag{17.6}$$

17.8. The Mapping $G \to G_1$

If the domain $G = G_0$, which is a subdomain of the unit disk $|z| < 1$ and contains the point $z = 0$, does not coincide with the unit disk, its boundary Γ has a minimum distance $r < 1$ from the origin. This minimum is achieved for at least one boundary point; let $z = r e^{i\phi}$ be one such point. We first rotate the z-plane by $z \to z e^{-i\phi}$, so that this boundary point goes into the point $z = r$. We denote by G the domain obtained by rotating G_0.

The equation (17.4) for the mapping defines w as a double-valued algebraic function of z. At $w = 0$, we fix that branch which vanishes for $z = 0$. This function-element can be continued throughout the domain G since the domain does not contain the branch points $z = r, 1/r$. Because G is *simply connected*, it follows from the monodromy theorem that the resulting function $w = w(z)$ is *single-valued* and regular in G; in addition, the function is continuous on the boundary Γ of G. If we bear in mind the properties of the transformation (17.4) mentioned earlier, we can further conclude that

1) $|w(z)| < 1$ for $z \in G$.

2) $w(0) = 0$ and $(dw/dz)_{z=0} = (1 + r)/2\sqrt{r}$.

3) $|w(z)| > |z|$ for $0 \neq z \in G$.

4) the mapping $z \to w$ is univalent (schlicht).

The last property follows from the fact that z is a *single-valued* function (17.4)' of w. The mapping $z \to w$ is therefore one-to-one in the domain G.

If we go from the variable w to the variable $e^{i\phi}w$, then the domain G_0 is mapped onto a schlicht subdomain G_1 of the unit disk. The shortest distance r_1 of the boundary Γ_1 of G_1 from the origin satisfies the condition $0 < r < r_1 < 1$. The origin remains fixed under the mapping $G_0 \to G_1$, and the derivative of the mapping function at the origin is real and positive $(= (1 + r)/2\sqrt{r})$. In this way we have carried out the first step in the iteration method.

17.9. The Mapping $G_0 \to G_n$

In a similar way, we map the domain G_1 by the transformation described above which differs from (17.4) only by a rotation of the z-plane and w-plane; it is only necessary to replace r by r_1. We obtain a schlicht domain G_2 as the image of G_0 under the transformation. By repeating this process, we obtain a sequence of schlicht subdomains $G_1, \ldots, G_n, \ldots$ of the unit disk.

The function $z_n = f_n(z)$ which maps the domain G_0 onto G_n is regular in G_0 and continuous on the boundary. As a consequence of (1)–(4), the function has the following properties:

1) $|z| \leqq |f_1(z)| \leqq \ldots \leqq |f_n(z)| < 1$ in G_0.

2) $f_n(0) = 0$ and

$$f_n'(0) = \left(\frac{dz_1}{dz} \cdots \frac{dz_n}{dz_{n-1}}\right)_{z=0} = \prod_{\nu=0}^{n-1} \frac{1 + r_\nu}{2\sqrt{r_\nu}},$$

where r_ν is the shortest distance of the boundary of G_ν from the origin $(0 < r_0 < r_1 < \ldots < r_n < 1)$.

3) The mapping $G_0 \to G_n$ is conformal and schlicht.

11

We now prove that

4) $\lim\limits_{n\to\infty} r_n = 1.$

To prove (4) we form the sequence

$$F_n(z) = \frac{f_n(z)}{z}.$$

The function f_n vanishes at the point $z = 0$ in G_0. Therefore $F_n(z)$ is regular in G_0 and

$$|F_1(z)| \leq |F_2(z)| \leq \ldots \leq |F_n(z)|. \tag{17.7}$$

We show next that this sequence is bounded. On the boundary Γ of the domain G_0, $|f_n| \leq 1$ and $|z| \geq r_0$; hence,

$$|F_n(z)| = \frac{|f_n(z)|}{|z|} \leq \frac{1}{r_0}. \tag{17.8}$$

By the maximum principle, this inequality holds throughout the domain G_0. In particular, for $z = 0$ we obtain

$$F_n(0) = f'_n(0) = \prod_{\nu=0}^{n-1} \frac{1 + r_\nu}{2\sqrt{r_\nu}} \leq \frac{1}{r_0}.$$

From this it follows that the limit

$$\lim_{n\to\infty} f'_n(0) = \prod_{n=0}^{\infty} \frac{1 + r_n}{2\sqrt{r_n}} \leq \frac{1}{r_0}$$

exists. On the other hand, it follows from the monotonicity of the sequence $f'_n(0)$ that $\lim f'_n(0) > 0$.

It follows from the theory of infinite products (cf. Section 13.1) that

$$\frac{1 + r_n}{2\sqrt{r_n}} - 1 = \frac{(1 - \sqrt{r_n})^2}{2\sqrt{r_n}} \to 0 \quad \text{as} \quad n \to \infty.$$

Since the denominator $2\sqrt{r_n}$ is less than 2, $1 - \sqrt{r_n}$ tends to zero, and assertion (4) is proved.

17.10. The Convergence Proof

It follows from properties (1) and (2) of the sequence $f_n(z)$ that the functions $F_n(z) = f_n(z)/z$ are regular in the domain G_0 and different from zero. At the origin we choose that branch of the function $\log F_n(z)$ which assumes the real value $\log F_n(0) = \log f'_n(0)$. Analytic continuation of this branch defines a *single-valued* regular function in G_0. Hence, $\log |F_n(z)|$ is harmonic in this domain and, by (17.8), is bounded ($\leq \log 1/r_0$). It follows from Harnack's principle (cf. Section 11.24 and Exercises 24 and 25 of Chapter 11) that the sequence $F_n(z)$, and therefore the sequence $f_n(z)$, converges in the domain G_0, and uniformly on any closed subset. The limit function

$$\lim_{n \to \infty} f_n(z) = f(z)$$

is a regular analytic function in the whole domain G_0.

17.11. The Mapping $w = f(z)$

The value of the limit function $f(z)$ at the origin is

$$f(0) = \lim_{n \to \infty} f_n(0) = 0.$$

Its derivative at the origin has the value

$$f'(0) = \lim_{n \to \infty} f_n'(0) > 0,$$

from which it follows that $f(z)$ is not constant.

It follows from property (1) of the sequence $f_n(z)$ that $|f(z)| \leqq 1$ for $z \in G_0$. Actually,

$$|f(z)| < 1$$

in this domain, for if $|f(z)|$ were to assume its maximum value 1 in G_0, then $f(z)$ would be a constant, in contradiction to what has just been proved.

As the non-constant limit of a sequence of schlicht functions $f_n(z)$, the function $w = f(z)$ is itself schlicht (cf. Section 9.28). Therefore it maps the domain G_0 one-to-one conformally onto a subdomain G_w of the unit disk $|w| < 1$ in such a way that the origin and the direction of the positive real axis at the origin remain invariant.

It remains to show that G_w coincides with the unit disk $|w| < 1$. As a first step, we prove:

At every point ζ of the boundary Γ of G_0,

$$\lim_{z \to \zeta} |f(z)| = 1.$$

To establish this result, we have to show that for every $\epsilon > 0$ there exists a $\rho > 0$ such that for z in the intersection G_ρ of the domain G_0 and the disk $|z - \zeta| < \rho$ we have $1 > |f(z)| > 1 - \epsilon$. We start by fixing a number n_0 such that $r_{n_0} > 1 - \epsilon/2$ (cf. Section 17.9, (4)). Then the function $f_{n_0}(z)$, which is continuous at the point ζ (cf. Section 17.9), satisfies the condition $|f_{n_0}(\zeta)| > 1 - \epsilon/2$. Next we choose $\rho > 0$ in such a way that $|f_{n_0}(\zeta) - f_{n_0}(z)| < \epsilon/2$ for $z \in G_\rho$. In this domain we have $1 > |f_{n_0}(z)| > 1 - \epsilon$, and, since $|f_n|$ is a monotone increasing sequence, it follows that $|f(z)| > 1 - \epsilon$, which is what we wished to prove.

If the image domain G_w does not coincide with the entire unit disk $|w| < 1$, then G_w must have a *boundary point* w_0 inside the disk $|w| < 1$.

We consider a sequence of points $w_\nu \in G_w$ with $\lim w_\nu = w_0$. This must correspond to a sequence $z_\nu \in G_0$ such that $f(z_\nu) = w_\nu$ $(\nu = 1, 2, \ldots)$ from which we may select a subsequence z_{ν_μ} $(\mu = 1, 2, \ldots)$ which converges to a point z_0 in G_0 or on its boundary. If z_0 were to lie in G_0, then $f(z)$ would be regular there and $f(z_0) = w_0$ would belong to G_w, contrary to assumption. On the other hand, if z_0 were a boundary point, then, by what we proved earlier, $|f(z_{\nu_\mu})| \to 1$ as $z_{\nu_\mu} \to z_0$, and this contradicts the fact that $f(z_\nu) \to w_0$, $|w_0| < 1$. Hence, $f(z)$ must assume every value w in the disk $|w| < 1$.

The image domain G_w therefore coincides with the disk $|w| < 1$, and the proof of the mapping theorem is thereby completed.

17.12. A Second Proof

We give now a second proof, based upon the argument principle, to show that the function $w = f(z)$ maps the domain G_0 onto the entire disk $|w| < 1$. What we must establish is that to any given point w_0 with $|w_0| < 1$, there exists a point $z_0 \in G_0$ for which $f(z_0) = w_0$.

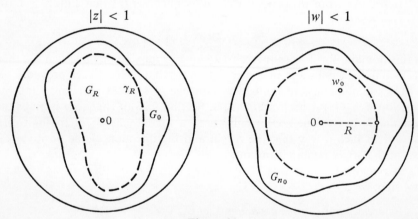

Figure 46

Let $1 > R > |w_0|$. Since $\lim_{n \to \infty} r_n = 1$, there exists an n_0 so large that the function

$$w = f_{n_0}(z) \tag{17.9}$$

maps G_0 onto a domain G_{n_0} whose boundary has a minimum distance $r_{n_0} > R$ from the origin. The domain G_{n_0} therefore contains the disk $|w| \leq R$. The boundary $|w| = R$ corresponds to a Jordan curve γ_R in G_0 and the domain G_R bounded by γ_R (see Fig. 46) is mapped by the function (17.9) onto the disk $|w| < R$. On the curve γ_R we have

$$|f_{n_0}(z)| = R > |w_0|, \tag{17.10}$$

and on the subdomain of G_0 outside this curve we have

$$|f_{n_0}(z)| > R > |w_0|. \tag{17.11}$$

Since $|f_n(z)| > |f_{n_0}(z)|$ for $n > n_0$, it follows from (17.10) and (17.11) that

$$|f_n(z)| \geq R > |w_0| \qquad (17.12)$$

for $n \geq n_0$ and $z \in G_0 - G_R$. From this it follows that the function $f_n(z)$, which maps G_0 onto a domain G_n containing the disk $|w| < R$ ($r_{n_0} < r_n$ for $n_0 < n$), assumes the value w_0 at some point in G_R.

We now assert that there is a point z_0 in the domain G_R at which $f(z_0) = w_0$. Let us write

$$f(z) - w_0 = [f_n(z) - w_0] + [f(z) - f_n(z)].$$

On the curve γ_R we have

$$|f_n(z) - w_0| > R - |w_0| \qquad \text{for} \qquad n > n_0.$$

Since $f_n(z)$ converges uniformly to $f(z)$ on the curve γ_R as $n \to \infty$, there exists an $n_1 \geq n_0$ such that, on γ_R,

$$|f(z) - f_n(z)| < R - |w_0|$$

whenever $n \geq n_1$. By Rouché's theorem (Section 10.10), the functions $f(z) - w_0$ and $f_n(z) - w_0$ have the same number of zeros in the domain G_R whenever $n \geq n_1$. But the function $f_n(z) - w_0$ has only a single zero in this domain. Hence, the function $f(z)$ assumes the value w_0 precisely once in the domain G_R, which proves our assertion.

§3. BOUNDARY CORRESPONDENCE UNDER CONFORMAL MAPPING

17.13. Boundaries and their Correspondence

By the Riemann mapping theorem, a simply connected domain G in the z-plane whose boundary Γ contains at least two points can be mapped conformally onto the unit disk $E: |w| < 1$, and this mapping is unique up to a conformal mapping of the unit disk onto itself. The group of such mappings consists of the linear transformations (17.2). In what follows, we shall study the behavior of the mapping $w = w(z)$ when the point $z \in G$ approaches the boundary Γ.

From the single fact that the mapping $G \leftrightarrow E$ is topological, we have first the following property.

If a point z of the domain G tends to a point ζ on the boundary Γ, then its image $w = w(z)$ tends to the boundary of the unit disk.

Proof. Let $z_1, \ldots, z_n, \ldots$ be a sequence of points in the domain G for which $z_n \to \zeta$ as $n \to \infty$. We must prove that $|w_n| = |w(z_n)| \to 1$ as $n \to \infty$, where $w = w(z)$ is the function mapping G onto the unit disk.

To begin with, we choose an arbitrary positive $r_0 < 1$. The disk $|w| \leq r_0$ then corresponds to a compact subset G_0 of G. The shortest distance of the point ζ from G_0 is a positive number δ. We choose n_0 so large that $|z_n - \zeta| < \delta$

for $n \geq n_0$. The points z_n $(n \geq n_0)$ lie outside G_0, and, from the one-to-one nature of the mapping it follows that the corresponding points w_n lie outside the circle $|w| = r_0$. Hence, $r_0 < |w_n| < 1$ for $n \geq n_0$, and this is what we wanted to prove.

17.14. Examples

The theorem we have just proved shows that the modulus $|w(z)|$ of the mapping function $w = w(z)$ is continuous on the boundary of the domain G. However, it does not follow from this that the mapping function $w(z)$ itself is continuous at the boundary Γ; for this to be the case, the argument arg $w(z)$ must be continuous in the approach to the boundary. In what follows, we shall see that this does not always happen. Let us consider some examples.

1) Let G be the domain bounded by the positive real axis Γ: $x \geq 0$, $z = x + iy$, of the z-plane. That branch of $\sqrt{z}$ which assumes the value i for $z = -1$ maps G onto the upper half-plane Im $(\sqrt{z}) > 0$. This half-plane is then mapped by a linear transformation onto the unit disk $|w| < 1$ in such a way that the positive real axis corresponds to the semicircle $|w| = 1$, Im $w > 0$, and the negative real axis corresponds to the semicircle $|w| = 1$, Im $w < 0$. If a point $z = x + iy$ tends towards a boundary point $x > 0$, $y = 0$ of G from the half-plane $y > 0$, then $w = u + iv$ tends to a well-defined point w $(|w| = 1, v > 0)$; if, however, z tends to the same point $x > 0$, $y = 0$ from the half-plane $y < 0$, $w(z)$ tends to the complex conjugate $\bar{w}$ of the limit value w found previously. The mapping $w = w(z)$ is therefore discontinuous at every boundary point $x > 0$, $y = 0$.

2) A more complicated example may be constructed in the following way. The exponential function $z = e^w = e^u(\cos v + i \sin v)$ maps the half-plane $u \leq 0$ onto an infinite-sheeted Riemann surface lying over the disk $|z| \leq 1$ and having $z = 0$ as a branch point. We now restrict the points w to the domain G_w: $u < 0$, $-(1/u) < v < -(1/u) + 2\pi$, whose boundary consists of branches of the hyperbolas $uv + 1 = 0$ and $uv + 1 - 2\pi u = 0$ (the second one is obtained from the first by a translation of 2π in the direction of the v-axis (Fig. 47)). The function $z = e^w$ maps this domain G_w one-to-one conformally onto a domain G_z obtained from the disk $|z| < 1$ by removing the spiral $z = e^u(\cos (1/u) - i \sin (1/u))$ $(-\infty < u < 0)$ corresponding to points on the bounding hyperbolas.

If the point w in the domain G_w now tends continuously towards the boundary point $u = 0$, $v = +\infty$, then its image point z winds infinitely often about the origin in such a way that $|z| \to 1$ (Fig. 48). Therefore the boundary correspondence under the mapping $w \leftrightarrow z$ is not continuous.

In this example the image of the domain G_z is not the disk E, but a domain G_w bounded by two hyperbolas. By the Riemann mapping theorem, this simply connected domain can be mapped conformally onto the unit disk.

Since the boundary of the domain G_w is a piecewise analytic curve, the mapping $G_w \leftrightarrow E$ is one-to-one and continuous on the boundaries (cf. Exercise 3, p. 339). In particular, there is a well-defined point P on the unit circle corresponding to the boundary point $u = 0$, $v = +\infty$ of G_w. The composite conformal mapping $E \leftrightarrow G_z$ is therefore discontinuous in the neighborhood of this point P: A continuous curve in E terminating at the point P corresponds to a curve in the domain G_z which spirals to the boundary $|z| = 1$ in such a way that every point of the boundary is a cluster point of the curve.

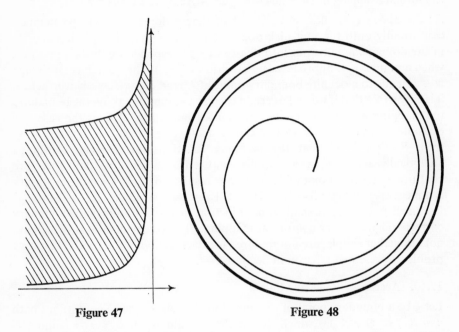

Figure 47   **Figure 48**

3) If we remove the segments $0 < x < \frac{1}{2}$, $y = 1/n$ $(n = 2, 3, \ldots)$ from the square $0 < x < 1$, $0 < y < 1$, we have left a simply connected domain G.† If we map G conformally onto the unit disk $|w| < 1$, we get an analytic function which is discontinuous on the missing segments. The nature of this mapping as it approaches the boundary segment $0 \leq x \leq \frac{1}{2}$, $y = 0$ is particularly complicated. To show this, we consider a sequence of points $z_n = x + in/(n^2 + 1)$ in G, where $n = 2, 3, \ldots$, and where x is a constant satisfying the inequality $0 < x < \frac{1}{2}$. As $n \to \infty$, the sequence z_n converges to the boundary point $z = x$. Under the mapping $G \leftrightarrow E$, the image points w_n of the points z_n tend to the boundary $|w| = 1$. We may choose an infinite subsequence $\{w_n\}$ from the sequence w_n which converges to a boundary point

---

† The simple connectivity of G follows from the fact that this domain can be mapped topologically onto an open square (Exercise 2, p. 339).

$w = w_0$. If we join successive points in the sequence by line segments, we obtain a polygonal path l_w in E with infinitely many sides terminating at the point w_0. The image of this path in G is a curve consisting of infinitely many analytic arcs. It passes through the image points $\{z_n\}$ of the points $\{w_n\}$ and oscillates as w tends to w_0 along l_w. Hence every point of the interval $(x, \frac{1}{2})$ of the real axis is a cluster point.

17.15. Boundary Correspondence under
Conformal Mapping of Domains Bounded by Analytic Curves

As the above examples show, that fact that a domain G may be mapped conformally onto the unit disk does not in itself imply that the boundaries of the domains may be put into one-to-one correspondence in the sense that when a point $z \in G$ approaches an arbitrary point on the boundary, its image $w \in E$ tends to a definite boundary point of E, and conversely. Nevertheless, it is easy to see that if we make certain special assumptions about the boundary, the mapping will also be continuous on the boundary. This is the case, for example, when the boundary Γ of G is an *analytic* Jordan curve. For it follows from Section 12.11 that the mapping function can then be continued analytically across Γ, which implies that it is analytic on Γ and therefore continuous at every point of Γ. The same result also holds when the boundary is a piecewise analytic Jordan curve (cf. Exercise 3, p. 339).

In what follows, we shall examine in more detail the nature of the boundary correspondence under conformal mapping. These considerations, which are not altogether simple, are not required for the solution of the special mapping problems presented later on in Sections 5–7.

17.16. Accessible Boundary Points

Let ζ be a boundary point of the domain G. If there exists a continuous path $z = z(\tau)$ $(0 \leq \tau \leq 1)$, which lies in the domain G for $0 \leq \tau < 1$ and terminates at the point ζ, $z(1) = \zeta$, then the boundary point ζ is said to be *accessible*. Accessible boundary points have particularly simple properties under conformal mapping, as we shall presently see.

To illustrate what we mean by an accessible boundary point, we consider the examples given above. In case (1) all boundary points of the domain G are accessible. In example (2), those boundary points ζ lying in the disk $|z| < 1$ are accessible, but none of the boundary points with $|\zeta| = 1$ have this property. All boundary points of the domain G in example (3) are accessible, with the exception of those lying on the segment $0 \leq x < \frac{1}{2}, y = 0$.

17.17. Classes of Boundary Elements

The notion of an accessible boundary point ζ involves not only the point ζ in the complex plane, but also a continuous path l: $z = z(\tau)$, lying in the domain G for $0 \leq \tau < 1$ and terminating at the point ζ when $\tau = 1$. Hence, we denote an accessible boundary point ζ by the pair (ζ, l_ζ) and call such pairs *boundary elements*. (It would really be enough to use the notation l_ζ, since this already determines the end-point ζ.)

Now let G be a simply connected domain and (ζ, l_ζ) a boundary element. To every value r of the interval $0 < r \leq |\zeta - z(0)|$ there corresponds a well-defined parameter value $\tau = \tau_r$ $(0 \leq \tau_r < 1)$ such that $|\zeta - z(\tau_r)| = r$ and $0 < |\zeta - z(\tau)| < r$ for $\tau_r < \tau < 1$. Let the corresponding subarc of l_ζ be l_r. The disk $|z - \zeta| < r$ and the domain G have a non-empty open intersection consisting of a countable set of disjoint connected subdomains or components. One of these subdomains contains the arc l_r; let us denote it by $G_r(l_\zeta)$.

Suppose now that (ζ_1, l_{ζ_1}) and (ζ_2, l_{ζ_2}) are two boundary elements. It follows from the definition that:

If $\zeta_1 \neq \zeta_2$, the domains $G_r(l_{\zeta_1})$ and $G_r(l_{\zeta_2})$ are disjoint for all sufficiently small values of r.

If $\zeta_1 = \zeta_2$, then either the domains $G_r(l_{\zeta_1})$ and $G_r(l_{\zeta_2})$ are disjoint, or they coincide.

If $G_r(l_{\zeta_1})$ and $G_r(l_{\zeta_2})$ coincide for every value of $r > 0$, the boundary elements (ζ_1, l_{ζ_1}) and (ζ_2, l_{ζ_2}) will be said to be *equivalent*. This relation has all the properties of an equivalence relation (cf. Section 8.16): it is reflexive, symmetric and transitive. The set of boundary elements corresponding to accessible boundary points admits a partition into disjoint equivalence classes such that two boundary elements are equivalent if and only if they belong to the same class.

For two boundary elements (ζ_1, l_{ζ_1}) and (ζ_1, l_{ζ_2}) to be equivalent, it is necessary for the "end-points" ζ_1 and ζ_2 to coincide, but this condition is not sufficient. Thus, every boundary point $\zeta = x > 0$ in Example (1) defines two different classes of elements, while the boundary point $\zeta = 0$ belongs to only one class. Similarly, in example (2), the points $\zeta(0 < |\zeta| < 1)$ define two distinct classes of elements, while the point $\zeta = 0$ defines only one. In example (3), each of the boundary points $\zeta = x + i/n$ $(0 \leq x < \frac{1}{2}, n = 2, 3, \ldots)$ belongs to two different classes, but the points $\zeta = \frac{1}{2} + i/n$ $(n = 2, 3, \ldots)$ and the other accessible boundary points of the bounding square belong to only one class.

The number of classes belonging to the same boundary point can also be infinite. Such is the case, for example, with the boundary point $\zeta = 0$ of the domain G obtained by removing from the plane $z \neq \infty$ the segments $r e^{i\phi}$ $(0 \leq r \leq 1, \phi = \pi/n, n = 1, 2, \ldots)$.

17.18. The Mapping of the Domains $G_r(l_\zeta)$

Let us examine the behavior of a boundary element (ζ, l_ζ) of a (bounded) simply connected domain G under the conformal mapping of G onto the unit disk E: $|w| < 1$. We may suppose that the point $z = 0$ is mapped into the point $w = 0$. For each positive number $r < |\zeta|$, let $G_r(l_\zeta) = G_r$ be the corresponding (connected) subdomain of G (cf. Section 17.17), and let $D_r \subset E$ be the (schlicht) image of G_r. As $r \to 0$, the domain G_r shrinks to the point ζ. We prove that D_r then tends to a well-defined point of the unit circle $|w| = 1$.

For this purpose, we consider (for a given r) two arbitrary points w_1 and w_2 of D_r which do not lie on the same ray through the origin, and we join them in D_r by a simple polygonal path. This contains as a subset at least one polygonal path λ which joins two points P_1 and P_2 of D_r lying on the rays $\phi = \arg w_1$ and $\phi = \arg w_2$, but which does not otherwise intersect these rays. The polygonal path λ lies in one of the two angular sectors bounded by the rays $0w_1$ and $0w_2$; we shall denote the one it lies in by $0Q_1Q_2$ and denote by α $(0 < \alpha < 2\pi)$ the value of the angular opening of $0Q_1Q_2$ at 0 (Figs. 49 and 50).

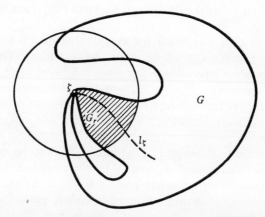

Figure 49

The simple closed polygonal path $0P_1P_20$ bounds a (simply) connected domain $E_0 \subset E$. We consider the harmonic function

$$u(w) \equiv \log |z(w) - \zeta| - \log M$$

defined in E_0, where M is the diameter of the domain G and where $z = z(w)$ effects the conformal mapping $E \to G$. Now $u(w) \leq 0$ on the rays bounding E_0, and $u(w) \leq \log r - \log M$ (< 0) on the polygonal path λ.

On the other hand, we form the harmonic measure $h(w)$ of the arc Q_1Q_2 with respect to the sector $Q_1 0 Q_2$†; it vanishes on the bounding radii and is equal to 1 at the interior points of the arc Q_1Q_2. Hence, $h(w) = 0$ on the

---

† This function can be determined in an elementary way (cf. Section 11.19 and Exercise 19, p. 210).

segments $0P_1$, $0P_2$ bounding the domain E_0, while $h(w) < 1$ on the (closed) polygonal path λ.

It follows that the harmonic function

$$U(w) \equiv u(w) + (\log M - \log r)h(w)$$

is less than or equal to 0 on the segments $0Q_1$ and $0Q_2$ and that the same is true at the points of λ. It then follows from the maximum principle that $U(w) \leq 0$ in the entire domain E_0. Hence, at every point w of this domain,

$$h(w) \leq \log \frac{M}{|z(w) - \zeta|} \Big/ \log \frac{M}{r}. \tag{17.13}$$

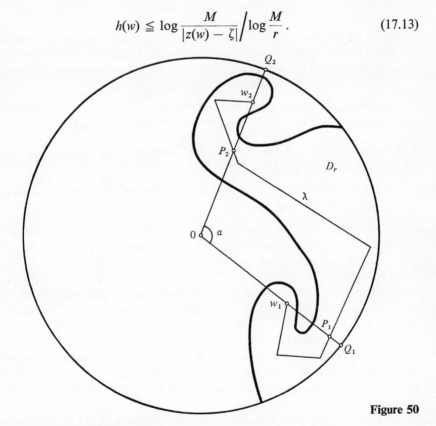

Figure 50

We now fix a number ρ_0 $(0 < \rho_0 < 1)$ such that

$$|z(w) - \zeta| \geq \frac{|\zeta|}{2}$$

in the disk $|w| \leq \rho_0$. Let w_0 be the midpoint of the subarc of $|w| = \rho_0$ which lies in the sector $0Q_1Q_2$. At the point w_0, $h(w_0)$ is a positive number which depends only upon the magnitude of the angle α. Its value $h(w_0) = f(\alpha) > 0$ decreases monotonically with α (see Exercise 4, p. 340).

It follows from inequality (17.13) that

$$f(\alpha) \leqq \log \frac{2M}{|\zeta|} \Big/ \log \frac{M}{r} .$$

Since the right-hand side vanishes when $r \to 0$, $f(\alpha)$, and therefore α itself, tends to zero with r. This means that the oscillation of the function arg w in the domain D_r must vanish when $r \to 0$. If we observe that $D_{r'} \subset D_r$ for $r' < r$, we see that arg $w(z)$ tends to a limit as $r \to 0$, $z \in G_r$. This proves our assertion.

In particular, it follows that

If (ζ, l_ζ) is a boundary element, and if the point z tends to the boundary point ζ along l_ζ, then the image point $w = w(z)$ tends to a well-defined limit ω $(|\omega| = 1)$. The limit point ω remains unchanged whenever the element (ζ, l_ζ) is replaced by an equivalent element (ζ, l'_ζ).

Therefore, to every given class of elements (ζ, l_ζ) there corresponds a uniquely determined point ω on the boundary of the unit disk.

17.19. The One-to-One Character of the Correspondence $(\zeta, l_\zeta) \to \omega$

We now prove the converse.

If (ζ_1, l_{ζ_1}) and (ζ_2, l_{ζ_2}) belong to distinct classes, then they correspond to distinct boundary points ω_1 and ω_2.

Proof. Suppose that the boundary elements (ζ_1, l_1) and (ζ_2, l_2) belong to different classes, and let w_1 and w_2 be the corresponding points on the circle $|w| = 1$. We assume that $\omega_1 = \omega_2 = \omega$ and show that this leads to a contradiction.

The paths l_1 and l_2, which we may assume are Jordan arcs (Exercise 5, p. 340), lead to two domains $G_r(l_1)$ and $G_r(l_2)$ (Section 17.17) which are disjoint for all sufficiently small values of r $(0 < r \leqq r_0)$. Let $l_1(r)$ be that part of the arc l_1 which lies in the domain $G_r(l_1)$ and connects the circumference $|z - \zeta_1| = r$ with the point ζ_1, and, similarly, let $l_2(r)$ denote the terminal part of l_2. Under the mapping $w = w(z)$, the arcs $l_\nu(r)$ $(\nu = 1, 2)$ correspond to two Jordan arcs $\lambda_\nu(r)$ which terminate at the point $w = \omega$ and which are disjoint except for this point.

We now apply Theorem 3 of Lindelöf (Section 11.21) to the function $z = z(w)$. This function is regular and bounded in the domain D bounded by the arcs $\lambda_\nu(r_0)$ $(\nu = 1, 2)$ and by an arbitrary Jordan arc λ_0 lying within the disk $|w| < 1$ and joining the initial points of $\lambda_\nu(r_0)$. It follows from this theorem that the limits ζ_ν to which $z(w)$ tends as w tends to ω along the arcs λ_ν are equal, $\zeta_1 = \zeta_2 = \zeta$, and that $z(w)$ tends to ζ as $w \in D$ tends to w. Moreover, the convergence is uniform: To every value r $(0 < r < r_0)$ there corresponds a value ρ such that $|z(w) - \zeta| < r$ whenever w lies in the intersection D_ρ of the domain D with the disk $|w - \omega| < \rho$.

The circle $|w - \omega| = \rho$ then contains a boundary arc λ of D_ρ joining two points w_1 and w_2 on the arcs $\lambda_1(r)$ and $\lambda_2(r)$. The corresponding points $z_\nu = z(w_\nu)$ $(\nu = 1, 2)$ lie on $l_\nu(r)$, so that $z_\nu \in G_r(l_\nu) \subset G_{r_0}(l_\nu)$ $(\nu = 1, 2)$. The image curve l of the arc λ joins the points z_1 and z_2. Since $G_{r_0}(l_1)$ and $G_{r_0}(l_2)$ are disjoint, the arc l which runs from the initial point z_1 to the end-point z_2, must intersect the boundary of the domain $G_{r_0}(l_1)$. But since l and the boundary Γ of G do not intersect, there must then be a point z_0 on the arc l which lies on the circle $|z - \zeta| = r_0$.

On the other hand, the inequality $|z(w) - \zeta| \leq r$ holds on λ. In particular, this is valid at the image point $w_0 \in \lambda$ of z_0, so that $|z(w_0) - \zeta| = |z_0 - \zeta| \leq r < r_0$, contrary to the previous assertion that $|z_0 - \zeta| = r_0$. The assumption $\omega_1 = \omega_2$ therefore leads to a contradiction, so that $\omega_1 \neq \omega_2$, which was to be proved.

17.20. The Conformal Mapping of Jordan Domains

The foregoing theorems yield a particularly simple result whenever the boundary of G is a Jordan curve Γ.

If a Jordan domain G (that is, a domain bounded by a Jordan curve) is mapped conformally onto the unit disk E ($|w| < 1$), then the mapping is continuous and one-to-one on the boundaries Γ and $|w| = 1$.

The proof is based upon the following facts.

1) Every boundary point ζ of a Jordan domain G is accessible, and it defines a single class of boundary elements (Exercises 6 and 7, p. 340).

2) Let (ζ, l) be a boundary element and $G_r(l)$ the associated "neighborhood" (cf. Section 17.17). As $r \to 0$, the image of $G_r(l)$ approaches a particular point ω of the circle $|w| = 1$ (as was shown in Section 17.18). To different boundary elements there correspond different image points. The boundary Γ is therefore mapped in a one-to-one manner onto a point-set (ω) on the circle $|w| = 1$.

3) The mapping $\Gamma \leftrightarrow (\omega)$ is continuous (Exercise 8, p. 340). As the point ζ varies on the boundary curve Γ, arg ω varies continuously. From the one-to-one character of the mapping $\Gamma \to \omega$ it follows that arg ω is a monotone function of ζ, that is, if $\zeta = \zeta(\tau)$ $(\tau_0 \leq \tau \leq \tau_1; \zeta(\tau_0) = \zeta(\tau_1))$ is the equation of Γ, then arg ω is a monotone increasing or monotone decreasing function of τ.

4) To the parameter interval $\tau_0 \leq \tau \leq \tau_1$ there corresponds a closed arc of the circle $|w| = 1$. Its end-points $\omega(\zeta(\tau_0))$ and $\omega(\zeta(\tau_1))$ coincide, since otherwise two distinct points on $|w| = 1$ would correspond to the point $\zeta = \zeta(\tau_0) = \zeta(\tau_1)$.

The mapping $G \leftrightarrow E$ therefore can be extended to the boundaries of the domains, and the correspondence between the boundaries Γ and $|w| = 1$ is topological. Q.E.D.

§4. THE CONNECTION BETWEEN CONFORMAL MAPPING AND THE DIRICHLET PROBLEM

17.21. The Solution of the Dirichlet Problem by Means of the Riemann Mapping Theorem

The Riemann mapping theorem has a close connection with the Dirichlet problem. In Chapter 11 we saw that a bounded harmonic function in a domain G is completely determined if its values on the boundary Γ of the domain are known. Suppose, then, that we are given an arbitrary, piecewise continuous function on Γ, and we seek to determine a bounded function which is harmonic in the interior of the domain G and assumes the given values on its boundary Γ. In Chapter 11 we have already given the solution to this problem whenever the domain G is a disk; it was constructed by means of the Poisson formula.

In the more general case of a *Jordan domain* G we can obtain the solution with the aid of the Riemann mapping theorem. Thus let G be a simply connected domain whose boundary is a Jordan curve Γ, and let $U(\zeta)$ be a piecewise continuous real function of the boundary point ζ. We seek a bounded harmonic function $u(z)$ in the domain G which assumes the value $U(\zeta)$ at each point of continuity of $U(\zeta)$.

By the Riemann mapping theorem, the domain G can be mapped one-to-one conformally onto the unit disk $|t| < 1$. The mapping is continuous on the boundary (cf. Section 17.20). The function $U(\zeta)$ is thereby transformed into a function $\bar{U}(\theta)$ of the point $e^{i\theta}$ on the unit circle, and the function $u(z)$, which we are seeking, goes over into a function $\bar{u}(t)$ which is harmonic in the disk $|t| < 1$ and which possesses the boundary values $\bar{U}(\theta)$.

From these boundary values $\bar{U}(\theta)$ we can construct the function $\bar{u}(t)$ by means of the Poisson integral. If we return to the z-plane, $\bar{u}(t)$ is transformed into a function $u(z)$, harmonic in the domain G, which possesses the given boundary values $U(\zeta)$. This solves the Dirichlet problem for a Jordan domain G.

17.22. The Green's Function

Conversely, whenever the boundary-value problem admits a solution for harmonic functions, the Riemann mapping problem may also be solved.

Let $w = w(z, a)$ be an analytic function which maps the simply connected domain G of the plane $z \neq \infty$ conformally onto the unit disk $|w| < 1$ in such a way that $z = a$ is mapped into the point $w = 0$. The single-valued function

$$g(z, a) = - \log |w(z, a)| \tag{17.14}$$

then has the following properties:

1) $g(z, a)$ is harmonic in G except at $z = a$, where it has a logarithmic pole:

$$g(z, a) = \log \frac{1}{|z - a|} + u(z, a); \tag{17.15}$$

here, the function $u(z, a)$ is harmonic throughout G.

2) $g(z, a)$ is continuous and equal to 0 on the boundary Γ of G.

The function g defined by (1) and (2) is called the *Green's function* of the domain G with pole $z = a$. Hence, there exists a Green's function for every simply connected domain G for which the Riemann problem can be solved. The uniqueness of the function $g(z, a)$ can be proved directly. For the difference of two such functions is harmonic everywhere in G and vanishes on the boundary. By the maximum and minimum principles, however, such a function must then be identically zero.

Conversely, let us now assume that the boundary-value problem can be solved for a given domain G in the plane $z \neq \infty$.† In order to construct the Green's function $g(z, a)$, we first solve the boundary-value problem for the boundary-values $\log |\zeta - a|$ ($\zeta \in \Gamma$). Denote the solution by $u(z, a)$. Then the sum (17.15) has both the defining properties (1) and (2) of the Green's function $g(z, a)$.

17.23. Solution of the Riemann Mapping Problem by Means of the Boundary-Value Problem

Formula (17.14) now permits us to construct the mapping function $w(z, a)$ from the Green's function $g(z, a)$ if we assume that G is *simply connected*.

We show first that there exists a single-valued analytic function $w(z, a)$, which is defined up to a constant factor of modulus 1 and which satisfies the relation

$$\log |w(z, a)| = -g(z, a).$$

To construct this function w, we first form the harmonic conjugate of the function g. The conjugate function of the first term in (17.15) is $-\arg (z - a)$. If we fix an arbitrary branch of $-\arg (z - a)$ at any point $z = z_0 \in G$ ($z_0 \neq a$), then the continuation of this branch for $z \neq a$ yields a multiple-valued function with periods $n \cdot 2\pi$, when n is an integer. On the other hand, by the monodromy theorem, the conjugate function $v(z, a)$ of $u(z, a)$ is *single-valued* once its value at $z = z_0$ has been fixed. Hence, the conjugate harmonic function $h(z, a)$ of g is uniquely determined up to the periods $n \cdot 2\pi$, so that the function

$$w(z, a) = e^{-g-ih} = (z - a) e^{-u-iv} \tag{17.16}$$

is a *single-valued* analytic function in G.

---

† For the moment, it is not necessary to assume that the domain G is *simply* connected.

17.24.

Now we shall prove that the function $w(z, a)$ defined by (17.16) maps the domain G one-to-one conformally onto the unit disk $|w| < 1$.

We remark that it follows from (17.16) that the following properties hold.

1) $w(z, a)$ has a simple zero at $z = a$, and does not vanish elsewhere in G.

2) $|w(z, a)| = e^{-g} < 1$, since the Green's function is positive in G. On the boundary Γ, $|w(z, a)|$ is continuous and is equal to 1.

Further, we shall prove that

3) The function $w(z, a)$ is one-to-one: it assumes different values at different points $z \in G$.

Proof of (3). Let $a \neq b \in G$. We shall show that $w(z, a) \neq w(b, a)$ for $z \neq b$. For this purpose, we form the linear transformation

$$\omega(z, a, b) = \frac{w(z, a) - w(b, a)}{1 - \overline{w(b, a)}w(z, a)}$$

of $w(z, a)$. Since $|w(z, a)| < 1$ in G, the same is also true for $\omega(z, a, b)$ (cf. Section 3.10). The latter is therefore regular for $z \in G$ and satisfies

$$|\omega(z, a, b)| < 1.$$

On the other hand, let us consider the function $w(z, b)$ obtained from (17.16) by replacing the pole a by b. Since this function has the point $z = b$ as its sole (simple) zero in G, the quotient

$$\frac{\omega(z, a, b)}{w(z, b)}$$

is regular in G. On the boundary Γ it has absolute value 1. Hence, by the maximum principle,

$$\frac{|\omega(z, a, b)|}{|w(z, b)|} \leq 1 \tag{17.17}$$

at every point in G.

If equality occurs in this relation at *one* point of G, then it holds identically in G. We shall show that equality does in fact hold at $z = a$.

It follows from (17.17), for $z = a$, that

$$\frac{|w(b, a)|}{|w(a, b)|} \leq 1,$$

for $\omega(a, a, b) = -w(b, a)$. However, since a and b are arbitrary points of G, this relation also holds if a and b are interchanged. Accordingly, we have

$$|w(a, b)| = |w(b, a)|.$$

But then equality must hold identically in (17.17):

$$|\omega(z, a, b)| \equiv |w(z, b)|.$$

However, since $w(z, b)$ vanishes *only* for $z = b$, we have $\omega(z, a, b) \neq 0$ for $z \neq b$. From the definition of the function $\omega(z, a, b)$ it follows that $w(z, a) - w(b, a) \neq 0$ for $z \neq b$, which proves our assertion.

Finally, we prove

4) The range of $w(z, a)$ is the full unit disk $|w| < 1$.

Proof. Suppose that there were a value w_0, $|w_0| < 1$, which is not assumed by $w(z, a)$. Form the expression

$$\frac{w(z, a) - w_0}{1 - \bar{w}_0 w(z, a)},$$

which defines a regular non-vanishing function for $z \in G$. On the boundary Γ its absolute value is continuous and is equal to 1. From the maximum and minimum principles it then follows that its absolute value is the constant 1. But for $z = a$ the absolute value is $|w_0| < 1$. This contradiction proves assertion (4).

Properties (1)–(4) show that $w = w(z, a)$ is the conformal mapping of G onto the unit disk $|w| < 1$ which we were seeking.

§5. THE CONFORMAL MAPPING OF POLYGONS

17.25. Analytic Continuation of the Mapping

Let P be a simply connected polygon in the w-plane whose boundary is a simple polygonal path with vertices at $w_1, w_2, \ldots, w_n$. Let the angles at these vertices be denoted by $\alpha_1\pi, \alpha_2\pi, \ldots, \alpha_n\pi$, so that

$$\sum_{\nu=1}^{n} \alpha_\nu = n - 2.$$

By the Riemann mapping theorem the interior of the polygon P can be mapped conformally onto the half-plane Im $z > 0$. The mapping function is uniquely determined up to a linear transformation of the half-plane onto itself. Since the boundary curves of the domain are piecewise analytic, the mapping is also continuous on the boundary. Consequently there exist points z_1, $z_2, \ldots, z_n$ on the real axis in the z-plane corresponding to the vertices w_1, $w_2, \ldots, w_n$ of the polygon. Three of these points may be chosen arbitrarily. If we take, say, $z_n = \infty$ and two others arbitrarily, the mapping is then uniquely determined. We denote the mapping function by $z = z(w)$ and its inverse by $w = w(z)$.

By the reflection principle the function $w = w(z)$ may be continued analytically across each segment $z_\nu z_{\nu+1}$ ($\nu = 1, 2, \ldots, n$) into the half-plane

*12

Im $z < 0$. When $w(z)$ is continued across z_1z_2, points which are symmetric with respect to the real axis are mapped into points which are symmetric with respect to the side w_1w_2. The function therefore maps the half-plane Im $z < 0$ conformally onto a polygon P' which is symmetric to the original polygon P with respect to the side w_1w_2 (Fig. 51).

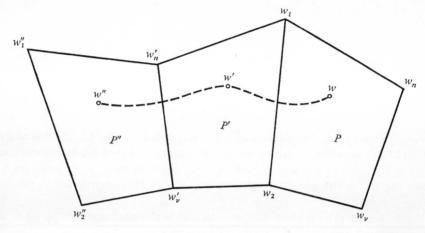

Figure 51

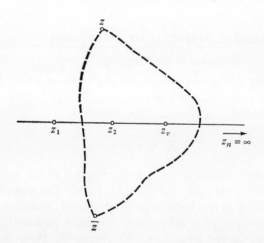

Figure 52

This branch of the function may be reflected back to the upper half-plane across any segment $z_\nu z_{\nu+1}$. The resulting function maps points which are symmetric with respect to the real axis into points which are symmetric with respect to the side $w'_\nu w'_{\nu+1}$ of P' corresponding to the side $w_\nu w_{\nu+1}$ of P. It maps the entire half-plane Im $z > 0$ onto a polygon P'' which is symmetric to P' with respect to the side $w'_\nu w'_{\nu+1}$. The polygon P'' is congruent to P and may be obtained from P by a translation and a rotation.

If we continue the mapping function $w(z)$ analytically in all possible ways, we obtain a multiple-valued analytic function whose branches are related by congruence transformations. From this it follows that any two branches, $w(z)$ and $\tilde{w}(z)$, satisfy the equation

$$\tilde{w}(z) = aw(z) + b, \tag{17.18}$$

where a and b are constants with $|a| = 1$.

From (17.18) we have

$$\frac{w''(z)}{w'(z)} = \frac{\tilde{w}''(z)}{\tilde{w}'(z)},$$

so that the function

$$f(z) = \frac{w''(z)}{w'(z)} = \frac{d}{dz} \log w'(z) \tag{17.19}$$

is single-valued in the entire plane. It is regular everywhere except at the points z_ν ($\nu = 1, 2, \ldots, n$), since apart from these points, $w(z)$ is regular and $w'(z) \neq 0$.

17.26. Singularities of the Function $f(z)$

We now examine the behavior of the function (17.19) at the points z_ν. At these points, the function $w(z)$ is not regular since it has branch-points. With w_ν as center we draw a small circle such that the sides of P emanating from w_ν determine a sector G_w of this circle which lies entirely in P. We map this sector conformally onto the semicircle G_ζ by the function

$$\zeta = (w - w_\nu)^{1/\alpha_\nu}. \tag{17.20}$$

Under the function $z = z(w)$ the sector G_w corresponds to a bounded domain G_z which lies in the half-plane Im $z > 0$ and which adjoins a segment of the real axis. Since $w = w(z)$ is regular in the domain G_z, it follows from (17.20) that ζ is also regular in G_z and

$$\zeta = (w(z) - w_\nu)^{1/\alpha_\nu} = \zeta(z). \tag{17.21}$$

Now $\zeta(z)$ maps this domain onto the semi-circle G_ζ. By the reflection principle, the function (17.21) may be continued analytically across the real axis; it therefore is regular even at the point z_ν. Hence, it may be expanded into a power series in $z - z_\nu$, in the neighborhood of the point z_ν. From (17.20) and (17.21) we obtain the expansion

$$(w - w_\nu)^{1/\alpha_\nu} = c_1(z - z_\nu) + c_2(z - z_\nu)^2 + \cdots$$
$$= (z - z_\nu)\{c_1 + [z - z_\nu]\}, \tag{17.22}$$

where $c_1 \neq 0$, since the mapping from the z-plane into the ζ-plane is conformal at the point z_ν (for the notation $[z - z_\nu]$ see Section 9.22). Hence,

$$w - w_\nu = (z - z_\nu)^{\alpha_\nu}\{c_1 + [z - z_\nu]\}^{\alpha_\nu}.$$

Since the expression in braces does not vanish in a sufficiently small neighborhood of z_ν, every branch of its power is regular there and admits an expansion into powers of $z - z_\nu$. Thus we obtain

$$w - w_\nu = (z - z_\nu)^{\alpha_\nu}\{b + [z - z_\nu]\}, \tag{17.23}$$

where again $b \neq 0$. By differentiating we obtain

$$w'(z) = \alpha_\nu(z - z_\nu)^{\alpha_\nu-1}\{b + [z - z_\nu]\}.$$

Consequently, we obtain the logarithmic derivative

$$f(z) = \frac{d}{dz}\log w'(z) = \frac{\alpha_\nu - 1}{z - z_\nu} + \mathfrak{P}(z - z_\nu),$$

where $\mathfrak{P}(z - z_\nu)$ is a series in positive powers of $z - z_\nu$. The function (17.19) therefore has a pole of first order with residue $\alpha_\nu - 1$ at the point z_ν ($\nu = 1, 2, \ldots, n - 1$).

We must still investigate the function (17.19) in the neighborhood of the point $z = z_n = \infty$. The transformation

$$z = -\frac{1}{t}$$

maps the upper half-plane onto itself in such a way that the origin corresponds to the point $z = \infty$. The function $w(z) = w(-1/t)$ maps the half-plane $\operatorname{Im} t > 0$ onto the polygon P in such a way that the point $t = 0$ goes into the point w_n. From (17.23), the function $w(-1/t)$ has the expansion

$$w\left(-\frac{1}{t}\right) - w_n = t^{\alpha_n}\mathfrak{P}(t) \qquad (\mathfrak{P}(0) \neq 0),$$

from which it follows that

$$w(z) - w_n = \left(\frac{1}{z}\right)^{\alpha_n}\mathfrak{P}\left(\frac{1}{z}\right). \tag{17.24}$$

For the function (17.19) we then have

$$f(z) = \frac{d}{dz}\log w'(z) = -\frac{\alpha_n + 1}{z} + \left[\frac{1}{z^2}\right].$$

Hence, $f(z)$ is regular at the point $z = \infty$ and vanishes there.

17.27. The Schwarz-Christoffel Formula

We have seen that the function $f(z)$ is regular everywhere except at the points $z_1, z_2, \ldots, z_{n-1}$, where it has poles of first order. By Section 9.23, it must be a rational function, and, since it vanishes at $z = \infty$,

$$f(z) = \frac{d}{dz}\log w'(z) = \sum_{\nu=1}^{n-1}\frac{\alpha_\nu - 1}{z - z_\nu}. \tag{17.25}$$

If we integrate this equation, we have

$$\log w'(z) = \sum_{v=1}^{n-1} (\alpha_v - 1) \log (z - z_v) + \log c,$$

where c is a constant. Going over to $w'(z)$ and integrating once more, we obtain the so-called *Schwarz-Christoffel formula*

$$w(z) = c \int_{z0}^{z} (z - z_1)^{\alpha_1-1}(z - z_2)^{\alpha_2-1} \ldots (z - z_{n-1})^{\alpha_{n-1}-1} \, dz + c'. \qquad (17.26)$$

Here z_0 is an arbitrary point and $c' = w(z_0)$.

We have derived formula (17.26) under the assumption that $z_n = \infty$. The point z_n then does not appear explicitly in the formula. If all the image points of the vertices are finite, a factor $(z - z_n)^{\alpha_n-1}$ would then appear in the integrand in (17.26). The function $w(z)$, as well as the function $f(z)$, would then be regular at infinity.

17.28. The Mapping of a Polygon onto a Disk

If we map the half-plane Im $z > 0$ conformally onto the disk $|\zeta| < 1$ in such a way that, for instance, the point $z = i$ goes into $\zeta = 0$, the mapping formula (17.26) is transformed into the formula

$$w = c \int_{0}^{\zeta} (\zeta - \zeta_1)^{\alpha_1-1}(\zeta - \zeta_2)^{\alpha_2-1} \ldots (\zeta - \zeta_n)^{\alpha_n-1} \, d\zeta + c'. \qquad (17.26)'$$

Here the points $\zeta_1, \zeta_2, \ldots, \zeta_n$ are the images on the unit circle of the vertices of the polygon. The proof of formula (17.26)' is left as an exercise (Exercise 17, p. 341).

The image points of three of the vertices of the polygon may be chosen arbitrarily (Section 17.25). The remaining images are then completely determined. In general they cannot be calculated explicitly in terms of the given vertices. In certain special cases, however, their positions can be computed, for example, if the given polygon is regular.

17.29. The Mapping of a Triangle

For a triangle we have

$$\alpha_1 + \alpha_2 + \alpha_3 = 1. \qquad (17.27)$$

Let $z = z(w)$ be a function which maps the triangle onto the half-plane Im $z > 0$. Let us investigate the conditions under which $z(w)$ can be continued analytically into the entire w-plane as a *single-valued* analytic function.

We start from a point z_0 in the half-plane Im $z > 0$ which corresponds to the point w_0 inside the triangle. If z winds once in the positive direction about the point z_1, we arrive at that branch of the function $w(z)$ which maps the upper half-plane onto a triangle P''. We obtain P'' by rotating P about the point

w_1 through an angle of $2\alpha_1\pi$. If z makes another circuit about z_1, the triangle is rotated once again through the same angle (Fig. 53). After a sufficient number of circuits the resulting branch of the function $w(z)$ maps the upper half-plane onto a triangle which covers the triangle P either completely or at least partially.

Let m denote the number of circuits made by z. If z returns to the point z_0 in this process, its image point w returns to the point w_0 if and only if the triangle returns to its initial position after m circuits.

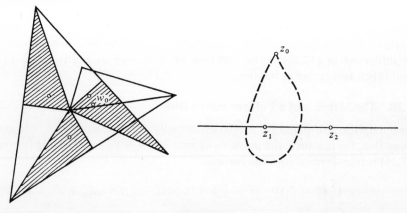

Figure 53

Therefore, in order that the function $z(w)$ be single-valued in the neighborhood of w_1, it is necessary and sufficient that the triangle be returned to its original position by an integer number m of rotations by the angle $2\alpha_1\pi$ about the point w_1. This means that α_1 must satisfy the condition

$$\alpha_1\pi = \frac{2\pi}{2m}, \qquad \alpha_1 = \frac{1}{m}.$$

If we repeat this argument for the other two vertices, we obtain $\alpha_1 = 1/n$, $\alpha_3 = 1/p$, where n and p are positive integers. By (17.27), these numbers must satisfy the condition

$$\frac{1}{m} + \frac{1}{n} + \frac{1}{p} = 1. \qquad (17.28)$$

The solutions of this equation in positive integers are easily determined:

$$m = 2, \qquad n = 4, \qquad p = 4$$
$$m = 2, \qquad n = 3, \qquad p = 6$$
$$m = n = p = 3.$$

17.30.

We consider the first case in detail; the given triangle is an isosceles right triangle. If we map the triangle onto the half-plane $\operatorname{Im} z > 0$ in such a way that its vertices are mapped into the points -1, 1, ∞, it follows from (17.26) that the mapping function assumes the form

$$w = c \int_{z_0}^{z} \frac{dz}{(1 - z^2)^{3/4}} + c',$$

where $z = \infty$ is the image of the vertex with the right angle. If z_0 is the image of the origin, then $c' = 0$; if the hypotenuse has the direction of the real axis, then c is real.

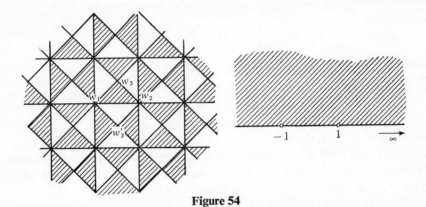

Figure 54

If we continue the mapping function analytically across the segment $(-1, 1)$ into the lower half-plane, the resulting mapping carries the plane, slit from the points -1 and 1 out to infinity, onto a square, half of which is the given triangle. By repeated analytic continuation we obtain, as images of the half-planes, triangles which come from the original triangle by successive reflections in the sides. In this way we obtain a network of triangles covering the entire w-plane once (Fig. 54). The function $z = z(w)$ is single-valued and maps the entire w-plane one-to-one conformally onto an infinite-sheeted Riemann surface whose branch points lie over -1, 1 and ∞. The branch points over -1 and 1 are of third order, those over ∞ of first order.

In the square $w_1 w_3' w_2 w_3$ (see Fig. 54, where the triangles corresponding to the half-plane $\operatorname{Im} z > 0$ are shaded), the function $z(w)$ assumes every value once. This square is therefore a fundamental domain of the function if we include a suitable portion of its boundary. The points of the w-plane where the function $z(w)$ assumes the same value may be obtained from the linear transformations $\tilde{w} = aw + b$, which form a group.

We see from the figure that $z(w)$ is doubly periodic. The period-parallelogram is a square which is made up of four smaller squares. The function assumes every value four times within the period-parallelogram. It is therefore a doubly periodic function of fourth order.

In the remaining cases mentioned at the end of Section 17.29, $m = 2$, $n = 3$, $p = 6$ and $m = n = p = 3$, the function also turns out to be doubly periodic.

17.31. The Mapping of a Rectangle

We now consider the corresponding question for the case $n > 3$. We want to know when the function $z(w)$ mapping an n-polygon onto the half-plane $\text{Im } z > 0$ is single-valued. The line of reasoning used in Section 17.29 remains valid. The necessary condition for single-valuedness turns out to be

$$\alpha_\nu = \frac{1}{m_\nu} \qquad (\nu = 1, 2, \ldots, n),$$

where the numbers m_ν are positive integers ≥ 2 and

$$\sum_{\nu=1}^{n} \frac{1}{m_\nu} = n - 2. \tag{17.29}$$

Since every $m_\nu \geq 2$, the left-hand side of (17.29) is less than or equal to $n/2$, and this is less than $n - 2$ whenever $n > 4$. The function $z(w)$ can therefore be single-valued only if $n = 4$. In this case, Eq. (17.29) holds if and only if every $m_\nu = 2$. The given polygon is therefore a rectangle.

We map the rectangle onto the half-plane $\text{Im } z > 0$ in such a way that its vertices map into the points $z = 1, -1, 1/k, -1/k$ $(k < 1)$. According to the Schwarz-Christoffel formula, the mapping is then given by

$$w = c \int_{z_0}^{z} \frac{dz}{\sqrt{(1 - z^2)(1 - k^2 z^2)}} + c',$$

where c and c' are constants. On the right-hand side we have an elliptic integral. We have already encountered this mapping function in another connection (Section 14.35).

The function $z = z(w)$ is a doubly periodic function whose period-parallelogram is made up of four smaller rectangles. The function is therefore of second order.

§6. TRIANGLE FUNCTIONS

17.32.

We now turn to a more general mapping problem. It is the question of mapping a circular curvilinear triangle conformally onto the half-plane $\text{Im } z > 0$.

Let w_1, w_2, w_3 be the vertices of the triangle, and let $\alpha_1 \pi$, $\alpha_2 \pi$, $\alpha_3 \pi$ be the angles at these vertices. We assume first that each of the angles is different from zero. By the Riemann mapping theorem, the triangle can be mapped one-to-one conformally onto the half-plane Im $z > 0$. Let the mapping function be $z = z(w)$ and let its inverse be $w = w(z)$. In view of Section 17.15, the mapping is continuous on the boundary. We may choose the images of the vertices to be three arbitrary points on the real axis; let these be the points 0, 1, ∞. The mapping function may be continued analytically into the lower half-plane. By repeated continuation, we obtain a function which maps the Riemann surface lying over the z-plane and having branch points over $z = 0$, 1, ∞ onto a Riemann covering surface of the w-plane

We now look for the conditions under which the inverse $z = z(w)$ of the function $w(z)$ is *single-valued*.

As in Section 17.29, we conclude at once that a necessary condition that $z(w)$ be single-valued is that

$$\alpha_1 = \frac{1}{m}, \qquad \alpha_2 = \frac{1}{n}, \qquad \alpha_3 = \frac{1}{p}, \qquad (17.30)$$

where m, n and p are positive integers.

In order to see that condition (17.30) is also sufficient, we must examine more closely the nature of the mapping at the vertices w_ν.

The sides of the triangle emanating from the vertex w_1 have a second point of intersection w_0 which lies outside the triangle. If we perform a linear transformation $\zeta = \zeta(w)$ which takes the point $w = w_0$ into the point $\zeta = \infty$, the triangle $w_1 w_2 w_3$ will be mapped onto a triangle such that the two sides emanating from the vertex $\zeta_1 = \zeta(w_1)$ are line segments. The third side is a circular arc through the points $\zeta_2 = \zeta(w_2)$ and $\zeta_3 = \zeta(w_3)$. Its center lies either on the same side of the line $\zeta_2 \zeta_3$ as the point ζ_1, or on the opposite side, according as the sum of the angles of the triangle is greater than π or less than π. The third side is a straight line if and only if the sum of the angles is π. We must therefore distinguish three cases:

$$\frac{1}{m} + \frac{1}{n} + \frac{1}{p} \gtreqless 1. \qquad (17.31)$$

17.33

In the first case, $1/m + 1/n + 1/p < 1$, it is easy to show that the sides of the triangle possess a common orthogonal circle containing the triangle in its interior. If we return from the ζ-plane to the w-plane by a linear transformation, we may conclude that the sides of the original triangle likewise have a common orthogonal circle C containing the triangle.

If we continue the mapping function analytically into the exterior of the given triangle by means of the reflection principle, we obtain a single-valued function. After two reflections, z returns to its original value. We have thus performed a linear transformation in the w-plane. The interior of the circle C is invariant under each of the reflections, while the sides of the triangle are mapped onto circles orthogonal to C.

By using the fact that the hyperbolic measure (the non-Euclidean length) of every arc is invariant under a conformal mapping of C onto itself (cf. Section 3.11), we conclude that the interior of C is *completely* covered once by the reflection of a network of triangles. The function $z = z(w)$ therefore maps the interior of C in a one-to-one manner onto an infinite-sheeted Riemann surface whose branch points lie over the points $z = 0, 1, \infty$. The mapping is conformal everywhere except at the branch points.

We leave the details of the proof to the reader (Exercise 23, p. 342).

In the circle C, $z = z(w)$ is a single-valued analytic function, with no singularities except for poles, which is invariant with respect to a certain group of linear transformations. It is an *automorphic* function under this group (cf. Section 14.31).

In the second case in (17.31), we get an ordinary rectilinear triangle as the image in the ζ-plane of the triangle $w_1 w_2 w_3$. The question of the single-valuedness of the mapping function $z = z(w)$ has already been answered in Sections 17.29 and 17.30.

17.34.

In the third case, the integers m, n, p satisfying the inequality $1/m + 1/n + 1/p > 1$ are:

m	n	p
2	2	Arbitrary
2	3	3
2	3	4
2	3	5

In these cases, the triangle $w_1 w_2 w_3$ may be mapped stereographically onto the Riemann sphere in such a way that all the sides of the image triangle are arcs of great circles. From this it follows that under repeated reflections of the triangle in its sides the surface of the sphere is covered once by finitely many triangles. In the first case, the number of triangles is $4p$, in the second, 24, in the third, 48, and in the last, 120. In the first case two vertices of the network of triangles lie at the poles of the sphere and the others lie on the equator. In the second case we obtain the network by projecting a regular inscribed tetrahedron onto the sphere from the center and then by drawing the altitudes (circular arcs) in each triangle. In the third and fourth cases the network of triangles leads to a regular octahedron and a regular icosahedron.

The domain consisting of two neighboring triangles is always mapped onto a full replica of the z-plane which has been suitably slit. The w-values belonging to the same point of the z-plane are obtained by substitutions of a group of linear transformations. The mapping function is therefore an automorphic function. Since it has no singularities other than poles, it is a *rational* function whose order, in the particular cases, is equal to $2p$, 12, 24, and 60. The reader is referred to Exercise 23, p. 342.

The investigations in this section and in the preceding sections were first carried out by H. A. Schwarz (1843–1921). The mapping by curvilinear triangles in the case treated in this section and its connection with the theory of regular polyhedra was investigated extensively by Felix Klein (1849–1925). The triangle functions constitute a particularly simple class of automorphic functions. A systematic general theory of automorphic functions was developed by Klein and, in particular, by Poincaré.

§7. THE PICARD THEOREM

17.35. Legendre's Modular Function

We have assumed up to now that all the angles of the circular triangles are positive. The investigation may be extended to the case where one or more of the angles is zero. In particular, we consider the conformal mapping of a triangle all of whose angles are equal to zero.

Let G be the domain $0 < \text{Re } w < 1$, $|w - \frac{1}{2}| > \frac{1}{2}$, $\text{Im } w > 0$. By the Riemann mapping theorem, G can be mapped one-to-one conformally onto the half-plane $\text{Im } \zeta > 0$ in such a way that the points $w = 0, 1, \infty$ go over into the points $\zeta = 0, 1, \infty$. Let the mapping function be denoted by $\zeta = \zeta(w)$.

Just as in the previous sections, we continue this function analytically by means of the reflection principle. If we reflect G in one of the two sides parallel to the imaginary axis, we obtain a triangle which is congruent to G. By repeated reflections of this sort we obtain a simple covering of the upper half-plane which includes all points except those which lie in the interior of the circles

$$|w - (n + \tfrac{1}{2})| = \tfrac{1}{2} \qquad (n = \ldots, -1, 0, 1, \ldots).$$

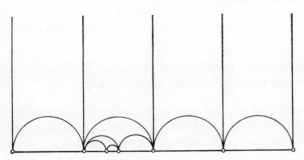

Figure 55

Now we reflect G in the semicircular arc on its boundary. The image of G is then a circular triangle with vertices at 0, $\frac{1}{2}$, 1, whose sides are orthogonal to the real axis. If we now reflect this triangle in the smaller circular arc which emanates from the origin and continue this process, the vertices will approach the origin and the radii of the circles will tend to zero. This we can see by first mapping the domain G onto itself in such a way that the side $(0, 1)$ goes over into the side $(\infty, 0)$. The mapping will be effected by a linear transformation $t = t(w)$ which maps the half-plane Im $w > 0$ onto the half-plane Im $t > 0$. The semicircular arcs emanating from $w = 0$ go over into the rays Re $t = n$ $(n = 0, \pm 1, \ldots)$, Im $t > 0$, and reflections in these semi-circles go over into reflections in the lines Re $t = n$. The images under these reflections of the points $t = 0$ and $t = 1$ have ∞ as a cluster point. If we return to the half-plane Im $w > 0$ by the inverse transformation $w = w(t)$, the rays Re $t = n$, Im $t > 0$ go over into semicircular arcs emanating from $w = 0$. Hence, the end-points of these arcs have the origin as a cluster point.

We can proceed in the same way with every curvilinear triangle. The radii of the circles then tend to zero. The circular triangles resulting from repeated reflections ultimately cover the entire half plane Im $w > 0$ just once without leaving any gaps. The real axis intersects all the sides of the triangles orthogonally.

The mapping function $\zeta = \zeta(w)$ is single-valued in the half-plane Im $w > 0$ and maps it onto an infinite-sheeted Riemann surface with infinitely many branch points of infinite order over the points 0, 1, ∞. Every sheet of this surface corresponds to a curvilinear quadrilateral in the w-plane composed of two neighboring circular triangles. The function $\zeta(w)$ has a singularity at every point of the real axis, so that it cannot be continued analytically across this axis.

The function $\zeta(w)$ is called the *Legendre modular function*.

If we make a linear transformation of the half-plane Im $w > 0$ onto the disk $|\omega| < 1$, then the modular function is defined in this disk, and it cannot be continued into the exterior of the disk. We denote this function by $\zeta = \lambda(\omega)$ and its inverse function by $\omega = \omega(\zeta)$.

17.36. The Picard Theorem

In conclusion, we shall use the modular function to prove *Picard's theorem* (Section 9.21).

An entire function $w(z)$ which does not reduce to a constant assumes every finite complex value with at most one exception.

The proof is indirect. Let us assume that $w(z)$ has two finite exceptional values a and b, $w(z) \neq a, b$, and show that the function then reduces to a constant. We may assume, without loss of generality, that $a = 0$ and $b = 1$, for otherwise we may replace w by the function $(w - a)/(b - a)$. The latter function we shall still denote by $w(z)$.

We substitute $\zeta = w(z)$ into the inverse function $\omega(\zeta)$ of the modular function. Every branch of the function $\omega(\zeta)$ is regular except for the points $\zeta = 0, 1, \infty$. However, the inner function $\zeta = w(z)$ is regular everywhere and does not assume the values 0, 1. It follows that the function $\omega(w(z))$ can be continued analytically throughout the whole plane. By the monodromy theorem, this function is single-valued. Since it is regular and bounded in the entire plane, it is a constant by Liouville's theorem. From this it follows that $w(z)$ is also constant. But this contradicts our assumption, and thereby completes the proof of Picard's theorem.

EXERCISES ON CHAPTER 17

1. Prove that a simply connected domain G having two distinct boundary points must have infinitely many boundary points.

Hint. First map G onto a domain which lies inside the unit disk, as in Section 17.5.

2. Map the rectangle $0 \leq x \leq 1$, $\alpha < y < \beta$ topologically onto itself by the functions $u = u(x, y)$, $v = v(x, y)$, defined as follows: $v = y$, and

$$u = 4 \frac{\beta - y}{\beta - \alpha + 2(\beta - y)} x \quad \text{for} \quad 0 \leq x \leq \frac{1}{2} + \frac{\beta - y}{\beta - \alpha},$$

$$u = 2x - 1 \quad \text{for} \quad \frac{1}{2} + \frac{\beta - y}{\beta - \alpha} \leq x \leq 1,$$

when $(\alpha + \beta)/2 \leq y < \beta$, while

$$u = 4 \frac{y - \alpha}{\beta - \alpha + 2(y - \alpha)} x \quad \text{for} \quad 0 \leq x \leq \frac{1}{2} + \frac{y - \alpha}{\beta - \alpha},$$

$$u = 2x - 1 \quad \text{for} \quad \frac{1}{2} + \frac{y - \alpha}{\beta - \alpha} \leq x \leq 1,$$

when $\alpha < y \leq (\alpha + \beta)/2$. Apply this mapping to the case $\alpha = 1/(n + 1)$, $\beta = 1/n$ $(n = 1, 2, \ldots)$ and prove that the square $0 < x < 1$, $0 < y < 1$, from which the segments $0 < x \leq \frac{1}{2}$, $y = 1/n$ $(n = 2, 3, \ldots)$ have been removed, can be mapped topologically onto the square $0 < u < 1$, $0 < v < 1$. Investigate the behavior of the mapping when the point (x, y) approaches the segment $0 \leq x \leq \frac{1}{2}$, $y = 0$.

3. Show that if a domain whose boundary is a piecewise analytic Jordan curve is mapped conformally onto the unit disk, the mapping is continuous on the boundary.

Hint. Make use of the reflection principle (Section 12.11) and Theorem 3 of Lindelöf (Section 11.21).

4. Let G be the circular sector $|z| < r$, $|\arg z| < \alpha/2$ and let $\omega(z_0)$ be the harmonic measure of the circular arc $|z| = r$, $|\arg z| < \alpha/2$ at the point z_0 $(0 < z_0 < r)$. Show that $\omega(z_0)$ increases monotonically with α.

5. Let (ζ, l_ζ) be an accessible boundary element of the domain G. Prove that l_ζ can be replaced by a Jordan arc which defines the same boundary element.

6. Prove that all boundary points of a Jordan domain are accessible.

Hint. Let $r_1 > \ldots > r_n > \ldots > 0$, $r_n \to 0$ as $n \to \infty$. The intersection of the disk $K_{r_1}: |z - \zeta| < r_1$ $(\zeta \in \Gamma = \partial G$, the boundary of G) with the domain G consists of at least one domain G_{r_1} which has ζ as a boundary point. In the intersection of the disk K_{r_2} with G there is a subdomain G_{r_2} of G_{r_1} which has ζ as a boundary point, and so on. If z_ν is an arbitrary point of G_{r_ν} $(\nu = 1, 2, \ldots)$, then z_1 can be joined to z_2 by a continuous path which does not leave G_{r_1}. Continuing in this manner, one obtains a path belonging to G and terminating at ζ.

7. Prove that every point ζ of the boundary Γ of a Jordan domain G defines a single class of boundary elements.

Hint. Let l_1 and l_2 be two simple arcs in G which terminate at the point ζ but otherwise have no common points. Join the points $z_1 \in l_1$ and $z_2 \in l_2$ by a Jordan arc $l \subset G$ which, except for its end-points, has no points in common with l_1 or l_2. The path $l_1' l_2' l$, where l_ν' denotes the subarc $z_\nu \zeta$ of l_ν $(\nu = 1, 2)$, is a Jordan curve which, by the Jordan curve theorem, bounds a domain D. We show that $D \subset G$. If there were a boundary point of G in D, then there would also be exterior points of G in D, since in the neighborhood of every boundary point of a Jordan domain there are both interior points and exterior points of the domain. The boundary Γ of G would then bound three distinct domains which, in view of the Jordan curve theorem, is impossible.

8. Prove that the correspondence $\Gamma \leftrightarrow (\omega)$ between the boundary Γ of a Jordan domain and the set of points (ω) of the circle $|\omega| = 1$ (Section 17.20) is continuous.

9. Show that there is one and only one way of mapping a given Jordan domain conformally onto the unit disk in such a way that three given boundary points on the Jordan curve are mapped into three given points on the unit circle.

10. Show that a given Jordan domain can be mapped conformally onto a rectangle in such a way that four given boundary points go over into the vertices of the rectangle.

11. Prove that the Green's function $g(z, a)$ of an arbitrary domain G satisfies the symmetry relation

$$g(a, b) = g(b, a).$$

Hint. Compare Section 17.24.

12. Form the Green's function $g(z, a)$ of the annulus $1/R < |z| < R$ $(R > 1)$.

Hint. Assume that $g(z, a)$ exists, and take $\zeta = \log z$ as a new variable. The Green's function is a single-valued periodic function of ζ for $|\text{Re } \zeta| \leq \log R$. The solution is obtained by continuing g harmonically into the whole ζ-plane according to the reflection principle. The result can be expressed with the aid of the Weierstrass $\wp$-function.

13. Discuss the mapping effected by the analytic function e^{-g-ih}, where g is the Green's function constructed in Exercise 12.

14. Does the domain $0 < |z| < 1$ possess a Green's function?

15. Let $0 < \alpha_\nu < 1$ $(\nu = 1, 2, \ldots, n)$, $\alpha_1 + \alpha_2 + \ldots + \alpha_n = n - 2$. Prove directly from the Schwarz-Christoffel formula (17.26) that $w = w(z)$ maps the half-plane $\text{Im } z > 0$ in a one-to-one way onto a polygon whose angles are $\alpha_\nu \pi$ $(\nu = 1, 2, \ldots n)$.

16. Prove directly (without the Riemann mapping theorem) that a given triangle can be mapped conformally onto a half-plane.

Hint. Make use of the Schwarz-Christoffel formula.

17. Derive formula (17.26)' for the function which maps a disk conformally onto a polygon (cf. Section 17.28).

18. Map a regular polygon of n sides conformally onto a disk, and treat the square as a special case.

Hint. Divide the polygon into central triangles and map each triangle onto a circular sector with central angle $2\pi/n$.

19. Show that the mapping function in Section 17.29 is a doubly periodic function in the cases $m = 2, n = 3, p = 6$ and $m = n = p = 3$.

20. Let $z = z(w)$ be a function which maps a triangle with angles π/m, π/n, π/p conformally onto the half-plane $\text{Im } z > 0$. Determine the fundamental substitutions of those groups of linear substitutions which leave the function $z(w)$ invariant, if

   a) $m = 2, n = 4, p = 4$

   b) $m = 2, n = 3, p = 6$

   c) $m = n = p = 3$.

21. Discuss the integral in the Schwarz-Christoffel formula (17.26) for $n = 2$ and $n = 1$, and determine the associated mapping function. What is the result in the case $n = 3$, $\alpha_1 = \alpha_2 = \frac{1}{2}$, $z_1 + z_2 = 0$?

22. Prove that in the case $1/m + 1/n + 1/p < 1$, the sides of the circular triangle have a common orthogonal circle containing the triangle in its interior.

23. Prove the theorems about the mapping of circular triangles announced in Sections 17.33 and 17.34.

24. If the function $w = w(z)$ maps the half-plane $\text{Im } z > 0$ conformally onto a circular triangle, the so-called Schwarzian derivative of $w(z)$,

$$\{w, z\} = \frac{w'''}{w'} - \frac{3}{2}\left(\frac{w''}{w'}\right)^2,$$

is a rational function. Find it.

Solution.

$$\{w, z\} = \frac{1 - \alpha^2}{2z^2} + \frac{1 - \beta^2}{2(1 - z)^2} + \frac{1 - \alpha^2 - \beta^2 + \gamma^2}{2z(1 - z)},$$

where $\alpha\pi$, $\beta\pi$ and $\gamma\pi$ are the angles of the triangle.

25. Find the Schwarzian derivative (see Exercise 24) of the inverse function of the Legendre modular function.

INDEX

343